FOUNDATION
INSTRUMENTATION

Other volumes in the

Series on Rock and Soil Mechanics
Vol. 1 (1971/73)

W. Reisner, M. v. Eisenhart Rothe:

Bins and Bunkers for Handling Bulk Materials
— Practical Design and Techniques —
1971

W. Dreyer:

The Science of Rock Mechanics
Part I: Strength Properties of Rocks
1972

Editor-in-Chief
Professor Dr. H. Wöhlbier

Series on Rock and Soil Mechanics

Vol. 1 (1971/73) No. 3

FOUNDATION INSTRUMENTATION

by

Thomas H. Hanna

B. Sc., Ph. D., C. Eng., M. I. C. E., A. M. A. S. C. E.

Professor of Civil and Structural Engineering
University of Sheffield, England

First Edition

1973

TRANS TECH PUBLICATIONS

Distributed in
North, Central and South America by
TRANS TECH PUBLICATIONS
21330 Center Ridge Road
Cleveland, Ohio 44116
USA

Distributed in
Africa, Asia, Australia and Europe by
TRANS TECH S. A.
CH-4711 Aedermannsdorf
Switzerland

International Standard Book Number
ISBN 0-87849-006-x

Library of Congress Catalog Card Number
LCC 72-90015

Printed in Germany

EDITOR'S FOREWORD

This volume represents No. 3 of Volume 1 of the Series on Rock and Soil Mechanics.

We are grateful to Dr. Hanna for his expert treatise on the subject of foundation instrumentation, and we believe that this volume will fill a gap in the book shelves of many civil engineers. This topic, foundation instrumentation, has become increasingly important over the past few years and the need has arisen for a comprehensive text on the principles of operation, installation and use of the various instruments and data processing systems as well as a thorough discussion on evaluation techniques.

This book, with its extensive references, numerous drawings and list of instrument suppliers and their representatives will soon become a day-to-day working tool for the engineer designing, constructing and evaluating the performance of foundations.

Special thanks go to the instrument manufacturers and the consulting companies who have found it worthwhile to place advertisements at the end of this book. With their contribution they have not only extended the scope of this volume, but also have made it possible to offer this book to students and Public Libraries throughout the world at a reduced price. These advertisements, though unusual in a textbook, underline the necessary cooperation between the researcher at the university, the equipment manufacturer and the consulting engineer in the field of foundation instrumentation.

We are confident that this volume, of which the philosophy of field instrumentation is the theme, will be considered a major contribution to the civil engineering profession.

December 1972

Professor Dr. H. Wöhlbier
Dr. Reinhard H. Wöhlbier
Editors

PREFACE

This book is about the instrumentation of field scale foundation structures and is written at the level of understanding of the final year undergraduate student of Civil Engineering. It should be of direct interest to the practising Civil or Structural Engineer who is associated with the design and construction of civil engineering works that are involved with the ground to a large extent. Research engineers should also find the text of value. The book is not intended to be a text book on soil mechanics, but is does refer to the applications of this science to foundation engineering as they affect foundation instrumentation.

The nature of all natural soils and their complex arrangements requires specialized approaches utilizing the science and skill of several professional disciplines in the solution of engineering associated with the ground. In the study of the behaviour of natural soil masses subjected to load changes, use is made of highly refined laboratory and in-situ testing techniques of "representative specimens" of the ground and of methods of analysis based on engineering mechanics. Most engineers are aware of the large differences between predicted and actual performance despite the enormous recent advances in knowledge of subjects such as soil mechanics, rock mechanics, engineering geology and associated methods of analysis. Most of these inadequacies are a reflection of the inadequate volume of available field evidence. The term "inadequate volume of available field evidence" does not imply any lack of basic ability amongst the many engineers and others who are involved with the design and construction of foundations. It is believed that the Civil Engineering profession is unaware, to a large extent, of the techniques that are available to enable the field performance of a foundation to be measured. Many of these measuring techniques can be used in other branches of Civil Engineering but some have specific uses in soil engineering only.

The primary purpose of this text is to focus the attention of the reader on the role of field instrumentation in the solution of practical foundation problems. To achieve this purpose a simple approach has been taken but the interested reader will wish to pursue the subject in much greater detail in the various references which are quoted. Many topics such as the instrumentation of rock masses and structures in rocks, dynamic and seismic study instrumentation, and the instrumentation of foundations in marine, desert and arctic environments have not been discussed. This omission is deliberate because these topics are not directly relevant to the primary purpose of this book. Costs of the various instruments are not considered.

It is assumed that the reader has a working knowledge of soil mechanics, engineering geology and foundation engineering as covered in standard text books such as Foundation Design and Construction by M. J. Tomlinson (1969), Soil Mechanics in Engineering Practice by K. Terzaghi and R. B. Peck (1967) or Soil Mechanics by T. H. Wu (1966). The material in this text is based in part on the professional experiences of the author, but relies heavily on data taken from a large number of publications, technical reports and instrument manufacturers' catalogues.

To create a background for the main theme of the book, Chapter 1 has been written as a review to draw the reader's attention to the approach followed by the foundation engineer in the solution of ground engineering problems. Chapter 2 discusses methods of force measurement of particular interest to the foundation engineer while Chapter 3 reviews piezometer theory and the various types of piezometers which are available as well as their field use and recording. Chapter 4 considers the measurement of total and effective earth pressure in soil masses and adjacent to soil/structure boundaries. Earth pressure cell theory and use are also discussed. In Chapter 5 methods of deformation measurement both at the ground surface and within the soil mass (three dimensional) are reviewed for a wide range of foundation problems. Having considered the various instruments and techniques which are available for field measurement in Chapters 2 to 5, Chapter 6 presents data for a number of foundations to illustrate how the various instruments were used and the type of information which they provided. This is followed in Chapter 7 by a general discussion of the collection of data and its analysis. To illustrate analysis of field data the finite element technique is referred to and, for a number of foundations field measurements are compared with analytical prediction. Finally, Chapter 8 describes some of the techniques which have been used by the research engineer to instrument laboratory-scale foundation structures. From a study of this chapter it will be seen that the principles of measurement are similar to those used at field scale but the quantities being measured are only a small fraction of the field values. Consequently, much more sensitive and delicate instruments have to be used.

This book, therefore, tries to show how the foundation engineer may benefit from the use of field instrumentation and to this end an attempt has been made to classify and describe the various instruments and their principle of operation which are currently available and to show how these instruments have and are being used to advantage on a number of sites. The subject of foundation instrumentation is a relatively new one but is gathering momentum. While the principles of field measurement are not expected to change very much, the techniques of measurement and the interpretation of the data provided by such programmes of instrumentation will change as experience is gained. This text may help to establish field instrumentation as a respectable and necessary part of foundation design, construction, and performance evaluation.

The author gratefully acknowledges the inspiration given by the many authors and instrument suppliers from whose reports and brochures the greater part of this book has been taken.

Grateful acknowledgement is also made to the following who have given permission to reproduce illustrations and other information.

American Society of Civil Engineers — Figs. 35, 36, 38, 62, 67, 73, 88, 90, 91, 94, 101, 102, 103, 104, 107, 108, 109, 113, 120, 127, 129, 130, 134, 135, 136, 148, 149, 150, 163, 164, 165, 166, 167, 168, 175, 176, 177, 178, 179, 180, 181, 182, 189, 191, 192, 193, 194, 220, 221, 226, 227, 228, 229, 234, 245, 250.
American Society for Testing and Materials — Figs. 61, 68, 96, 97, 98, 183, 184.
Australian Road Research Board — Fig. 82.
British Geotechnical Society — Figs. 159, 160, 195.
British Society for Strain Measurement — Fig. 93.
Bureau of Reclamation — Fig. 190.
Civil Engineering and Public Works Review — Figs. 99, 100, 121, 124, 235, 236, 237.
Director, Building Research Establishment. — Figs. 30, 31, 32, 33, 78, 83, 105, 114, 115, 116, 169, 170, 185, 210, 211, 212, Table 2.
Electrical Research Association — Figs. 161, 162.
Engineering — Figs. 18, 19, 20.
G. T. Foulis & Co. Ltd. — Figs. 117, 233, 247 (a).
Geonor A/S — Figs. 37, 55, 58, 66.
Grafische Betriebe und Verlag GmbH — Figs. 230, 231, 232.
H. M. S. O. — Fig. 65.
Institute of Physics and The Physical Society — Fig. 87.
Institution of Civil Engineers — Figs. 56, 57, 75, 76, 119, 122, 123, 125, 151, 153, 154, 158, 199, 200, 201, 222, 223, 224, 225, 244, 249, Table 5.
Institution of Highway Engineers — Figs. 186, 187, 188.
Institution of Structural Engineers — Fig. 40.
Interfels — Figs. 21, 22, 23, 132, 133, 137, 143, 144, Table 1.

Journal of Mechanics and Physics of Solids — Figs. 85, 86.

National Research Council of Canada — Figs. 43, 59, 69, 71, 72, 92, 112, 128, 145, 146, 147, 155, 156, 157, 213, 214, 216, Table 4.

Slope Indicator Company (Seattle) — Figs. 63, 139.

Sociedad Mexicana de Mecanica de Suelos A. C. — Figs. 171, 172, 173.

Soil Instruments Ltd. — Figs. 77, 79, 81, 118, 126.

Terrametrics — Figs. 26, 27, 28, 64, 131.

University of Toronto Press — Figs. 174, 251, Table 6.

Waterways Experimental Station (U. S. Army) — Figs. 45, 46, 47, 48, 49, 50, 51, 52.

John Wiley & Sons Ltd. — Fig. 24.

December 1972

T. H. Hanna
University of Sheffield

CONTENTS

Chapter 7 — The Recording and Processing of Field Data

Chapter 8 — Instrumentation of Laboratory Scale Foundations

1 | Introduction

1.1. Soil Occurrence and the Influence of Geology

This text is concerned with the behaviour of soil masses in the vicinity of engineering structures. Because the composition of natural and artificial soil masses will be referred to throughout the text and because the ability to predict and also interpret soil mass behaviour depends on the skill of the engineer in describing the soil both quantitatively and qualitatively, it is useful to review very briefly the occurrence of natural soils. Soils may be divided into two wide groups on the basis of origin: (a) residual soils which were derived in place from the parent bedrock, and (b) transported soils which were deposited by the action of processes such as wind, water and ice. These groups cover a wide range of physical and chemical characteristics because the parent bedrock materials, from which all soils are derived, have varying characteristics depending on their origin. Excellent descriptions of soil occurrence are to be found in a number of soil mechanics textbooks (e. g. Leonards [1962]).

The processes of geology form rock and soil masses into land forms with their varying topographies. Land topography and its historical development is an important topic at the reconnaissance and planning stages of an engineering project and is usually studied in association with soil maps and aerial photography.

Geologic processes also control the future behaviour of the soil mass under load. An excellent example of the influence of geological factors

on the engineering properties of water laid sediments is the case of
the varved clay. (Leggett [1958]). Such materials are believed to have
formed in glacial lakes, a coarse silt size layer being deposited during
the summer and a thinner and finer layer being deposited during the
cold winter periods. Hundreds, and in some cases thousands, of
repeated layers have been encountered and because the individual
layers have different strength and deformation characteristics, the
behaviour of the soil mass is difficult to predict. Erosion of overlying
deposits of the soil stratum causes the underlying soil to rebound, but
because the soil is not unloaded in the horizontal direction, large lateral
stresses are locked in the soil mass and such deposits are known as
overconsolidated soils. (Terzaghi [1943]). With clays subjected to
overconsolidation a system of joints and cracks may result, especially
near to the ground surface, and the behaviour of the mass of clay is
controlled, therefore, to a large extent by the crack or joint pattern
present. An excellent example of such deposits is the London clay
formation (Bishop [1966]). Alteration of the chemical composition of
the water in the pores of a soil also may have important consequences
and perhaps the best known examples are the post-glacial clays of
eastern Canada and Scandinavia which have been subject since deposition
to (a) uplift above sea level and (b) percolation of fresh water through
the uplifted soil mass. (Kenny [1964]). The effect of leaching the
saline solution from the clay pores has been to increase the sensitivity
of the clay to disturbances and strain. Thus, while these clays are
stable in their undisturbed state, they can become very unstable when
subjected to slight changes in external loading with catastrophic
consequences. (Crawford and Eden [1967]). These three examples
draw attention to the influence of geological factors and a thorough
survey of such factors has been presented by Terzaghi (1955).

In examining a site for a proposed construction the engineer, and in
some cases the engineering geologist, draws on the geological information which is available for that area. Such information varies widely
throughout the world and the information at their disposal usually
depends on the previous construction activity in the area. Use is made
of geological maps, well records, soil maps, old mining records, old
reports and maps of the area plus local knowledge and the history of
any buildings in the region. Additional information may be obtained
from a site inspection and, if warranted, trial pits, sampled borings
etc. may be put down. The nature of the site study depends to a

large extent on the proposed structure and the general soil conditions, but the main object of the study is to determine the nature of the ground and ground-water and provide quantitative measures of expected soil behaviour.

From this very brief glimpse of soil occurrence and the influence of geology it is hoped that the reader will be made aware of the basic differences between soil engineering and other branches of engineering mechanics. The difference lies not in the mechanics used but in the physical behaviour of a naturally occurring material (soil) compared with that of a material such as steel whose parametric constants can be controlled within very fine limits during the manufacturing process. Perhaps this difference and its recognition holds the key to the future developments in the field of foundation analysis. Unfortunately it is still impossible to describe an ideal soil, let alone a natural soil, using engineering mechanics methods, although fascinating developments in this pursuit have taken place during the last half century since the subject was first tackled by Terzaghi using the principles of engineering mechanics. For this reason foundation engineering is both an art and a science and will always remain so. To bridge the gap, in part, between the art and the science, more and more engineers are turning to the use of field instruments to enable them to observe foundation performance and thus evaluate their designs. This text is devoted to this general problem.

1.2. Site Investigations

Most practising civil engineers recognise the need for a sub-surface investigation of the soil and ground water conditions prior to the design and construction of any engineering or building structure. The primary purpose of the investigation is to assess the suitability and characteristics of sites as they affect the design and construction of civil engineering works and the security of neighbouring structures. Adequate and reliable information concerning the ground and soil conditions is fundamental to the design of any structure founded on the ground or constructed of earth material. The required information is usually obtained by one or more of three general methods: (a) remote sensing from aircraft, airphoto interpretation (Mekel [1970]) and geophysical methods, (b) the interpretation of standard mechanical and physical tests for representative but "slightly disturbed" samples and (c) the retrieval and testing of "undisturbed" samples of the highest quality. Methods of mapping from air photographs and the various geophysical techniques are now widely used in civil engineering practice. However, they still lack the precision attainable from well executed borings but they have the advantages of speed and greatly reduced costs for preliminary exploration. Mapping by remote sensing is still at the development stage and is not in general use by the civil engineer.

The recovery of "slightly disturbed" samples of soil covers the vast majority of site investigation work. These "slightly disturbed" samples are usually obtained in clay soils by pushing, or in hard clays by driving, an open tube into the bottom of a borehole. The sampling tube is usually of 50 to 100 mm diameter and the borehole may be lined with a steel casing or unlined depending on the ground conditions. Sampling is discontinuous but by arranging that samples are taken from different elevations in adjacent boreholes, the ground is assumed to be properly sampled. Such samples are carefully sealed to prevent loss of moisture, packed in special crates and sent to the laboratory either for storage at constant temperature and humidity, or for testing. It is now recognised that all samples recovered in this manner are subject to an unknown amount of mechanical disturbance due to the combined actions of drilling the borehole, installing the sampler in the ground at the base of the borehole, recovering the sample, waxing and transporting it to the laboratory and finally preparing it in the laboratory for testing. The amount of disturbance varies with the ground conditions, the skill of the personnel involved, the machinery used and the degree of soil stratification. Extensive research at laboratory and field scale by Rowe (1968, 1972) has demonstrated the importance of the last mentioned variable and has shown that very large sampling of such soils may be required.

"Undisturbed" samples are very expensive and can hardly be planned until representative samples and exploration holes on the site have been evaluated. In soft clays which are sensitive to "disturbance" piston sampling techniques in association with large diameter samplers are used. This is a highly specialized operation and details are given by Rowe (1968).

To get even larger samples of "partly disturbed" stiff clay, block sampling methods may be employed either from the side or bottom of an excavation or trench, or from the bottom of a specially drilled shaft of about 1 m diameter (U. S. B. R.). Samples are recovered at preselected vertical intervals as the excavation or shaft is advanced. Such methods have been in use for several decades and one of their primary virtues is that the ground is exposed to the engineer and consequently he can select the soil of greatest engineering significance and include it in the sample.

In sands and gravels undisturbed samples are impossible to recover with the techniques currently in use. The engineer may require a knowledge of the laminations present, the grading, the in-situ density, permeability, compressibility and angle of internal friction. With the Bishop sand sampler (Bishop 1948) it is possible to recover and inspect the laminations present but the natural density of the sand is likely to be affected. For the other quantities mentioned, in-situ test methods are used and semi-empirical techniques of interpretation are followed to provide quantitative data.

In-situ testing is now a recognised and growing part of site investigation practice. At present the vane shear apparatus is used for the in-place strength determination of soft and sensitive clays (Skempton [1948]) whereas dynamic testing methods are extensively used for the assessment of sands and gravels as well as very dense glacial tills (Fletcher [1965]). Permeability testing of soils in-situ is also well established and a wide range of techniques is available to cater for most ground conditions (ASTM [1967]).

For strength and deformation measurement or prediction the trend is towards "static" test methods. The Dutch cone apparatus has been used extensively for the assessment of the competence of sands and their variability. (De Beer [1963]). Semi-theoretical methods have enabled the resistances recorded by this apparatus to be translated into strength and compressibility data suitable for design use. In clays and "soft" rocks, equipment established as a small scale laboratory tool has been taken into the field and the 0.6 m square shear box apparatus is now a fairly common sight on large sites where the strength of fissured clays is required. (Bishop [1966]). Plate bearing tests, either at the base of excavations or pits, against the walls of trenches, or at the base of a lined shaft, are now common and plates of up to about 1 m diameter are in use. (Burland and Lord [1970]). Testing at this scale and degree of sophistication is expensive and is performed in association with other tests and perhaps large scale block sampling (Lo, Adams and Seychuck [1969]).

At the site investigation stage, ground water samples and ground water observations are made. The samples enable the quantitative determination of soluble sulphates, chlorides and the degree acidity or alkalinity present. The position of the static ground water table requires the use of a sensing device referred to as a piezometer. The purpose of the piezometer is to record accurately the position of the ground water table corresponding to different depths. Thus artesian conditions can be delimited. This subject is reviewed in some detail in Chapter 3.

Large scale testing is becoming part of the site investigation process and it is not uncommon to encounter full size pile and anchor test programmes, trial embankments, trial slopes, compaction trials for the selection of plant, de-watering studies and large scale bearing tests such as tank testing. With all of these methods and types of tests a certain minimum degree of field monitoring is demanded and certain features of these tests are covered in Chapter 6.

It should be appreciated that all site investigations are limited because only a very small part of the soil mass is sampled and described quantitatively. It is usual, therefore, that design recommendations are generally covered by the terms "errors and omissions" or "errors in assumptions". For this reason it is imperative that all general statements given in a design report are qualified where the engineer can only obtain a partial idea of the ground conditions. Thus it is recognised that the design process is far from perfect because the materials being used cannot be described with a high degree of engineering precision.

1.3. The Behaviour of Soil Under Load

All soils comprise discrete particles, but some particles are so small that they can only be viewed by microscopy. The discrete particles are not regular shaped but range from near spherical (sands, silts and gravels) to highly angular, to near plate shaped and needle shaped in the clay size range. Because soil particles are not strongly bonded they are free to move (relatively) with respect to one another. Hence soil mass behaviour is controlled by the laws pertaining to a system of particles. This is another basic difference from solid mechanics and fluid mechanics.

When a mass of soil is loaded, force is transmitted through the soil at the points of contact between adjacent particles. These forces comprise a normal and a tangential component at each point of contact. Very small deformation of the individual soil particles is caused by these forces. The vectorial summation of the individual load changes at the points of contact equals the applied external load change, while the movement of the soil mass is the vectorial sum of the individual movements of the individual particles. These individual movements comprise elastic and plastic type deformations. The plastic deformations occur when the shear force between adjacent particles equals the shear resistance. When soil particles slide relative to one another, a rearrangement of the soil particles occurs and as soon as sliding at the point of contact develops an irreversible deformation has taken place. Consequently the load-deformation behaviour of all soils is non-linear even at low load levels. From a fundamental viewpoint the stress system at the points of contact of individual particles controls behaviour but it is impossible to build up a load-deformation relationship for a soil in this manner owing to the very large number of points of contact involved. The study of soil behaviour, therefore, relies on the measurement of the parametric constants of an element of soil (the sample) consisting of a large and unknown number of particles.

With natural soils the space between the individual particles is filled with air and/or water. Therefore soils are multiphase comprising a mineral phase and a pore phase. These phases interact chemically and physically as follows. First, water or air or both can flow through the soil and alter the forces at the points of contact between the individual particles. Secondly, when load is applied to a soil mass part is carried by the mineral skeleton and part by the pore fluid. The load is distributed to the two phases in relation to their stiffnesses. Because water is almost incompressible, all of the applied load is resisted by an increase in the pore fluid for a fully saturated soil. However, water can slowly flow through the pores in the soil mass and with time the applied load is slowly transferred to the soil grains, the rate depending on the pore size. This process is known as consolidation and is dealt with in some detail later. As the water escapes from the soil pores, the soil compresses and the amount of compression depends on the difference between the applied stress and the stress in the water in the pores. This difference is known as the effective stress, and the discovery of this

relationship led to the development of soil mechanics. This was the first
major contribution by Terzaghi about 1920 to the establishment of the
science of Soil Mechanics.

In soil engineering work the engineer usually tests representative elements of the soil to be loaded by the structure foundations. By use of
Soil Mechanics Theory he checks stability and predicts movements using
very simplifying assumptions as discussed in Section 1.4. Of greatest
importance in analysis are the results of tests used to quantify the stress-
strain behaviour of the soil element. In the following paragraphs a very
brief review of a few of the standard tests is given.

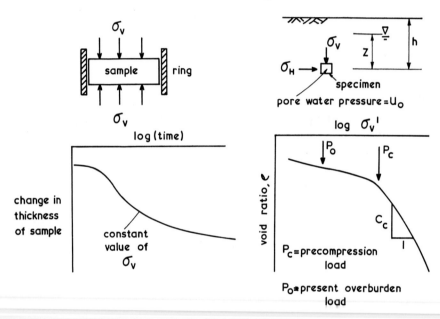

Fig. 1: The oedometer test and typical test results.

The oedometer or one dimensional compression test causes stress to be
applied to the soil specimen along the vertical axis, while strain in the
horizontal direction is prevented. Hence the axial strain is equal to the
volumetric strain. Figure 1 shows a sketch of the commonly used oedometer and typical test data which it provides. During a test the ratio
of the lateral effective stress to the vertical effective stress is constant
and is denoted by K_o, the coefficient of earth pressure at rest. When a
soil specimen is tested in the oedometer apparatus, load increments are
applied and the corresponding axial compression of the specimen with

time provide data which, when interpreted, give measures of the coefficient of consolidation c_v, the compression index C_c, the coefficient of volume compressibility m_v and the overconsolidation ratio. Details are given in most standard soil mechanics texts and the reader is referred to Wu (1966). There are several shortcomings to the standard oedometer test and this has resulted in the development of a number of more versatile and larger machines. The hydraulic oedometer developed by Rowe and Barden (1964) appears to be the most versatile and has enabled the consolidation of natural soils to be measured with confidence.

For ultimate strength determination the triaxial apparatus is extensively used both at a commercial and research level. There are, however, basic limitations as discussed by Roscoe (1970). A cylindrical specimen of soil is subjected to a confining pressure σ_3 which hydrostatically stres-

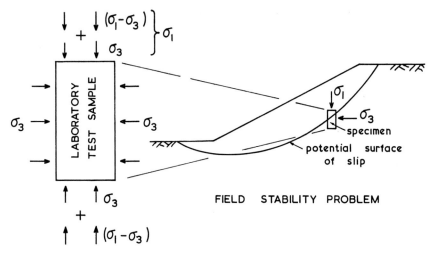

Fig. 2: The triaxial test.

ses all surfaces of the specimen equally. The axial stress σ_1 is increased until the specimen fails. The specimen diameter is usually in the range 40 mm to 250 mm although larger sizes are occasionally in use for special testing of gravels and rock fill. (Marsal [1966]). The length of the specimen is up to twice the diameter. The arrangement for application of the confining pressure σ_3 and the axial pressure σ_1 is shown in Figure 2. By use of a null device or transducers it is possible to measure the pressures generated in the pore fluid inside a specimen and techniques are available for volume change measurement. The standard text dealing with all aspects of triaxial testing is due to Bishop and Henkel (1962). Depending on the drainage conditions permitted during a triaxial test, the tests are usually referred to as quick or undrained (no drainage), drained (full

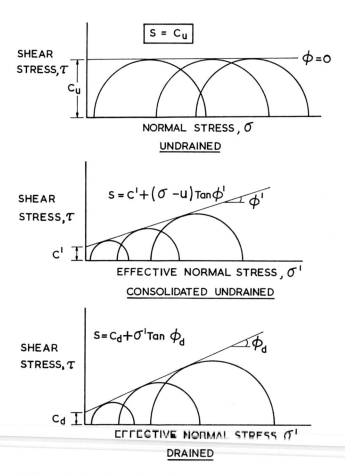

Fig. 3: Mohr circle plots for undrained, consolidated undrained and drained triaxial tests.

dissipation of pore water pressure) and consolidated undrained with pore water pressure measurement. Test information is usually presented in Mohr circle plots of stress, Figure 3, the strength parameters being the "cohesion" intercept and the slope of envelope tangential to the circles, ϕ. A large number of symbols, sometimes confusing, are in use to denote details of the different tests that can be used. As the axial stress, σ_1, is increased the specimen deforms and where drainage is permitted during the test a volume change results. Figure 4 gives a typical stress-

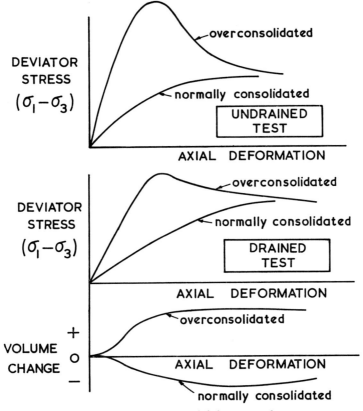

Fig. 4: Deviator stress — axial deformation diagrams.

strain diagram and illustrates the general features of the triaxial test result. The slope of the stress-strain diagram, at any stress level, provides a measure of the modulus of deformation of the soil.

Many other standard and special laboratory tests are used to describe and classify soils. Most of the classification tests are described in B. S. 1377 (1967) or in A. S. T. M. manual on soil testing.

The behaviour of soils under load is complex and today very sophisticated test equipment, methods of sample preparation and interpretation are in use. Several excellent text books are available as well as a number of leading journals and conference proceedings and some of these are referred to in the list of references.

1.4. Soil Problems in Civil Engineering — A Review

The design and construction engineer has to deal with the ground in all projects. These encounters with soil and rock are diverse. For example he uses the soil to carry the weight of structures; he uses the soil as an engineering material for construction purposes; he forms structures within the ground; he designs structures to retain soils in the vicinity of excavations and other openings, and he has to deal with soil in a number of special areas such as under dynamic loads. Over the years the engineering and construction industry has built up techniques for the description and solution of such problems. This section draws attention to some features of these general problems.

1.4.1. Foundations

For economy reasons most foundations are placed in the soil or rock near to the ground surface. The design of the foundation requires that it performs satisfactorily when loaded during the lifetime of the struc-

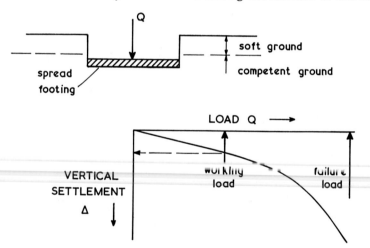

Fig. 5: A spread foundation.

ture. Several general types of foundation are in use depending on the strength of the ground. Where competent soil is near to the ground surface loads are transmitted to the soil by spread footings. Today almost all spread footings are of reinforced concrete construction. Figure 5 sketches a spread foundation. In many site conditions a stratum of highly compressible soil may be encountered near to the ground surface and where buildings are of considerable weight the most usual method of support is by a system of vertical columns passing through the soft soil to an underlying bearing stratum. Such members are referred to as piles and the foundation is known as a piled foundation or a deep foundation. Figure 6 illustrates a structure supported on piles.

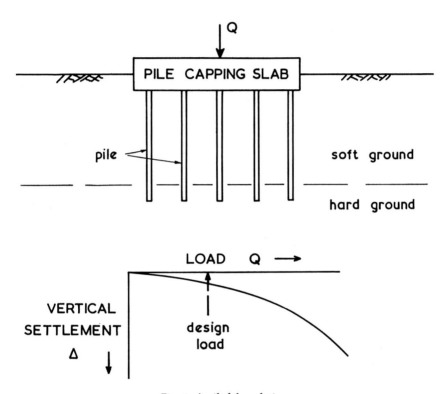

Fig. 6: A piled foundation.

The size of a foundation is controlled by the loads it is required to carry. The loads are due to self weight (dead load) and other loads from furnishings, storage etc. which are not of a permanent nature (live loads). Because foundations are placed a finite distance below ground level, the weight of soil excavated reduces the gross building load to the net load (Skempton [1951]). Figure 7 illustrates the concept of net and gross loads for a structure supported on a mat or raft foundation i. e. a footing which covers the plan area of the structure. The technique of reducing the net load by soil removal is sometimes referred to as flotation. Few building foundations are entirely compensated (i. e. the net load is zero), but partial flotation is a very common design technique used primarily for the control of settlement (Golder [1964], D'Appolonia and Lambe [1971]) because structures are normally very sensitive to structural distress from movement and differential movement. (Skempton, Peck and MacDonald [1956]).

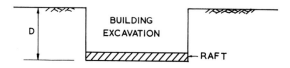

ORIGINAL PRESSURE AT FOUNDATION BASE LEVEL = γD

GROSS PRESSURE = q_{gross} = TOTAL WEIGHT OF STRUCTURE TO BASE OF FOUNDATION $/$ TOTAL AREA OF FOUNDATION

NETT PRESSURE = q_{nett} = $q_{gross} - \gamma D$

Fig. 7: The concept of net and gross loads.

1.4.2. Soil as a construction material

In use as a construction material soil is selected and controlled during placement. The placing and control during placement are referred to as stabilization and the soil is known as fill. Because large quantities of fill may be required and the available source soil may vary widely, the purpose of site control is to ensure that the properties of the fill correspond to those assumed or employed in design.

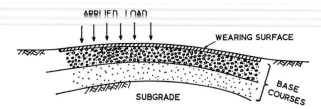

Fig. 8: A highway foundation.

Most roads and airfields use soil as a construction material. To transmit the large surface forces to the relatively weak soil either flexible or rigid pavements are in use. A general sketch of a highway pavement is given in Figure 8.

Road embankments and water retaining embankments (earth and rock-fill dams) are good examples of soil as a construction material. In the water retaining embankment an impermeable zone is required to control leakage. Usually highly permeable zones are located on either side of the impervious core to add to stability (Figure 9). Control of seepage forces within the structure is accomplished by filter layers to prevent the washing of fine soil particles through the voids of the coarser adjacent material. In all embankment construction work it is essential that a high degree of quality control is achieved on site, especially for high structures. Perhaps the earth dam structure is the best example where use has been made of field instrumentation to monitor actual behaviour and compare with design assumption during and subsequent to construction.

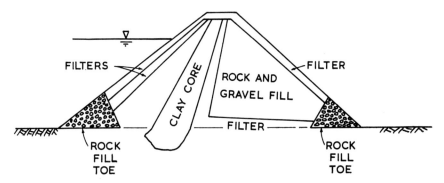

Fig. 9: An earth-rock fill dam.

There are several special areas where soil is used to create a foundation. The writer has used a pad of well compacted granular fill to span a soft foundation soil and thus permit a fairly large load to be carried (see also Mitchell and Gardner [1971]). In other circumstances fill has been used to cause a soft stratum of soil to compress. After the consolidation has reached a predetermined degree, the fill is removed and the structure is placed on the strengthened ground. This technique is referred to as preloading and is considered in detail by Aldrich (1964). Land reclamation entails the filling of large enclosures of low lying and usually soft ground with fill. The fill is either pumped into the enclosures and allowed to sediment, usually in a controlled manner, or it is placed mechanically. An excellent treatment of this topic is given by Whitman (1970). An extension of land reclamation to the reclamation structure has been brought about by the need for harbour and terminal facilities and airports. The site for such a facility may be built by filling, and in one or two cases artificial islands have been built by filling inside a sheet pile retaining structure.

1.4.3. Underground Structures

The loading of structures built below the ground surface and completely surrounded by soil is complex and depends on the interaction between the soil and the structure. The buried pipeline is a good example and it may be flexible or rigid in construction. The design of such pipes is based primarily on semi-empirical methods supported by many successful uses. Figure 10 shows an illustration of a pipe of 0.9 m diameter buried in a trench. In other cases pipes may be placed beneath embankments. With both conditions a number of design considerations arise and these are dealt with by Clarke (1966).

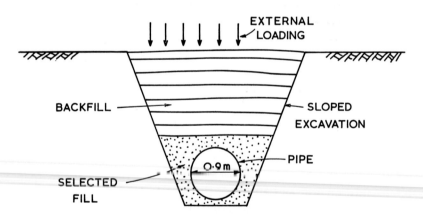

Fig. 10: A buried pipeline.

Tunnels through soft ground such as clays and sands are another type of structure which demand much greater design and construction control owing to the fact that (a) they may be located at considerable depth, (b) they may be driven near to adjacent settlement sensitive structures and (c) operational requirements demand that they deflect a few millimeters only under load. (Peck [1969]).

Structures for underground subways formed by a cut and cover method of construction are intermediate between the earth retaining structure (1.4.4.) und the underground structure. One of the most successful applications of the cut and cover technique was in the new Oslo subway (N.G.I. [1962]).

1.4.4. Earth Retaining Structures

A common type of earth retaining structure is the gravity wall, as illustrated in Figure 11. The structure has a large base in contact with the foundation soil and is designed to be stable with respect to sliding, overturning and vertical loading of the foundation soil. The gravity wall has several disadvantages and in some situations a driven sheet pile wall supported by an anchor tie, Figure 12, is a more economical solu-

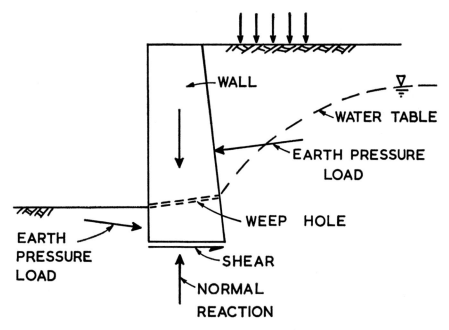

Fig. 11: Gravity retaining wall.

tion especially for high walls or walls built as part of a shiploading dock. An extension of the anchored bulkhead is the multiple anchored wall. The primary use of anchors was as a construction convenience in the solution of the deep excavation problem, Hanna and Littlejohn (1969).

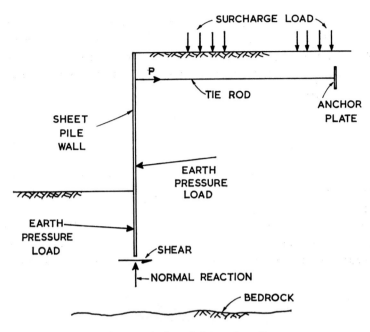

Fig. 12: Anchored sheet pile wall.

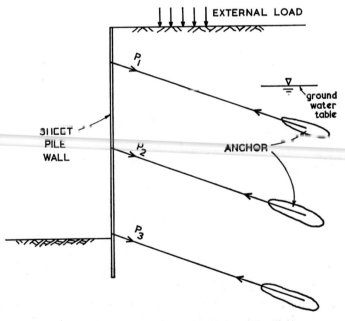

Fig. 13: Tied-back sheet pile wall.

With this method of wall support internal strutting (Figure 13) can be eliminated. The design and construction problem is one of anchor length, load and inclination selection to ensure that the retaining structure is safe and does not move excessively. Over the last decade many novel wall and anchor systems have been introduced by the construction industry. The most recent is the use of reinforced earth in which tensile membranes are installed in the retained soil at close vertical intervals and attached to a special wall skin, Figure 14. In this manner the ideas of Vidal (1966) have been applied to the solution of a practical problem.

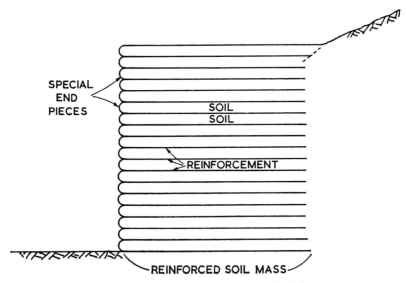

SPECIAL END PIECES

SOIL
SOIL

REINFORCEMENT

REINFORCED SOIL MASS

Fig. 14: A reinforced earth vertical-sided slope.

In all earth retaining problems the selection of the wall cross section and the design of the anchoring system require the computation of the loads exerted by the soil against the wall and their distribution. Their distribution is controlled by the movements in the soil adjacent to the wall which in turn are controlled by the rigidity of the wall. Movements may present a design problem in the bracing of deep excavations in clay. In such circumstances the earth retaining structure problem cannot be divorced from the excavation problem. As detailed in a later chapter enormous progress is being made with this problem by the use of elaborate field monitoring of performance coupled with sophisticated methods of data analysis.

1.4.5. Slopes and Excavations

Figure 15 illustrates a natural slope on which a building is placed. Because the soil surface is not horizontal, there is the gravity component of the soil-weight tending to move part of the slope downward. The increased load from the building, and perhaps decrease of soil shear strength in the slope with time, can lead to the instability of slopes which have been stable for many years prior to construction activity.

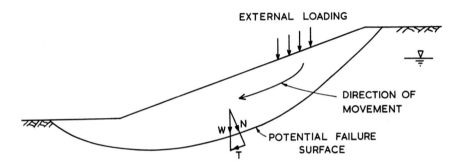

Fig. 15: The slope stability problem.

Stability problems of a similar nature arise with most artificial cuttings in clay soils and some of the problems which they may present to the civil engineer are reviewed by Bishop and Bjerrum (1960).

Sloped excavations may be on a relatively small scale such as are encountered in the construction of irrigation canals. The main problems demanding solution are protection against erosion from flowing water; protection against drying followed by wetting of the lining; and the natural variability of the ground from one location to another. Several large scale excavations have been required for ship canals and perhaps the best known is the Panama Canal where many stability problems were encountered during and subsequent to construction through the notoriously soft clay shales of the Cucuracha formation.

More modest and also more numerous excavation problems arise with the laying of underground services such as pipelines. Such excavations may be braced or unbraced depending on their depth and the ground

conditions encountered, Figure 16. For temporary excavations a temporary bracing system is usually required to retain the vertical-sided slope
or to control clods of dirt falling into the excavation.

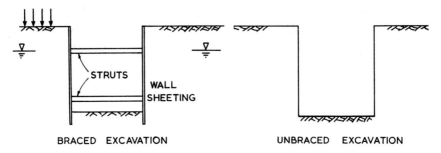

Fig. 16: Braced and unbraced excavations.

1.4.6. Special Problems

In addition to the more common types of problem illustrated in the
above sections there are other problems which can be extremely important. Included are the problems presented by ground subsidence due to
mineral extraction such as water, coal, oil, gas and salts. Ground surface
movements of up to 8 m have resulted from oil extraction in Long Beach,
California and movements of equal magnitude have taken place in parts
of Mexico City since the beginning of the present century as a result of
water extraction from the aquifer beneath that city. Such movements
present very difficult problems in the solution of foundations for proposed constructions and in these areas many novel solutions have been
adopted.

Construction in the permanently frozen regions of the world present
problems of soil thawing and the resulting deterioration of the ground
composition and strength. (Brown and Johnston [1964]). In other parts
some soils are susceptible to freezing temperatures and very large heaves
can result if a supply of free water is available to permit the freezing
process to proceed. These problems are usually encountered in highway
construction works although special problems may also arise in the
design of the foundations for refrigeration plant.

Some granular soil deposits can be densified by vibrations. Such vibrations are normally transmitted to the foundations of buildings by equipment like large compressors, drop forge hammers and turbines. In circum-

stances where it is believed that the frequency of the vibration may coincide with the natural frequency of the soil foundation, the engineer has the choice of several methods of prevention. He can alter the frequency of vibration by increasing the mass of the foundation or he may improve the foundation soil by a stabilization technique, either mechanical or chemical, thereby altering its natural frequency and settlement potential. (Major [1962]).

Some soil formations are found naturally in a metastable structure and when loaded by either a static force or by an explosive or earthquake load they become highly unstable, and in some cases are transformed into a liquid phase thus permitting the disturbed soil mass to flow. The sensitive clays of Eastern Canada and Scandinavia are well known (Hutchinson [1962]) while other soils, e. g. loess deposits, may also provide spectacular flow behaviour under exceptional loading conditions (see Kezdi [1969]).

Earthquakes can present problems depending on the type of soil on which a building rests and the type of foundation employed. The 1964 earthquake in Alaska caused a very large earth slide as well as near complete damage to most of the buildings in Anchorage (Seed and Wilson [1966]).

There are many other equally important special foundation problems and the interested reader is referred to the various technical journals and specialist conference proceedings for further details.

1.5. The Principles of Foundation Design

In section 1.4. attention was drawn to a number of foundation problems which the civil engineer may be called upon to solve. The successful solution of each problem usually involves making use of soil mechanics theory in association with engineering geology knowledge, experience and cost considerations. From country to country and within a particular country it will be noted that the blend of these components varies widely and depends on the nature of the problem under consideration, available soils knowledge and construction know-how. Soil mechanics theories are used to describe in a quantitative manner the stress strain behaviour of "undisturbed elements" of soil which are subsequently used in the theoretical analysis of the soil mass under load. In the theoretical analysis of the soil mass, theories of continuum mechanics have been applied to stress distribution and stability problems and an example is given in a later part of this section. A knowledge of engineering geology aids in the selection of test specimens for laboratory testing because the behaviour of the soil en masse is regulated by the discontinuities present, the variability in plan and elevation, and the loading history to which it has been subjected in its geological past. In the selection of motorway routes, for example, the engineering geologist is of prime importance in the defining of former areas of mass instability which may be reactivated by construction activity (Symons and Booth [1971]).

Experience is a misnomer if it is associated with design and construction only. Today many engineers recognise the need for field evaluation and the feeding back of this information into the design process. Thus experience is the comparison of measured field performance against design assumptions. As one accumulates such knowledge, one's experience increases. Measured field performance not only relies on field instrumentation to record preselected quantities at predetermined positions, but it also requires observations of the problems encountered during construction; the differences between the ground conditions as exposed, say, in an excavation and the profile assumed in the analysis and any difficulties which arose during the construction of the design. Only by a thorough evaluation of the act of constructing does the foundation engineer add to his knowledge. This increase in knowledge relies on the availability and use of reliable methods of behaviour prediction. It is only in recent years that such methods have come within the grasp of the civil engineer. (Zienkiewicz and Cheung [1967]).

The selection of the best solution from a number of possible solutions is usually influenced by cost considerations and materials available and perhaps this is best illustrated with respect to earth fill dams where considerations such as climate, as it affects placement water content, may have a significant influence on the design and method of construction chosen. One major cause of variation in costs of construction of foundation works is uncertainty in dealing with unexpected foundation problems and the use of sophisticated methods for getting out of trouble. With modern methods of scientific management being applied in construction it is fairly common to find that the foundation specialist is only expected to provide a safe and quick method of forming a foundation. This of course depends on the nature and complexity of the problem.

All soil problems are highly complex and cannot be solved by "exact" methods because the science of soil mechanics is unable to describe soil behaviour in absolutely precise terms as discussed in 1.3. In addition it must always be remembered that soils possess several characteristics which are only partly understood and which cannot be quantified with rigour. These are: (1) the load-deformation behaviour of natural soils is non-linear, (2) behaviour is stress, time and environment sensitive, (3) natural soils vary both in plan and elevation and on every job only a very small part of the soil mass is seen. Consequently the soil mass has to be described with the aid of a number of small samples obtained from isolated areas. (4) all soils are sensitive to disturbance during the process of recovery from the ground. The disturbance may be with respect to strength, deformability or permeability, and thus the quantities determined from laboratory tests may be unlike those of the in-situ soil. Also the method of test can produce additional errors due to undesirable features of the test apparatus and method of test preparation (Roscoe [1970]), Rowe [1968]). Because of the nature and variability of soil masses and because of the many unknowns present, the theoretical model which uses soil mechanics principles may not represent the actual field problem with the required degree of accuracy. Therefore a trend which is emerging is that as construction progresses and more information is accumulated, the soil and boundary conditions are re-evaluated and the engineering solution is modified. The term "observational method" is sometimes used and this was set out by Peck (1969) in his Rankine lecture as follows:

1. Carry out exploration sufficient to establish at least the general nature, pattern and properties of the deposits, but not necessarily in detail.

2. Assess the most probable site conditions and the most unfavourable conceivable deviations from these conditions. In this assessment geology often plays a major role.

3. Establish the design based on a working hypothesis of behaviour anticipated under the most probable conditions.

4. Select quantities to be observed as construction progresses and calculate their anticipated values on the basis of the working hypothesis.

5. Calculate the values of the same quantities under the most unfavourable conditions compatible with the available data concerning the subsurface conditions.

6. Select in advance a course of action or modification of design for every foreseeable significant deviation of the observational findings from those predicted on the basis of the working hypothesis.

7. Measure the quantities to be observed and evaluate the actual conditions.

8. Modify the design to suit the actual conditions.

Peck has successfully used this method and he cites several cases.

From the above reasoning it will be appreciated that the interpretation of complex soil data, the selection of appropriate soil parameters and the modification of solutions require experience and intuition. Thus the requirements for the design of foundation structures are a sound knowledge of the principles of soil mechanics used in association with experience and intuition. If the latter is lacking many mistakes will occur. This judgement for engineering design can only be obtained by the careful measuring of the differences between the performances of real field structures and the idealization made in the mathematical models used for their analysis.

To illustrate the basic principles used in design, the case of foundation design is very briefly considered. Foundation engineering is the art of applying building loads to the ground so as to avoid excessive deformations. The general requirement is an assessment of the site conditions which are related to the type of the structure proposed. Soil borings provide the soil succession, bedrock position and the positions of the ground water table. Quantitative information on soil strength and compressibility is obtained from representative "partly disturbed" samples from these borings. Factors such as climate, building use and seismic activity have to be considered as they affect the type of foundation structure to be used. Having established the general foundation layout the engineer makes use of quantitative methods to check on bearing capacity and settlement. The requirements of a bearing capacity calculation are available soil strength data appropriate to the problem (e. g. immediate or long term) and a theory which makes use of the strength information (bearing capacity theory). For the settlement prediction calculation, use is made of "elastic" stress distribution theory to describe the stress changes caused in the ground by the applied foundation loads. The immediate settlement requires an estimate of the modulus of deformation of typical soil elements and is obtained by either laboratory or field testing. (Hanna and Adams [1968]). The magnitude and the rate of consolidation testing depend on the results of oedometer tests to provide the relevant coefficient of volume compressibility and coefficient of consolidation constants and on the site investigation to define the thicknesses of compressible layers and the drainage conditions present. In turn the magnitude, and in some cases the rate of settlement, control the allowable loads. The applied load becomes very important and it is imperative that the significance of the concepts of net and gross pressures are appreciated (Skempton [1957]). The requirements of, say, a slope design or a retaining structure design follow the same general approach but there are differences in detail pertaining to each. Excellent design information is provided by Tomlinson (1969), Wu (1962) and Lambe and Whitman (1969) dealing with most of the standard foundation problems and more sophisticated aspects are dealt with in the state-of-the-art review presented to the International Conferences (e. g. VII Conference [1969]).

1.6. Limitation in the Present Methods of Design

A survey of the relevant literature will suggest that the "properties" of undisturbed soils are more complex than laboratory tests on "undisturbed" samples indicate. Part of this complexity is regulated by the conditions under which the soil was deposited (e. g. the sedimentation of clays) and part resulted under the influence of the environment in which the soil aged. As mentioned earlier, during the processes of sampling, transportation and testing some of the basic or essential features of natural soils are damaged — hence the laboratory test displays only a distorted characteristic of the real soil.

The application of theories directly to the design of foundation structures requires complete test data pertaining to the sub-soil conditions. As mentioned above, the real nature of natural soils can only be determined by comparison of observed field performance with predictions based on laboratory tests. Thus field sampling in association with laboratory testing and the monitoring of field behaviour are complimentary facets of foundation design. Nevertheless, it is rare that a site comprises a uniform stratum of soil, yet almost all theories pertaining to foundation analysis are based on the assumption that the subsoil conditions may be approximated to a homogeneous stratum or several homogeneous strata. If this idealization of the subsoil condition is not possible, then it is very difficult to find out by observation the accuracy of soil mechanics theories. In such cases design can only be based on semi-empirical rules which are occasionally updated as data are accumulated, e. g. the standard penetration test for settlement prediction of foundations in sands. The design of foundation structures based on semi-empirical methods requires field and laboratory testing which will describe in an approximate manner the properties of the soil and in particular delimit the properties of the weakest and the strongest zones. Use of such data is most effective when analysed statistically. To make use of statistical techniques it is imperative that data from a number of sites pertaining to a particular soil formation are available. The procuring of such large amounts of statistical data is controlled by economic considerations and consequently only records from a soil stratum in a large city like London (Bishop [1966] may be subjected to statistical examination. Lumb (1970) discusses the role of statistics in the design of foundations in the Hong Kong region.

Much sound commentary has been given by Terzaghi (1942) and his remarks with respect to tunnel design are of interest and relevant. "... the inevitable shortcomings of pertinent theories in general should serve as a guide for judging to what extent the theoretical results can be depended upon. According to my opinion much steel could be saved by establishing a closer approximation between the assumptions and reality. The real load and stress conditions and the scattering of the conditions around the average will be disclosed by pressure cell and extensometer observations . . ." This philosophy of design could apply equally to slope stability, retaining structure or foundation design.

It is encouraging to note that the general approaches set out in Section 1.5, while not accepted by the majority of civil engineers dealing with foundation problems, are being pursued by an ever-increasing number. No doubt this trend is due in part to the feed-back of information on the successful completion of projects such as those described by Peck. Another reason is the introduction of the digital computing machine coupled with the finite element idealization of soil/structure representation and the availability of more rigorous methods of soil behaviour description (e. g. Schofield and Wroth [1968] and Rowe [1968]).

The current procedure for tackling soil problems is first to obtain as clear a picture as possible of the pattern and the extent of the subsurface conditions present at the site. The second procedure is to quantify the soil properties and their variability and hence 'average' values of the soil properties are selected for use in the design method. It is not surprising, therefore, that the degree of accuracy of the design method varies (a) with the problem under study and (b) with the ground conditions present and in particular their complexity. The design of foundation structures, therefore, is always subject to limitations usually of unknown magnitude. For this reason further progress depends mainly on improvements in methods of field measurement, on the quality of field observation programmes, particularly their scope and detail, and on the use of the results of such field observations to define limitations in design methods and to provide a reliable basis for the development of more logical approaches to design.

In future work it is to be expected that the traditional methods of design will become more scientific as the advantages and benefits of such methods become accepted and the profession has access to the services which are required to enable effective use to be made of field data. The next section reflects on the general requirements of field instrumentation.

1.7. Comment

It is essential that the engineer should be able to quantify his design before he can speak with authority. In foundation engineering the quantities of direct interest to the engineer are usually forces and displacements. Because some foundation structures are large and behave in a complex and redundant manner, it is essential to obtain knowledge about the distribution of forces and displacements and to preselect the measuring locations of these quantities so that the data can be used to advantage in subsequent interpretation and in the control of construction progress.

During the last five years or so the civil engineer has become more aware of the many limitations of the routine approach to foundation design based on site investigation techniques which rely on a quantitative assessment of the parametric constants of the ground based on a physical examination of samples of soil in a partly disturbed condition recovered from small diameter boreholes and their testing in the laboratory using standard testing techniques which are known not to provide very realistic parameters. As mentioned in Section 1.3. these limitations are related in part to:

1. mechanical damage (disturbance) to the soil specimen during the sampling process,

2. a change in the stress and strain state of the specimen during sampling, which invariably changes the measured behaviour of that specimen from its real in-situ behaviour,

3. variability of the ground in plan and elevation resulting in the small test specimens being unrepresentative of the mass of ground as a whole, in many cases important structural features being completely missed,

4. the inflexibility of commercial test equipment which cannot reproduce the complex stress changes that occur under field loading conditions,

5. the fact that stress changes are seldom independent of the ground and in particular the variability of the ground from one location to another.

The limitations are also related to the simplifications which are required to translate the field design problem into the analytical model which is analysed by engineering mechanics methods. This simplification in the past was due to the enormous physical effort required to solve even the most simply defined boundary conditions. Today, thanks to the contribution made by the finite element representation of engineering problems and the powerful and efficient digital computing machines, it is possible to carry out "stress" and "strain" analyses for complex problems with a fair degree of success, provided it is possible to determine parametric constants which are representative of soil field loading behaviour. (Penman, Burland and Charles [1971]).

To overcome these limitations in part and to provide a design and predict the behaviour of a foundation structure with confidence, the foundation engineer is turning to large scale in-situ testing and evaluation techniques which overcome some of the five limitations mentioned above and hence provide more realistic design data. The in-situ testing techniques usually comprise large-scale loading tests such as tank testing, plate bearing tests, trial embankments and pile tests, where comprehensive instrumentation enables basic quantities of use in subsequent analyses

to be determined. The evaluation techniques usually consist of the monitoring of one or more aspects of field behaviour of actual structures.
As a rule, in the field observation of a foundation structure, the primary
objective is to assess its safety under service loading conditions whereas
in a minority of cases the objective may be to improve the basic knowledge of behaviour and hence improve the methods of designing similar
structures in the future. In the former case it is usual to measure displacements only, and these data when checked against predicted behaviour provide a measure of actual performance against anticipated
performance. With the exception of very special cases, safety problems
should not arise unless the movements exceed the anticipated values
by an appreciable amount and the environmental conditions are such
that adjacent foundations and their superstructures will be subject to
distress. When the behaviour of the foundation structure is to be investigated in more detail, the sophistication of the observations increases and
both deformation and load measurements may be required. The primary
importance of such measurements is, after all, a consequence of the fact
that the design engineer interprets the behaviour of the structures and
designs them by considering the propagation of the external forces inside
the structure. It will be appreciated that the determination of stresses
and strains in a foundation structure does not eliminate the measurement
of displacements. In effect, the primary purpose of an overall displacement measurement programme is to delimit zones of importance where
it was not feasible to install load measuring and other instruments owing
to cost limitations or other factors.

Despite these general observations it must be emphasised that considerable difficulty arises in the measurement of forces and displacements under field conditions due to the often hazardous site conditions
present and the change in conditions of most soils and rocks with time,
even under constant loading. Consequently all measurement work
requires experience which can allow for variables such as the ground
conditions and the structure or component to be monitored, the accuracy
required, the time scale of observation, the robustness of instruments bearing in mind the installation environment and the site control of personnel.
Finally, the purpose of the observation work has to be clear and it is imperative that consideration has been given to the subsequent interpretation of the observations and the feed-back of these results into future
design work. If this vital link is missing, then the value of any field
evaluation programme is greatly reduced.

In conclusion, it is universally agreed in the foundation engineering field and also in civil engineering in general that knowledge of the real behaviour of field structures is, in general, inadequate and consequently the engineering profession must promote and finance systematic studies into an evaluation of the behaviour and the prediction of behaviour of real structures, in collaboration with national and international research institutes and universities. The following chapters of this text draw the attention of the reader to some of the instruments which are available and to some installations where this philosophy has been pursued to advantage.

References

ALDRICH, H. P. (1964), "Precompression for the support of shallow foundations", Design of foundations for the control of settlement, American Society of Civil Engineers, 471—505.

American Society for Testing and Materials (1967), Special Technical Publication No. 417, — Permeability and Capillarity of Soils.

American Society for Testing and Materials (1966), "Book of Standards — Part II"

BISHOP, A. W., (1966), "The strength of soils as engineering materials", Geotechnique, Vol. 16, No. 2, 89—130.

BISHOP, A. W., and Henkel, D. J., (1962), "The measurement of soil properties in the triaxial test", Arnold, London, Second Edition.

BISHOP, A. W., and BJERRUM, L., (1960), "The relevance of the triaxial test to the solution of stability problems", Norwegian Geotechnical Institute, Publication No. 34.

British Standard 1377, (1967), "Method of testing soils for civil engineering purposes". British Standards Institution, London.

BROWN, R. J. E., and JOHNSTON, G. H., (1964), "Permafrost and related engineering problems", Endeavour, Vol. 23, No. 89, 66—72.

BURLAND, J. B., and LORD, J. A., (1970), "The load deformation behaviour of middle chalk at Mundford, Norfolk: a comparison between full scale performance and in-situ and laboratory measurement", In-situ Investigations in Soils and Rocks, British Geotechnical Society, 3—16.

CLARKE, N. W. B., (1966), "The load imposed on conduits lead under embankments or valley fills", Proceedings, Institution of Civil Engineers, London, Vol. 36, 63—98.

CRAWFORD, C. B., and EDEN, W. J., (1967), "Stability of natural slopes in sensitive clay", Proceedings, American Society of Civil Engineers, Vol. 93, No. SM 4, 419—436.

D'APPOLONIA, D. J., and LAMBE, T. W., (1971), "Floating foundations for control of settlement", Proceedings, American Society of Civil Engineers, Vol. 97, No. SM 6, 899—915.

DE BEER, E. E., (1963), "The scale effect in the transposition of the results of deep-sounding tests on the ultimate bearing capacity of piles and caisson foundations", Geotechnique, Vol. 13, No. 1, 39—75.

FLETCHER, G., (1965), "The standard penetration test: Its uses and abuses", Proceedings, American Society of Civil Engineers, Vol. 91, No. SM 4, 67—76.

GOLDER, H. Q., (1964), "State of the art of floating foundations", Design of Foundations for the Control of Settlement, American Society of Civil Engineers, 555—576.

HANNA, T. H., and ADAMS, J. I., (1968), "Comparison of field and laboratory measurements of the modulus of deformation of a clay", Soil Properties from in-situ measurements — A symposium. Highway Research Record, No. 243, 12—22.

HANNA, T. H., and LITTLEJOHN, G. S., (1969), "Design and construction consid-erations associated with retaining walls supported by prestressed tie backs". The Consulting Engineer (London) Part I, May, 50—53; Part 2, June, 49—52.

HUTCHINSON, J. N., (1961), "A landslide on a thin layer of quick clay at Furre, Norway", Geotechnique, Vol. 11, 69—94.

KEZDI, A., (1969), "Landslide in loess along the bank of the Danube", Proceedings, Seventh International Conference on Soil Mechanics and Foundation Engineering, Vol. 2, Mexico City, 617—626.

KENNY, T. C., (1964), "Sea level movements and the geologic histories of the post-glacial marine soils of Boston, Nicolet, Ottawa and Oslo", Geotechnique, Vol. 14, No. 3, 203—230.

LAMBE, T. W., and WHITMAN, R. V., (1969), "Soil Mechanics", John Wiley & Sons.

LEONARDS, G. A., (1962), "Foundation Engineering", McGraw Hill.

LO, K. Y., ADAMS, J. I., and SEYCHUCK, J. L., (1969), "The shear behaviour of a stiff fissured clay", Proceedings, Seventh International Conference on Soil Mechanics and Foundation Engineering, Mexico City, Vol. 1, 249—256.

LUMB, P., (1970), "Safety factors and the probability distribution of soil strength", Canadian Geotechnical Journal, Vol. 7, No. 3, 225—242.

MAJOR, A., (1962), "Vibration analysis and design of foundations for machines and turbines". Collett's Holdings Ltd. (London).

MARSAL, R. J., (1966), "Large scale triaxial testing of granular materials", American Society of Civil Engineers Structural Engineering Conference, Miami, Florida, Jan. 31 — Feb. 4.

MEKEL, J. F. M., (1970), "ITC Text Book of Photo interpretation Vol. VIII — Use of air photographs in geology and engineering", International Institute for Aerial Survey and Earth Sciences Delft.

MITCHELL, J. K., and GARDNER, W. S., (1971), "Analysis of load bearing fills over soft sub-soils". Proceedings, American Society of Civil Engineers, Vol. 97, No. SM 11, 1549—1571.

N.G.I., (1962), "Measurement at a strutted excavation, Oslo Subway, Vaterland I, Km 1.373", Tech. Report No. 6.

PECK, R. B., (1968), „Advantages and limitations of the observational method in applied soil mechanics", Geotechnique, Vol. 19. No. 2, 171—187.

PECK, R. B., (1969), "Deep excavation and Tunnelling in soft ground", Proceedings, Seventh International Conference on Soil Mechanics and Foundation Engineering, Mexico City, State of the Art Volume, 225—290.

PENMAN, A. D. M., BURLAND, J, B., and CHARLES, J. A., (1971), "Observed and predicted deformations in a large embankment dam during construction", Pro-ceedings, Institution of Civil Engineers, London, Vol. 49, May, 1—21.

ROSCOE, K. H., (1970), "The influence of strains in soil mechanics", Geotechnique, Vol. 20, No. 2, 129—170.

ROWE, P. W., and BARDEN, L., (1964), "The importance of free ends in triaxial testing", Proceedings, American Society of Civil Engineers, Vol. 90, No. SM 1, 1—17.

ROWE, P. W., (1968), "Failure of foundations and slopes on layered deposits in relation to site investigation practice", Proceedings, Institution of Civil Engineers, London, Paper 7057 S. Supplementary Volume, 73—131.

ROWE, P. W., (1971), "Theoretical meaning and observed values of deformation parameters for soil", Stress Strain Behaviour of Soils Symposium, Cambridge, 143—194.

ROWE, P. W., (1972), "The relevance of soil fabric to site investigation practice", Geotechnique, Vol. 22, No. 2, 19—30.

SCHOFIELD, A. N., and WROTH, C. P., (1968), "Critical state Soil Mechanics", McGraw Hill.

SEED, H. B., and WILSON, S. D., (1966), "The Turnagain Heights Landslide in Anchorage, Alaska", Soil Mechanics and Bituminous Material Laboratory, University of California, Berkley, Report.

Seventh International Conference on Soil Mechanics and Foundation Engineering, Mexico City, State of the Art Volume, 1969.

SKEMPTON, A. W., (1948), "Study of the geotechnical properties of some post-glacial clays", Geotechnique, Vol. 1, 7—22.

SKEMPTON, A. W., (1951), "The bearing capacity of clays", Building Research Congress, London, 180—189.

SKEMPTON, A. W., PECK, R. B., and MacDONALD, D. H., (1955), "Settlement analysis of six structures in London and Chicago", Proceedings, Institution of Civil Engineers, London, Vol. 4, No. 4, Part 1, 525—544.

SYMONS, I. F., and BOOTH, A. I., (1971), "Investigation of the stability of earthwork construction on the original line of Sevenoaks By-Pass Kent", Road Research Laboratory, Report LR 393.

TERZAGHI, K., (1942), "Shield tunnels of the Chicago subway", Journal of the Boston Society of Civil Engineers, Vol. 29.

TERZAGHI, K., (1943), "Theoretical Soil Mechanics", John Wiley & Sons.

TERZAGHI, K., (1955), "Influence of geological factors on the engineering properties of sediments", Economic Geology, Fiftieth Anniversary Volume, 557—718.

TOMLINSON, M. J., (1969), "Foundation design and construction", Pitman, Second Edition.

United States Bureau of Reclamation, (1963), "Earth Manual", U.S. Govt. Printing Office, Washington D.C.

VIDAL, H., (1966), "La Terre Armée", Annales de L'Institut Technique du Bâtiments et des Travaux Publics, No. 223—224, 888—937.

WHITMAN, R. V., (1970), "Hydraulic fills to support structural loads", Proceedings, American Society of Civil Engineers, Vol. 96, No. SM 1, 23—47.

WU, T. H., (1966), "Soil Mechanics", Allyn and Bacon Inc.

ZIENKIEWICZ, O. C., and CHEUNG, Y. K., (1966), "The finite element method in structural and continuum mechanics", McGraw Hill.

| 2 | Load Measurement |

2.1. Introduction

The construction of load measuring devices is quite simple and there are a number of commercially available types of acceptable design. It is, therefore, relatively easy to obtain readings of load on a foundation or a foundation component. However, because of the range of loads to be measured, the environments to be encountered, and the need in some cases to keep costs to a low level, load cells of differing principles of operation, differing degrees of sophistication and differing methods of site installation may be used. The choice of load cell type is usually controlled by three factors (i) the costs involved, (ii) the environment in which it is to be used. This term includes items such as access for reading, temperature, humidity and susceptibility to damage from construction works and (iii) the nature of the load to be measured and the accuracy required.

The purpose of this chapter is to review some of the load cells which may be used for foundation instrumentation, to consider the calibration of load cells, to mention the problem of errors and their control and to draw attention to some of the field problems which arise with load cell installation and subsequent recording. Because the subject is a relatively large and dynamic one the reader is referred to a number of standard references on the subject for fuller details. Most load cells are available commercially but with good workshop facilities and trained personnel it is possible to design and build load cells for a particular requirement.

In the past this has been a fairly common practice to field instrumentation problems in general, but with the rapid development of companies which provide field measuring equipment, installation, recording and interpretation services this is no longer common except for non-routine jobs.

2.2. The Mechanical Load Cell

In almost all load cells the principle of the deformation of an "elastic" body under the influence of an external force is utilized to determine the applied force by means of a cell calibration factor.

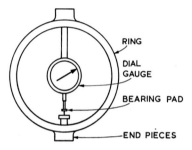

Fig. 17: The Proving Ring Principle.

The proving ring is a precision elastic load measuring device and, as its title suggests, it is usually used for the 'proving' or 'verification' of load in a testing machine, the ring being inserted in the test machine. There are many other uses for proving rings such as the measurement of tensile or compressive loads in field tests, e.g. plate bearing tests and pile loading tests. Rings are manufactured from high quality steel and in use are loaded diametrically through special loading plates which may be integral with the ring (bosses) or are clamped to the ring by bolts. Bolting of the load plates to the ring reduces the costs of manufacture but such rings are more susceptible to changes in calibration during use. However, careful machining of the loading pad which is clamped to the ring can reduce these disadvantages to an acceptable practical level and the great majority of proving rings in use, other than those used for test machine calibration purposes, are of the clamped loading pad type. The actual elongation or compression of the proving ring along the diameter of load application is measured by a micrometer screw or dial gauge mounted within the ring or is transduced into an electrical signal by means of a linear displacement transducer attached to the dial gauge and to a semi-automatic or automatic recording system (Chapter 7). The principal features of the proving ring are shown in Figure 17.

Compressive loads are applied to the ring through the end loading plates or bosses. There are several methods of arrangement of load application to the loading plates. In some designs one loading plate is machined plane and perpendicular to the axis of loading, the other being finished in the same manner or having a spherical radius. This spherical radius bears on a hardened steel pad. The load may be applied to the ring through screwed threads attached to the bosses and with this system much greater stability of the ring can be achieved by provision of a large diameter base plate.

For tensile load measurement screw adaptors are used which have spherical seatings incorporated to ensure axial loading of the ring. Where this arrangement is not possible, the tensile load is converted to a compressive load by the use of a stirrup.

The dial gauge or micrometer gauge must be positively secured to the proving ring so that the diametral change of the ring in the direction of loading is measured. With most rings small holes are drilled and the deflection measuring instrument is attached. Excellent repetition of reading over long periods of use results.

In most proving rings a dial gauge is used which reads direct to 0.002 mm. Such a system offers the advantage of providing a direct reading without recourse to any action on the part of the operator other than the customary light tap on the face of the dial to ensure that the gauge follows the deflection of the ring. The bearing pad on which the dial gauge spindle bears must be rigidly fixed to the ring and have a ground surface whose plane is normal to the line of load application. The chief disadvantage of the proving ring is that the dial gauge is not perfectly linear in the measurement of displacement and consequently, for very high accuracy work, the more cumbersome micrometer is preferred. For most field measurements the dial gauge is satisfactory. After repairing a dial gauge it is good practice to re-calibrate the ring.

Proving rings in use have a maximum load capacity from a few kilogrammes to about 200 t. Generally the small load carrying capacity rings are much more sensitive, in proportion to their maximum loads, than the large rings partly owing to the thickness of the ring. The reason for the upper load limit of about 200 t is primarily the size and weight involved and for the measurement of large forces other load measuring devices which are more stable (structurally) become more convenient.

The principles of proving ring design are covered in most standard text books on Strength of Materials, e. g. Timoshenko (1955).

Calibration of proving rings is carried out in a testing machine against a standard. For the highest precision work a "standard" deadweight machine such as that used by the National Physical Laboratory in England is used and an accuracy of about 1 in 25000 can be achieved. For field-use proving rings the standards of calibration required are not so high and the ring is usually calibrated against a "standard" load cell or proving ring maintained in the laboratory. With such methods of test calibration loads in tension or compression of $\pm 1\%$ accuracy for loads of 250 t will result.

In use the hysteresis of a proving ring is usually very small provided the end loading plates are satisfactory. The hysteresis of the dial gauge may be as much as one half of a division and for the great majority of load readings on site this error can be tolerated.

Variation in temperature has little effect on the elasticity of steel and except in cases where a very high degree of accuracy is demanded, no allowance for variations in the proving ring deflection due to temperature change is required. Laboratory calibrations are usually performed at 20° C and the correction to be applied to the measured deflection reading follows from the expression:

$$D_{20} = D_t [1 - R (t - 20)] \hspace{3cm} (2.1)$$

where D_{20} is the deflection corresponding to a temperature of 20° C, D_t is the deflection corresponding to a temperature of t° C, and R is the temperature coefficient of the ring which is approximately 0.0003 per degree C. Thus for a temperature rise of 5° C and a ring axial deflection of 1000 divisions the correction to the deflection reading is only 1.3 divisions.

Each proving ring is provided with a calibration against a standard. Because a direct plot of deflection against load usually cannot conveniently be drawn to a scale to give the desired accuracy, a calibration factor is provided which is the ratio of applied load to measured deflection. The calibration factor is usually assumed constant but for high accuracy work each calibration load should be divided by the deflection and the ring calibration constant plotted against deflection, a smooth line being drawn through the points.

Proving rings used on site are subjected to rough treatment and it is imperative that they are calibrated against a standard prior to use, subsequent to use and, if possible, during use. Only by so doing is it possible to guarantee the accuracy of the measured load readings.

The primary disadvantage of proving ring use in the field is the difficulty of ensuring that the applied load is axial. Attempts are made to achieve this by the use of ball bearing supports and by the very careful plumbing of the ring at the beginning of a test or measurement. Despite such precautions it is still possible for the ring to be loaded at an inclination with resulting error. Also, large capacity rings are heavy and cumbersome to use on site; they require access for reading and they are susceptible to damage.

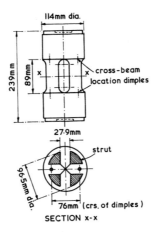

Fig. 18: Force Measuring Block — Strut Type (Swindells and Goymour [1963]).

There are also several other elastic mechanical load measuring units. The force measuring block is a very good example and several models have been used. The original National Physical Laboratory (NPL) instrument comprised a steel cylinder machined from a solid bar to form four struts, Figure 18. The load on the cell is determined by measurement of the average shortening of the struts. A mechanical dial gauge is used for this purpose in association with a lever mechanism to give a four-to-one magnification. The lever arms are held apart by a helical compression spring with its centre line on the axis of the load block. Details of this cell are given by Swindells and Goymour (1963). In a more recent and improved design the points of deflection pick-up are on the centre line of the column.

These load cells have several advantages over the proving ring, especially with respect to stability. They are much smaller and lighter and blocks with a capacity of 1000 t or greater can be manufactured.

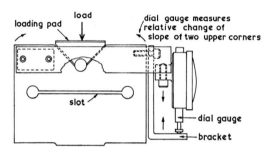

Fig. 19: Force Measuring Block — Slotted device (Swindells and Goymour [1963]).

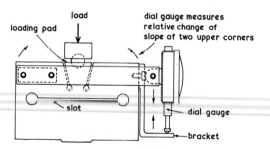

Fig. 20: Force Measuring Block — Slotted device with pivoted loading pad
(Swindells and Goymour [1963]).

A more compact and more versatile cell is the slotted type device also developed by N.P.L. The load cell consists of two end-to-end C-shaped devices (Figure 19) with a relatively flexible hinge joining the upper members together whereas the lower members are joined very rigidly. In use the slope of the two upper corners is measured by dial gauge.

Because the effective position of load application to the cell may change, the loading pad instead of being integral with the main block is made free and rests on a hardened steel roller as shown in Figure 20. With this load application arrangement errors due to frictional effects and angular changes in the position of the loading pad are small and accuracies of less than $\pm$ 0.4 % can be obtained over the full working load range. The instrument is proportioned so that, at design load capacity, the deflection of the dial gauge is about 1000 divisions. Other variants of this load cell are described by Goymour (1969).

The main limitation of the force measuring block is the requirement of access to read the dial gauge and the vulnerability of the dial gauge to damage. Remote reading of the dial gauge is possible by use of a displacement transducer.

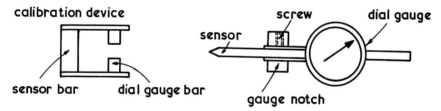

Fig. 21: Manual reading device for disc load cell (Interfels).

The disc load cell manufactured by Interfels GmbH has an elastic element consisting of a cup spring. The element, fixed between an abutment plate and a top yoke plate, deflects when loaded and a dial gauge measures the distance between the abutment and yoke plates. A steel peripheral ring protects the elastic element and the system is waterproofed by the use of 'O' rings between moving parts. The reading of the spring deflection is achieved by dial gauge with a special feeler-end reading to about 0.01 mm accuracy (Figure 21). A calibration device ensures that the same initial value is used for each measurement. Long term registration of load is achieved by a mechanical recorder. In cases where remote readings are necessary, electrical or electronic methods of recording may be used.

A sketch of the disc load cell in use for anchor load measurement is shown in Figure 22 and, while it is possible theoretically to manufacture any capacity of disc load cell, such cells are available in the range 25 to 450 t with a 25 % maximum overload. The measuring accuracy is about ± 0.5 %. Table 1 lists the dimensions of some of the standard disc load cells which are available.

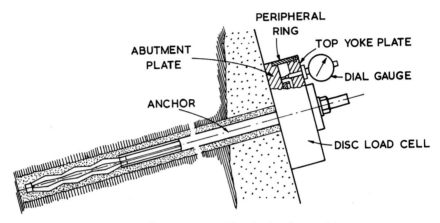

Fig. 22: Schematic view of disc load cell (Interfels).

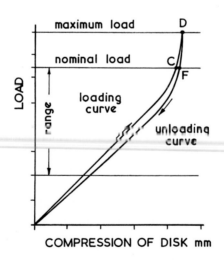

Fig. 23: Calibration curve for disc load cell (Interfels).

Because of hysteresis of the cup springs, the applied load — disc compression relation is non-linear and Figure 23 provides such a curve.

This load cell is simple and of robust construction with a weather and winterproof mechanism which is suitable for both short and long term measurements. No special expertise is required during cell installation and the recording device can be used with other devices such as the multiple position extensometer, see Chapter 5.

Nominal load (t)	Maximum load (t)	Diameter of central hole (mm)	Weight (kg)	Overall height (mm)	Overall diameter (mm)
32	40	102	15	84	230
72	90	113	35	94	330
96	120	140	45	99	350
136	170	165	55	107	395
187	230	176	80	124	455

Table 1. Dimensions of standard Interfels disc load cells.

2.3. Indirect Methods

Numerous indirect and inexpensive methods of load measurement may be used depending on environmental conditions. The most common is the measurement of the deformation of a member, e. g. a strut or pile, over a known gauge length. Knowledge of the sectional area and modulus of deformation of the member material permits the determination of average load provided bending effects are small. The commonest mechanical deformation gauges are those in which the deformations are measured by dial gauge. The National Civil Engineering Laboratory (LNEC), Lisbon, has developed several gauges which operate on the principle shown in Figure 24. In this deformation gauge the measuring

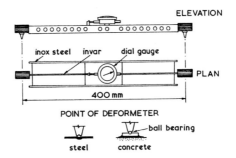

Fig. 24: LNEC deformation gauge (Rocha [1965]).

points are provided with a hemispherical cavity which is applied to steel balls fixed on the surface of the member under measurement. The balls, of 3 mm diameter, are fixed as shown in Figure 25. The deformation gauge is always used in association with a reference bar and accuracies within the range 10.10^{-4} to 40.10^{-4} cm for a 40 cm gauge length are quoted by Rocha (1965).

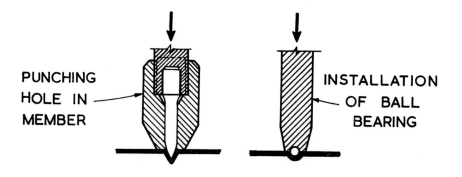

PUNCHING HOLE IN MEMBER

INSTALLATION OF BALL BEARING

Fig. 25: Detail of method of fixing gauge length on member.

Several other deformation gauges work on the LNEC principle and the Demec gauge developed by Morice and Nurse (1953) is widely used. The usual gauge length is 50 mm, 100 mm or 200 mm and deformation is recorded by dial gauge actuated by a simple lever magnification system. The gauge comprises an invar steel beam with two conical-shaped gauge points, one fixed at one end of the beam and the other pivoting on a knife edge. The pivoting motion is transferred to a 0.002 mm dial gauge. Temperature compensation is with respect to a standard invar steel reference bar. The gauge points are attached to the structural element by small, drilled, stainless steel discs with an epoxy, their spacing being fixed by a special locating bar. Accuracies of up to 3.10^{-6} are possible.

Despite the accuracies of these deformation gauges, their use is somewhat limited in the field of foundation instrumentation to structural members which are accessible to the observer. It should be noted that to take a reading the observer must be in a relatively comfortable position. Only static measurements are possible.

2.4. Photoelastic Load Indicators

The principle of operation of these load cells is that when a cylinder of optical glass is strained by application of load to the body of the cell, photoelastic interference fringe patterns are visible in the glass cylinder when it is illuminated with polarized light. The fringe pattern observed is a direct measure of the load applied to the load cell. The optical glass cylinder is placed in a hole in the cell body, load being applied through end plates. These plates are usually domed and are arranged to accommodate eccentricity of loading. Spring washers retain the loading plates in position under zero load. Figure 26 illustrates the general features of the photoelastic load cell being used to monitor the load in a strut.

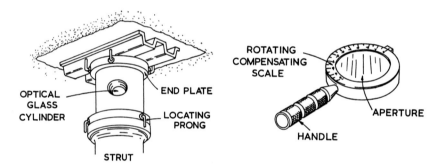

Fig. 26: Photoelastic load cell (Terrametrics Inc.).

Fig. 27: Hand viewer for fringe count determination (Terrametrics Inc.).

The stressed optical glass cylinder is read by use of a hand-viewer. Various sizes of hand-viewer are available depending on the degree of accuracy required. The viewer is normally fitted with a standard miner's cap lamp housing, which polarizes the light. In some cell designs the polarizer is inserted into the opposite side of the cell. A red filter is occasionally incorporated in the polarizer to give monochromatic light. The aperture of the hand-viewer, Figure 27, has a rotating compensating scale marked 0 to 1.0 with 0.01 subdivisions. With the precision hand-viewer compensation scale initially set to zero, the number of fringes visible in one half the disc are counted as shown in Figure 28. An exact count is made when the fringe at the centre forms a cross (x) as illustrated. Where this is not the case, e. g. at 1½ fringes, the full fringes (one) are

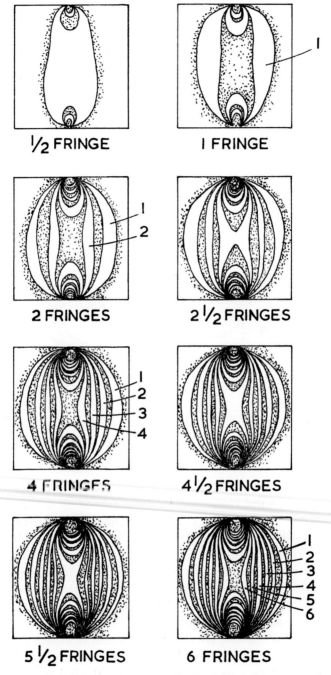

Fig. 28: Patterns of photoelastic interference fringes (Terrametrics Inc.).

counted and the compensation scale is then rotated clockwise until the last fringe counted (i. e. that nearest the centre) has moved back to form a cross. The fractional fringe reading on the scale is added to the initial full fringe count. In this manner the fringe count can be obtained to about ± 0.05 of a fringe and with skill to perhaps ± 0.02 or better. The fringe count is multiplied by the load cell calibration factor to give the applied load. Up to five fringes usually cover the normal working capacity of the cell and hence it is possible to read to an accuracy of about ± 0.5 % with practice.

Using the photoelastic principle of measurement, tensile loads can be measured by use of a steel tube with the optical glass inserted in the tube wall. Such cells are very convenient for the measurement of the forces in anchor bars, for example (Moore [1971]).

For field use the load cells are plated and water and dust proof caps cover the optical glass when the cell is not in use. Special locating prongs are used to align the load cell and hold it in position during use.

The main advantages of this load indicator, from a field use point of view, are that it is relatively cheap to manufacture, easy to install, easy to replace a broken glass transducer, and easy to use. The limitation of the system is that access to near the load cell is required for viewing purposes; although it is possible to overcome this limitation in part by the use of a system of viewing tubes with mirrors and prisms and a light source near to the load cell. However, the costs involved with such an elaborate viewing layout system may make other forms of load cell which rely on an electrical recording system more acceptable.

The load capacity of cells which use the photoelastic transducer principle is controlled by the physical dimension of the element. For large cell capacities several transducer elements may be used and equally spaced in a circular pattern. The limitation of the multi-element load cell is the problem of viewing the photoelastic discs.

Details relating to the development of the photoelastic load cell and its application to the instrumentation of foundations are given by Hawkes, Dhir and Rose (1964), Moore (1971), and Hooper (1972).

2.5. The "Strain Gauged" Load Cell

The operating principle of these cells relies on the basic property of a metal that its electrical resistance varies directly in response to deformation caused by applied mechanical load. Details of strain gauges and their use are reviewed by Hickson (1965) and an excellent survey is given by Hendry (1964) and Scott (1972). A predetermined number of resistance strain gauges is bonded on the surface of carefully machined metal elements of accurately known dimensions. Application of load to this element results in a strain, which is proportional to the material stress, occurring at the position of the strain gauge attachment. This principle of operation is employed in all such load cells, the differences in cells being in the shape and size of the metal element or elements, the arrangement of the strain gauges and the technique of measuring the output signal from the strain gauges.

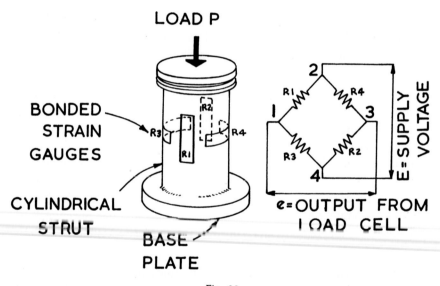

Fig: 29:

(a) View of strain gauge layout on load cell element;

(b) Circuit diagram of strain gauges.

Figure 29 shows the load measuring element of a load cell in which four strain gauges are used in the measuring circuit and all are subjected to strain. The element is a cylinder of steel and the strain gauges R_1 to R_4 are bonded with gauges R_1 and R_2 along the longitudinal axis of the cylinder while gauges R_3 and R_4 are in the circumferential direction.

Under axial load the resistances of R_1 and R_2 decrease owing to axial shortening of the element while resistance in R_3 and R_4 increases. When the strain gauges are connected up in the Wheatstone Bridge circuit configuration shown in Figure 29, then as the cylindrical element is compressed, the output as measured between 1 and 3 will vary proportionately to the load applied.

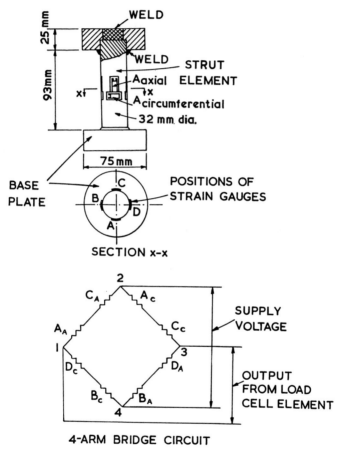

Fig. 30: Detail of strain gauged element used by Whitaker (1963).

In some designs eight resistance strain gauges are attached to the load element. The usual layout is to have four T-shaped groups equally spaced around the circumference of the strut to give four axial and four circumferential gauges. The gauges are then connected to form a 4-arm bridge circuit. Such an arrangement was chosen by Whitaker (1963) for the load cells used to measure the base load in bored piles. Figure 30 shows details of the method of element construction used and the strain gauge layout.

Supply voltages between 2 and 4, Figure 29, are generally in the order of 10 volts and the output from the cell under full load conditions is in the order of 10 millivolts.

Load elements may also include rectangular and square-shaped metallic pieces and tubes, but the solid cylinder is the more common shape.

For high precision work the columnar element integral with its base is machined from a one-piece forging of heat-treated high-tensile steel. The top end of the column is shaped to provide a good bearing surface. The strain gauged element is enclosed within a strong casing, usually cast iron, and sealed to it by 'O' rings. In some designs the space surrounding the strain-gauged column is oil-filled to ensure temperature equalization along the length of the stressed element. Electrical connections are made via a lead entering the cell through a sealed gland.

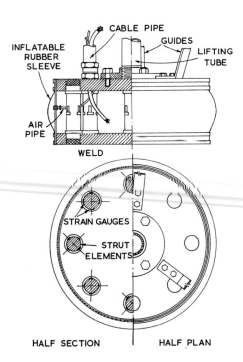

Fig. 31: Diagram of a load cell for a 400 mm diameter pile shaft (Whitaker [1963]).

Load cells for tensile force measurement are of a similar construction. The stressed element is machined with integral ends from a single forging and the ends are provided with self-aligning eyes for the elimination of non-axial loads. Tensile loads may also be measured with compression cells by transformation of the tensile load into a compressive load by the use of stirrups.

Single element load cells are available in capacities from a few to 500 t and greater. For example, typical dimensions of a 500 t compression cell are : end plate diameter = 300 mm; overall length = 300 to 400 mm; weight = 100 kg; deflection under load = 0.5 mm. These cells are designed to withstand an overload of 150 % nominal capacity and operate in the temperature range — 20° C to + 40° C. Accuracies of better than ± 0.2 % of full load output are possible with the high precision cells.

In order to keep the overall height of the load cell small and to enable large capacity load cells to be constructed which have the facility to compensate for eccentricity of loading, several load elements may be

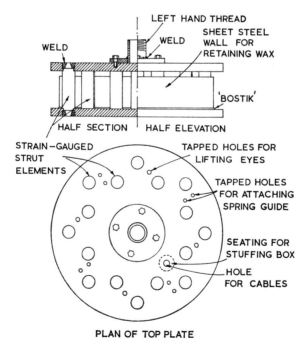

Fig. 32: Detail of a 16 element strain-gauged load cell (Whitaker [1963]).

used. Much pioneering work has been carried out by Whitaker (1963) into large capacity cells for bored pile instrumentation. He designed cells of capacity 50 to 600 t having 8 to 24 load measuring elements. In the eight element cells the pillars were equally spaced in a ring. In cells with 16 and 24 strain-gauged elements, the elements were arranged in two concentric rings with equal numbers in each ring. Figures 31 and 32 show details of construction of load cells with 8 and 16 measuring elements respectively and dimensions of a number of the load cells designed for this project are given in Table 2. The strain gauges on the elements in each quadrant of the cell were wired to form a 4-arm bridge circuit, a typical example of which is shown in Figure 33. Complete details of these cells including waterproofing, calibrating, installation on site and recording are given by Whitaker and he has shown conclusively that this type of load cell design is very satisfactory for pile base instrumentation.

Many other forms of load cell are available and where it is necessary to have a low height, the toroidal type of cell is advantageous. It com-

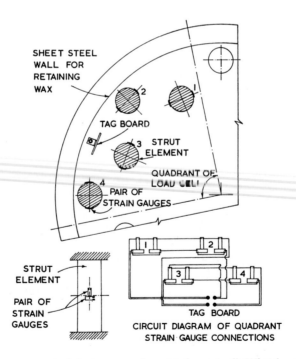

Fig. 33: Arrangement of strain gauges for a 16 element cell (Whitaker [1963]).

Pile shaft diameter (m)	Load capacity (t)	Cell diameter (m)	End plate thickness (mm)	Number of elements	Pitch circle diameter of elements (m)	Diameter of elements (mm)	Clear height of elements (mm)
0.6	305	0.546	31.7	16	0.343 0.47	44.5	127
0.6	51	0.571	25.4	8	0.406	28.5	89
0.6	203	0.571	31.7	16	0.343 0.470	38.1	114
0.75	102	0.724	31.7	8	0.508	38.1	114
0.75	305	0.724	31.7	16	0.444 0.571	44.5	127
0.75	406	0.724	31.7	16	0.444 0.571	50.8	152
0.9	152	0.875	25.4	16	0.521 0.698	31.7	101
0.9	610	0.875	31.7	24	0.521 0.698	50.8	152

Table 2. Dimensions of load cells used by Whitaker for underreamed bored pile instrumentation.

prises a high tensile steel toroidal loading element enclosed within a forged steel casing, the two parts of the case being hermetically sealed by 'O' rings. Strain gauges bonded to the internal and external peripheries of the torus are connected in a temperature-compensated Wheatstone bridge circuit. Load is applied to the element via a special diaphragm section through a self-aligning loading cap acting through a hemispherical pad.

The principal feature of the "strain gauged" load cell is its simplicity. The element is very rigid and displacements of a fraction of a mm only are required to develop the full load. They have a rapid response to applied load and are suitable for the recording of rapidly varying loads. By virtue of the method of construction, the sensitivity of the load cell can be predetermined by the choice of the number of elements used and the arrangement of the strain gauge circuits (Whitaker [1963]). The cells are relatively flat and stable. Great care during construction is required to ensure that (i) all gauges are correctly and positively bonded, (ii) the cell is completely waterproofed.

The recording of the electrical signal from the strain gauges is achieved by supplying the load cell elements from a stable precision d.c. voltage source and amplifying the output. Because variation in the supply of current causes error, a d.c. voltage regulator which can either be energised from an a.c. main supply or an accumulator is required. The output signal from the load cell, in d.c. form, can be conducted directly to a suitable indicator or recorder and details of recording systems are given in Chapter 7.

2.6. Vibrating Wire Load Cells

In contrast to the various types of strain-gauged load cell, the vibrating wire cell is essentially a very simple mechanical gauge which is capable of maintaining its dimensions and frequency of vibration to a very high degree. The basic principle of operation is that the change in natural frequency of vibration of a stretched wire depends on the change of tension in the wire. In practice a gauge wire is stretched between two points on a structural member or load cell transducer element used to sense the load change. When the gauge wire is caused to oscillate, it will vibrate at its resonate or natural frequency. If strains are induced in the element on which the wire is mounted, the distance between the points of support changes, the tension in the wire changes and its natural frequency of vibration will change. This change in frequency of vibration of the wire is a measure of the strain in the element of the transducer.

The theoretical solution of the governing differential equation of a tensioned wire in vibration relates the frequency of vibration and the strain in the tensioned wire by the following expression:

$$\varepsilon = \text{Constant.} \frac{4 \cdot L \cdot {}^2\varrho}{E \cdot g} (f^2 - f_0^2) \qquad (2.2)$$

where L = length of the wire, ϱ = density of the wire material, E = modulus of deformation of the wire material, f_0 = zero strain vibrating frequency, f = vibrating frequency, g = gravity constant and ε = strain in the wire. The Constant depends on the design of the gauge.

Temperature change will affect the gauge only if the coefficient of thermal expansion of the wire differs from that of the gauge body. Usually they are identical and, provided that temperature gradients throughout the gauge are avoided, the output of the vibrating wire is not affected by ambient temperature effects.

The gauge contains two electromagnets which are positioned about 1 mm clear of the tensioned wire. One magnet excites the gauge-wire and as it oscillates, the size of the air gap changes. An alternating current is induced in the coils of the second electromagnet which acts as the pick-up. The induced emf will be of a frequency equal to that of the vibrating wire and this signal, when amplified, can be recorded or measured.

Following from equation 2.2., once the change in the square of the frequency of the gauge wire is known, the change in load can be determined from a knowledge of the physical dimensions of the load cell unit and its modulus of deformation. The load P is given by the expression:

$$P = K \cdot (f^2 - f_0^2) \qquad (2.3)$$

the constant K depending on the physical dimensions of the element and the length and method of support of the wire.

This principle of load measurement has been used extensively by civil engineers. The most common shape of load cell using the vibrating wire principle is the thick-wall high-tensile steel tube. The vibrating wires are placed in holes drilled in the tube wall, special clamping devices being used to fix the ends of the pretensioned wires. It is usual to place three wires spaced symmetrically 120° apart but with large capacity load cells which require a fairly large internal clearance and when there is a possibility of eccentricity of loading, six or more wires are used and are equally spaced around the cylinder. The ends of the load cell cylinder are machined, and after the wires have been installed and pretensioned, the ends of the holes are sealed to protect the wires against damage. The leads to each vibrating wire element are conducted to a socket outlet for connection to the frequency recording unit. Figure 34 shows in line drawing a plan and elevation for a 100 t capacity load cell comprising six vibrating wire elements. A protective outer casing guards the leads from the vibrating wire elements to the waterproof outlet socket.

Several other forms of vibrating wire load cell are available and the Norwegian Geotechnical Institute (NGI) developed a watertight cell,

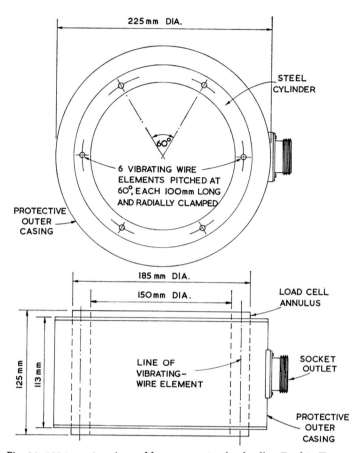

Fig. 34: 100 t prestressing-cable compressive load cell - Deakin Type.

details of which are shown in Figure 35. Three vibrating wires are mounted on the inside of a steel cylinder to which watertight end plates are attached. The cable from the vibrating wires is conducted through a watertight port and connects to a terminal box. The load cell is calibrated, the mean value of $(f^2 - f_0^2)$ for the three wire gauges being graphed against applied load. The method used by the NGI for strut load measurement is shown in Figure 36.

The NGI have also developed a surface mounting gauge which is fastened by two posts previously attached to the structural element. General features of this gauge are given in Figure 37. This unit is waterproof and the detailed precautions which have been taken during manufacture are

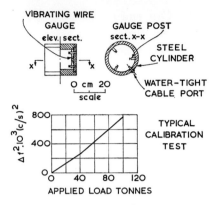

Fig. 35: NGI Compressive load cell (Bjerrum et al [1965]).

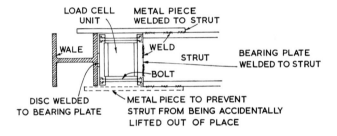

Fig. 36: Detail of attachment of NGI cell to a strut (Bjerrum et al [1965]).

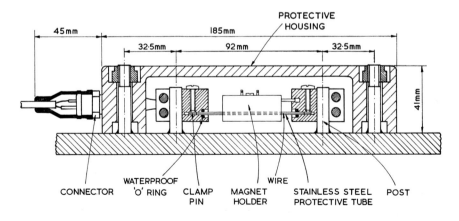

Fig. 37: NGI Vibrating wire strain gauge (Bjerrum et al [1965]).

evident from Figure 37. One end of the wire is clamped and the other end is fixed by a set-screw during field assembly. The vibrating wire is housed in a stainless steel tube. Accuracies of ± 5% are quoted by the manufacturer.

An earlier version of this gauge was used by NGI for strut load measurement. Two vibrating wires, one on each side of the web of the steel strut and along its neutral axis, were mounted as shown by Figure 38. The tensioned wires and electromagnets were fastened to posts bolted into the web of the steel section.. The average of the "strain" measurements from these two tensioned vibrating wires equals the average strain, ε, in the strut and is independent of any bending of the strut. Consequently the strut load, P, was obtained from the product of the average axial strain, ε, the sectional area, A, the modulus of the metal, E, and the constant of the strain gauge, G.

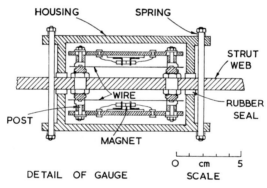

Fig. 38: Use of Vibrating Wire Strain Gauge to measure strut loads
(Bjerrum et al [1965]).

A number of vibrating wire elements each comprising a thick-walled tube and having a tensioned wire may be used. The layout of the system is somewhat similar to that used by Whitaker for his multi-element strain-gauged cells.

The main advantages of the vibrating wire principle of load measurement are that (i) it is convenient, accurate, sensitive and stable, (ii) the form of construction is rugged and the element is contained within a watertight housing, (iii) installation is simple to perform, (iv) repair of a damaged wire is possible, (v) measurement may be remote and it is fast. The advantages and disadvantages of the strut instrumentation system (Figure 38) are given by Bjerrum, Kenney and Kjaernsli (1965).

During the last twenty years the vibrating wire load cell has been accepted as a reliable method of load measurement by the foundation engineer. These load cells have different shapes and sizes and in some instances they were designed for a specific purpose — e.g. the measurement of strut loads by the NGI. Several reasearch engineers are responsible for the application of the vibrating wire principle of load measurement. The papers of Cooling and Ward (1953), Ward (1955), Skempton and Ward (1951), NGI (1962), Ward and Cheney (1960), Di Biagio and Kjaernsli (1961), Sutherland and Findlay (1961), and Cooling (1962) present details of some of the uses and applications of these load gauges. Today the vibrating wire load cell is available commercially in capacities from a few t to 1000 t or greater. With most designs the overall height is less than 150 mm. The problems of eccentricity of loading are overcome, to a practical extent at least, by the use of a number of vibrating wire elements (3 or more) and by end plates which centralize the load. A detail of such a load centralizer is shown in Figure 39. Here the load in a ground anchor is being measured by the load cell shown in Figure 34. Ground and recessed steel plates with accurately located guide holes fixed the positions of the individual strands to apply the load centrally to the cell.

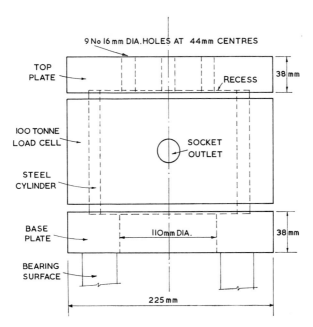

Fig. 39: Method of load centralizing for a prestressed anchor.

Electronic equipment is used to measure the frequency of vibration of the wire. However, the vibrating-wire instrument is, in reality, a mechanical gauge because the oscillation of the gaugewire is a mechanical phenomenon. It is for this reason that this type of load cell has distinct practical advantages over most other load cells. For example, instability due to moisture, contact resistance, and lead wire resistance is not significant.

2.7. Other Methods of Load Measurement

A load cell working on a hydraulic principle is sometimes useful. The simplest form is the hydraulic jack with oil pressure measurement by a pressure gauge. Friction effects in the ram of the jack make this method of measurement unattractive and it is usual to use it in association with an "elastic" load cell in series e.g. pile load testing.

Hydraulic load capsules are available but are not often used for field measurements. Flack jacks have been used and the use of a Freyssinet type jack by Frischmann and Fleming (1962) to measure the base load in a large diameter underreamed pile illustrates the principle of the jack. The arrangement of the jack is shown in Figure 40 (a) and a detail of the method of incorporating the jack as a load cell in the pile is given in Figure 40 (b).

For wire ropes and multi-strand cables a convenient method of tensile force determination is by use of a tension meter. The general principle of operation is illustrated in Figure 41. The cable or rope is engaged between two wheels or shoes separated at least 200 mm. A third wheel between the two outer wheels causes the gauge length to deflect by a known amount (about 0.02 mm). By measurement of the force applied normal to the cable, F, the axial load P is related to the deflection, Δ, and the gauge length, ℓ, by

$$P = F \cdot \frac{2}{\ell} \cdot \sqrt{(\ell/2)^2 + \Delta^2} \qquad (2.4)$$

Hanna and Seeton (1966) made use of this principle to construct a simple mechanical tension meter capable of recording the forces in the individual cables of a multi-strand rock anchor. The gauge length, ℓ, was 200 mm and the force, F, normal to the axis of the cable was determined by the deflection of a cantilever measured by dial gauge.

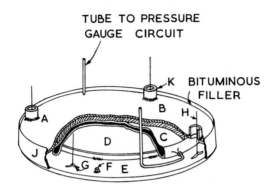

A. COVER PLATE
B. TOP SPACER PLATE
C. FREYSSINET TYPE JACK
D. LOWER SPACER PLATE
E. BASE PLATE

F. NUT FOR ATTACHMENT OF COVER PLATE
G. REFERENCE WIRE ANCHORAGE
H. REFERENCE WIRE
J. CELL WALL PLATE
K. WIRE DUCT SOCKET

(a)

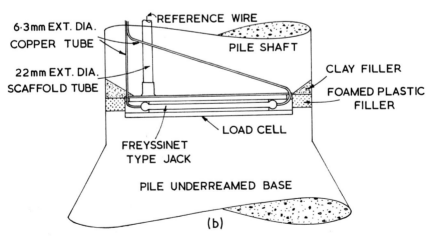

(b)

Fig. 40: (a) Freyssinet jack load cell arrangement;
(b) Arrangement of load cell in the pile (Frischmann and Fleming [1962]).

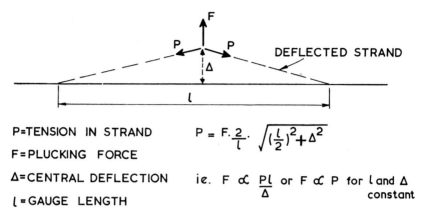

P=TENSION IN STRAND

F=PLUCKING FORCE

Δ=CENTRAL DEFLECTION

ℓ=GAUGE LENGTH

$$P = F \cdot \frac{2}{\ell} \cdot \sqrt{\left(\frac{\ell}{2}\right)^2 + \Delta^2}$$

i.e. $F \propto \dfrac{P\ell}{\Delta}$ or $F \propto P$ for ℓ and Δ constant

Fig. 41: The principle of the Tension Meter.

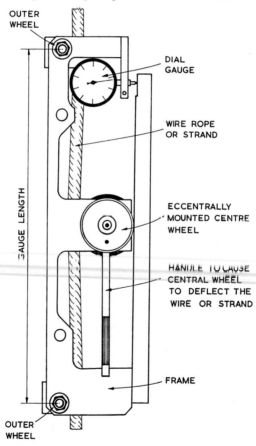

OUTER WHEEL

DIAL GAUGE

WIRE ROPE OR STRAND

ECCENTRALLY MOUNTED CENTRE WHEEL

HANDLE TO CAUSE CENTRAL WHEEL TO DEFLECT THE WIRE OR STRAND

FRAME

GAUGE LENGTH

OUTER WHEEL

Fig. 42: The Fulmer Tension Meter.

Portable tension meters are available commercially and the Flumer meter (Figure 42) operates on the principle that the deflecting force, F, acts upon the frame of the meter and causes it to bend in proportion to the applied force. This bending is recorded by a dial gauge or by a displacement transducer attached to a recorder. With the Fulmer meter an accuracy of $\pm 5\%$ on cable and $\pm 3\%$ on wire is quoted. Its gauge length is about 400 mm and it weighs between 2 and 5 kg depending on its capacity.

The chief advantage of the tension meter is that it is a mechanical gauge. The main limitations to its use are (i) access to the cable or wire is required for measurement, (ii) errors may result with repeat readings if the same points of contact are not used, (iii) calibration charts are required for each size of cable or wire to be measured.

Occasionally both tension and compression members are strain gauged and part of the member becomes a "load cell". There are numerous disadvantages to this method of load measurement in the field particularly moisture proofing and physical protection and its use is not recommended for general application in foundation instrumentation.

The scratch strain gauge is another form of mechanical load or strain measuring device. Strain recordings are made on a brass disc about 25 mm in diameter. The brass target disc can be removed from the gauge and the recorded strain data are extracted either manually or automatically. These discs may be stored as a permanent record of movements which have occurred. Thus the scratch strain gauge accomplishes in a mechanical manner what the electric resistance gauge does electrically. The gauge is ideally suited for attachment to structures by clamps, adhesives or screws. Details are given by Tatnall (1969), Haglage and Wood (1969), Chironis (1970) and Haglage (1970) of the development and use of the scratch gauge.

2.8. Special Load Cells

In some foundation measurements it is necessary to have gauges capable of measuring both tensile and compressive forces, capable of withstanding severe impact forces and capable of measuring bending moments. The Swedish Geotechnical Institute has developed a load cell, operating on the vibrating wire gauge principle, which is capable of withstanding the forces due to pile driving (Fellenius and Haagen [1969]).

The cell comprises three elements placed symmetrically and between two steel plates. The steel plates are specially locked into the body of the Hercules pile by a standard pile joint. Impact of the pile hammer does not alter the tension in the wire-element. A layout of the pile force gauge is shown in Figure 43. This cell gives frequencies f_a, f_b and f_c

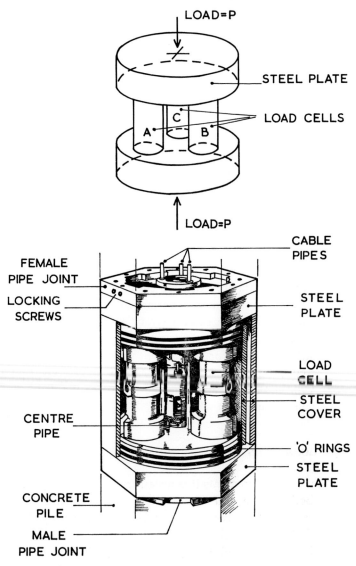

Fig. 43: Pile force gauge (Fellenius and Haagen [1969]).

from which the applied load P, the bending moment M, and the direction β of the bending moment are evaluated. The loads in the separate elements are P_A, P_B and P_C and the total load $P = P_A + P_B + P_C$. The moment vectors M_X and M_Y are

$$M_y = (P_A + P_C) \cdot R \cdot \cos 60° - P_B \cdot R \qquad (2.5)$$

$$M_x = (P_A - P_C) \cdot R \cdot \sin 60° \qquad (2.6)$$

R being the radius of the pitch circle of the elements. The resulting moment M is

$$M = \sqrt{M_x^2 + M_y^2} \qquad (2.7)$$

and the direction β of the moment is

$$\tan \beta = M_y/M_x \qquad (2.8)$$

The principle of this special load cell may be extended to other types of piles and to other problems where the cell has to withstand severe dynamic loadings prior to its use for static load measurement.

2.9. Summary

A large range of load cells and force measuring instruments is available. The selection of an instrument for a particular problem will be conditioned to a large extent by environmental factors such as accessibility, presence of water, damage potential. In use the most important detail is to ensure that eccentric loading of the cell is either measured or prevented. For long term measurement the stability of the load cell must be considered and the vibrating-wire type cells are believed to be the most suitable. The other forms of load cell may also be considered for this purpose but it is essential to check on their stability over a period of time. Installation of load cells requires care and common sense and consequently experience of the operator is important. Most load cell manufacturers provide an installation service or provide detailed instructions with each cell. Consultation of a number of the references will delimit most of the problems associated with load cell use in the field. It is imperative that all load cells are calibrated prior and subsequent to use. This is a standard procedure and for field use the cells may be calibrated against a second order accuracy load indicator.

The principle of load measurement is not expected to change in the near future although there will be changes in the sizes and shapes of cells, in the reliability of cells for both static and dynamic load recording processes. A review of force measuring is given by Profos and Ruhm (1971).

References

BJERRUM, L., KENNEY, T. C., KJAERNSLI, B., (1965), "Measuring instruments for strutted excavations", Proceedings American Society of Civil Engineers, Vol. 91, No. SM 1, 111—141.

CHIRONIS, N. P., (1970), "Simple mechanical gauge keeps a running record of strains". Product Engineering, September 28.

COOLING, L. F., (1962), "Field measurements in soil mechanics", Geotechnique, Vol. 12, 77—103.

COOLING, L. F., and WARD, W. H., (1953), "Measurements of loads and strains in earth supporting structures", Proceedings, Third International Conference on Soil Mechanics and Foundation Engineering, Zurich, 162—166.

DI BIAGIO, E., and KJAERNSLI, B., (1961), "Strut loads and related measurements on Contract 63a of the Oslo subway", Proceedings, Fifth Conference on Soil and Foundation Engineering, Paris, Vol. 2, 395—401.

FELLENIUS, B. H., and HAAGEN, T., (1969), "New pile force gauge for accurate measurements of pile behaviour during and following driving", Canadian Geotechnical Journal, Vol. 6, No. 3, 356—362.

FRISCHMANN, W. W., and FLEMING, W. G. K., (1962), "The use and behaviour of large diameter piles in London clay", The Structural Engineer, Vol. 40, 123—131.

GOYMOUR, E. P., (1969), "Force measuring blocks", Engineering, Sept. 12th, 298—299.

HAGLAGE, T. L., (1970), "The installation and operation of the Scratch strain gauge on a C-5A aircraft", Technical Memorandum 70-6-FBR.

HAGLAGE, T. L., and WOOD, H. A., (1969), "Scratch strain gauge evaluation", Technical Report AFFDL-TR69-25, Wright Patterson Air Force Base, Ohio, July.

HANNA, T. H., and SEETON, J., (1967), "Observations on a tied-back soldier-pile and timber-lagging wall", Ontario Hydro Research Quarterly, Vol. 19, No. 2, 22—28.

HAWKES, I., DHIR, R. K., ROSE, H., (1964), "An application of photoelastic transducers to load measurement in building foundations", Civil Engineering and Public Works Review, Vol. 59, November, 1536—1540.

HENDRY, A. W., (1964), „Elements of experimental stress analysis", Pergamon Press, pp 193.

HOOPER, J. A., (1972), "The theory and design of photoelastic load gauges incorporating glass element transducers", International Journal of Rock Mechanics and Mining Sciences, Vol. 9, No. 3, 363—401.

MORICE, P. B., and BASE, G. D., (1953), "The design and use of a demountable mechanical strain gauge for concrete structures", Magazine Concrete Research, Vol. 5, No. 13, 37—42.

N.G.I., (1962), "Measurements at a strutted excavation, Oslo Subway, Vaterland 1, km 1.373", Technical Report No. 6, Norwegian Geotechnical Institute.

PROFOS, P., and RUHM, K., (1971), "New trends in measuring and control instruments", Swiss Technics, Vol. 3, 29—40.

ROCHA, M., (1965), "In-situ strain and stress measurements", In Stress Analysis (Edited by O. C. Zienkiewicz and G. S. Holister), Wiley, 425—461.

SCOTT, A., (1972), "Strain gauges", Engineering, London, May, 482—485.

SKEMPTON, A. W., and WARD, W. H., (1951), "Investigations concerning a deep cofferdam in the Thames estuary clay at Shellhaven", Geotechnique, Vol. 3, 119—139.

SUTHERLAND, H. B., and FINDLAY, J. A., (1961), "The measurement of load distribution under two adjacent column footings", Proceedings, Fifth International Conference on Soil Mechanics and Foundation Engineering, Paris, Vol. 1, 829—835.

SWINDELLS, M. A., and GOYMOUR, E. P., (1963), "Measuring compressive forces accurately", Engineering (London), October 4th, 418.

TATNALL, F. G., (1969), "Development of the scratch gauge", Experimental Mechanics, SESA Spring 1968 Meeting, Albany, N. Y. May.

TIMOSHENKO, S., (1955), "Strength of materials", Van Nostrand, Vols. 1 and 2.

WARD, W. H., (1955), "Techniques for field measurement of deformation and earth pressure", Conference on the Correlation between calculated and observed stresses and displacement in structures, Institution of Civil Engineers, London, 28—40.

WARD, W. H., and CHENEY, J. E., (1960), "Oscillator measuring equipment for Vibrating Wire Gauges", Journal of Scientific Instruments, Vol. 37, 88—92.

WHITAKER, T., (1963), "Load cells for measuring the base loads in bored piles and cylinder foundation", Building Research Station, Current Papers, Engineering Series 11, 1—9.

	Pore Water
3	Pressure
	Measurement

3.1. The Effective Stress Principle

In Chapter 1 it was mentioned that soils are multi-phase materials and comprise a mineral and a pore phase. These phases interact chemically and physically. When load is applied to a soil mass, part is carried by the mineral skeleton and part by the pore fluid(s), the load being distributed in direct proportion to the relative stiffnesses of the phases. If one denotes the pressures in the air and water, which fill the pore space, by u_a and u_w respectively, and the total applied stress by σ, then the manner in which the effective stress is related to these known stresses is important because this distribution of stresses controls the strength and deformation behaviour of the soil. For fully saturated soils it was shown by Terzaghi (1923) that the effective stress $\sigma' = \sigma - u_w$ and this experimental finding has been confirmed by subsequent work (e. g. Skempton [1960]).

Consider a section through a soil mass at rest, Figure 44. The pressure in the pore water is $\gamma_w \cdot h_w$. Consider an element of soil of area A. The total vertical force is $\sigma \cdot A$ which equals $(\gamma_{sat} \cdot h_2 + \gamma_w \cdot h_1)$ A. The force from the pore water pressure acts over an area $(1 - a)$ A and by definition the total vertical force is

$$\sigma \cdot A = \sigma' \cdot A + u_w \cdot (1 - a) A \qquad (3.1)$$

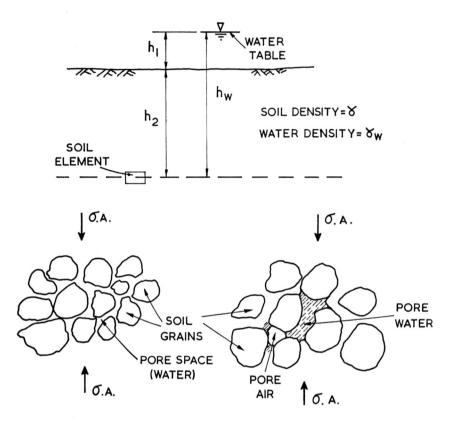

Fig. 44: Stresses in a soil mass.

The value of a, the fraction of the cross-sectional area that is occupied by the points of contact of the soil grains is very small (Bishop and Eldin [1950]), and without serious loss in accuracy may be assumed to be zero to give

$$\sigma' = \sigma - u_w \qquad (3.2)$$

At any point the pore water pressure, u_w, acts equally in all directions causing hydrostatic compression of the soil particles. Because the modulus of compression of the soil particles is very large, this compression is negligible in the civil engineering range of pressures.

In a partly saturated soil the water is restricted to some of the pores between the soil particles as shown in Figure 44. Here the water is not continuous but is surrounded by air and the meniscus at the air/water interface reduces the pressure in the water phase. It can be shown that the total force $\sigma.A$ is due to three components as follows:

$$\sigma \cdot A = \sigma' A + u_w \chi \cdot A + u_a (1 - a - \chi) A \qquad (3.3)$$

where $\chi.A$ is the fraction of the section that passes through the water phase, u_a is the pore air pressure. The pore water pressure u which represents the effects of the pore air and pore water pressures is

$$u = u_a - \chi (u_a - u_w) \qquad (3.4)$$

In a fully saturated soil $\chi = 1.0$ and in a perfectly dry soil it is 0. This relationship was put forward by Croney et al. (1958), Bishop et al. (1961) and since that time much experimental and theoretical study has been devoted to the examination of the parameter χ (Matyas [1963]).

Because the strength and the deformation behaviours of soil masses are controlled by the effective stresses, it is imperative that techniques are available to the foundation engineer for the prediction of pore water pressure changes in a soil mass due to change and also for the field checking of these predictions. Skempton (1954) derived the expression

$$\Delta u = B [\Delta \sigma_3 + A (\Delta \sigma_1 - \Delta \sigma_3)] \qquad (3.5)$$

where Δu is the change in pore water pressure due to stress changes of $\Delta \sigma_1$ and $\Delta \sigma_3$ acting on a soil element, A and B being dimensionless parameters. Techniques for the laboratory determination of the values of A and B were developed (Bishop and Henkel [1962]) and the field measurement of pore water pressure in soil deposits under buildings and in earth structures has shown that the values of A and B determined in the laboratory are close to those occurring in the field (Lambe [1962], Bishop and Bjerrum [1960]).

In many foundation problems it is impossible to predict pore water pressures with any degree of confidence. In other cases it is necessary to record pore water pressure development at pre-selected positions as a means of either construction control or stability checking, or both. The subject of the field measurement of pore water pressures, therefore, is the most important aspect of foundation instrumentation. In this chapter most of the standard methods of pore water pressure measurement are considered and some special methods are referenced. It should be appreciated that despite the use of extensive field instrumentation programmes for the measurement of water pressures, failures of foundations still occur. In many cases such failures are due to geological causes where the quantitative description of the ground conditions was poor. The use of any field instrument to record pore water pressure, therefore, must only be considered whenever the geological history of the ground has been worked out. If this appreciation of site geology is lacking, then the use of the field data provided by the instruments will be limited and in some cases false conclusions may be drawn.

3.2. Piezometers

The basic principle of operation of all piezometers is that a porous element is placed in the ground so that the soil water is continuous through the pores of the element and this water is collected in a container unit. The level of the water in the container unit may be measured or the pressure of the water in the container unit may be recorded and hence the water pressure in the ground is determined. A large range of pore water and pore air measuring elements has been developed which are available for pore pressure recording in fully or partially saturated natural soils, in rolled earth fills (dams), on the interface of structures such as retaining walls, and on structures subject to dynamic loading. As mentioned in Chapter 1 the coefficients of permeability of soils may vary by a factor up to 10^8. In the selection of a piezometer it is essential that the permeability of the ground be considered if it is to record faithfully and accurately ground water pressures in such materials. The following parts of this section examine the factors which control the design and use of a piezometer.

3.2.1. Piezometer Requirements

The primary requirements of any piezometer are (1) that it should record accurately the pore pressures in the ground, whether positive or negative (suction) and that the errors are within known and tolerable limits, (2) that the piezometer should cause a minimum of interference to the natural soil and hence to the response of the natural soil in which it is embedded, (3) that the piezometer should respond quickly to changes in ground water conditions (4) that the piezometer should be rugged and reliable and should remain stable over long periods of time, (5) that the piezometer can be recorded continuously or intermittently if required. There are many types of piezometer available commercially and the selection of the best system for a particular installation is not easy. Many piezometers which perform well under laboratory conditions are not well suited to long term field use and information on piezometer types is given in (3.3). The first two requirements usually do not present the foundation engineer with difficulty provided that good practice is followed. The third factor has been recognised for a long time, Hvorslev (1951); and the basic problem with any piezometer system is that a finite flow of water from the adjacent soil to the piezometer element is required to pressurize the system, and this prevents the instrument from recording a pore water pressure change immediately. For a known pressure change this energy is directly proportional to the volume of water that must flow into the piezometer system. Because all soils have a finite permeability, a time lag exists between the change in the ground water pressure state and the recording of that pressure state by the piezometer element. The time required for equalization of pressures may be computed if the "flexibility" of the piezometer system and the permeability and compressibility of the soil are known. Solutions for the time lag have been presented by Hvorslev (1951) for incompressible soils, and by Gibson (1963, 1966) for compressible soils whereas Penman (1960) has examined the time lag of a range of piezometer tips by experiment.

Because it is possible to compute the time lag of a piezometer system by knowing the pertinent piezometer and soil data, it is also possible to estimate the in-situ permeability of a natural soil from a knowledge of the time lag. During the last decade the potential of using a piezometer as an in-situ permeameter has been recognised and utilized (see Bishop and Al-Dhahir [1970] for example).

3.2.2. Time lag

As mentioned above, a time lag in pore water pressure measurement exists because the pressure in the measuring system initially differs

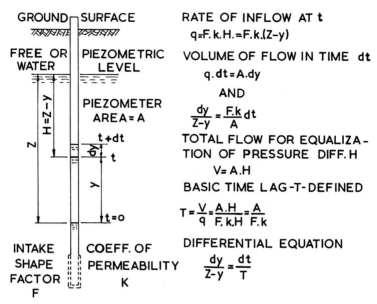

Fig. 45: Basic Definitions for Time Lag (Hvorslev [1951]).

from that in the soil thus requiring flow into or out of the piezometer measuring element before equilibrium is reached. A finite time is required for this to occur and it depends primarily on the soil permeability. When water flows to or from the measuring device the measured equilibrium value will usually differ from the value that it was intended to measure. For these reasons efforts have been made to reduce the flexibility of piezometer systems, e. g. Kallstenius and Wallgren (1956), Penman (1960). Flexibility occurs due to (i) the presence of trapped air or gas in the lines of the piezometer, (ii) expansion of the piezometer body and lines due to pressure change. With proper precaution the first limitation can be overcome (flushing of the lines, selection of impermeable tubing, prevention of cavitation at the piezometer tip).

The theory for the determination of hydrostatic time lag is similar to that for a falling head permeameter. The head, H, at any time t is $H = (Z - y)$, Figure 45. The flow may be expressed

$$q = F \cdot k \cdot H = F \cdot k \cdot (Z - y) \qquad (3.6)$$

where F is a shape factor which depends on the dimensions of the piezometer tip. Values of the shape factor according to Hvorslev (1951)

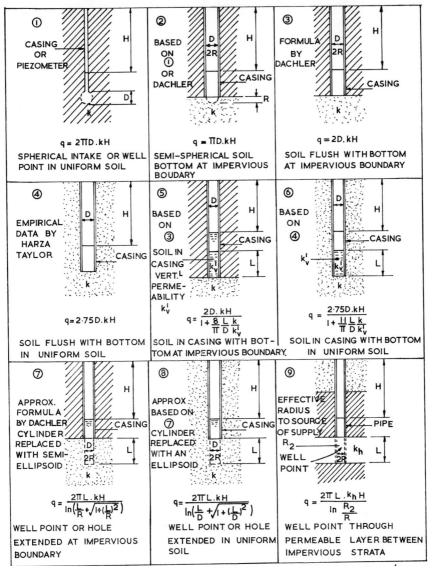

Fig. 46: Inflow and shape factors for piezometers (Hvorslev [1951]).

are given in Figure 46. Consideration of the flow during time dt leads to the equation

$$q \cdot dt = A \cdot dy \qquad (3.7)$$

and on combination with equation (3.6) gives the differential equation

$$\frac{dy}{Z - y} = F \frac{k}{A} dt. \qquad (3.8)$$

The total volume for pressure equalization is V = A.H, and the basic time lag, T, is the time required for equalization of this pressure difference when the original rate of flow, q = F.k.H, is maintained.

$$\text{i.e. } T = \frac{V}{q} = \frac{A \cdot H}{F \cdot k \cdot H} = A/F \cdot k. \qquad (3.9)$$

Rewriting equation (3.8) gives

$$dy/(Z - y) = dt/T. \qquad (3.10)$$

This is the basic differential equation for the determination of hydrostatic time lag and solutions have been presented by Hvorslev (1951) for constant and variable ground water conditions. Figure 47 shows the

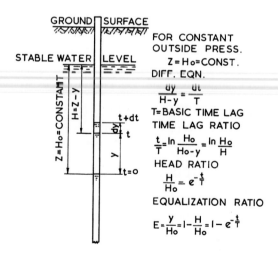

Fig. 47: Rise of water in piezometer tube for constant ground water conditions (Hvorslev [1951]).

set-up for constant ground water pressure. Use of the above expression gives the time lag ratio, t/T, as

$$t/T = \log (Ho/H) \tag{3.11}$$

where Ho/H is the head ratio and is equal to

$$H/Ho = e^{-t/}T \tag{3.12}$$

and the equalization ratio, E, is

$$E = 1 - Ho/H = 1 - e^{-t/}T \tag{3.13}$$

Figure 48 shows a graph of equalization ratio, E, against time lag ratio, t/T. The basic time lag T corresponds to an equalization ratio of 0.63. An equalization ratio of 0.9 corresponds to 2.3 times the basic time lag and is considered adequate for most practical purposes.

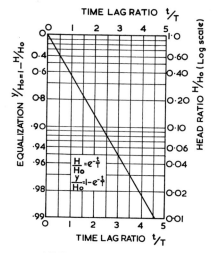

HEAD AND EQUALIZATION RATIOS

$\frac{t}{T}$	$\frac{H}{Ho}$	$\frac{y}{Ho}$
0·69	0·50	0·50
1·00	0·37	0·63
2·30	0·10	0·90
3·00	0·05	0·95
4·60	0·01	0·99
6·91	0·001	0·999

Fig. 48: Equalization ratio, E, against time lag ratio, t/T (Hvorslev [1951]).

If the static water table is not known it may be determined by observation of successive levels h_1, h_2, h_3 in the standpipe for equal time intervals, t. The time lag is then equal for the three intervals, Figure 49, i. e.

$$t/T = \log H_0/H = \log H_1/H_2 = \log H_2/H_3$$

Hence $\quad H_0/H_1 = H_1/H_2 = \dfrac{H_0 - H_1}{H_1 - H_2}$ \hfill (3.14)

$$H_0 = \frac{h_1^2}{h_1 - h_2}, \quad H_1 = \frac{h_2^2}{h_2 - h_3} \text{ etc.}$$

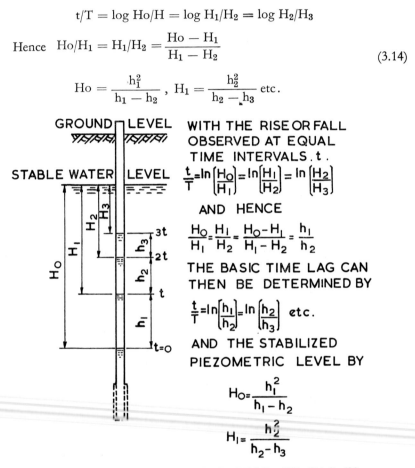

GROUND LEVEL

STABLE WATER LEVEL

WITH THE RISE OR FALL OBSERVED AT EQUAL TIME INTERVALS . t .

$$\frac{t}{T} = \ln\left[\frac{H_0}{H_1}\right] = \ln\left[\frac{H_1}{H_2}\right] = \ln\left[\frac{H_2}{H_3}\right]$$

AND HENCE

$$\frac{H_0}{H_1} = \frac{H_1}{H_2} = \frac{H_0 - H_1}{H_1 - H_2} = \frac{h_1}{h_2}$$

THE BASIC TIME LAG CAN THEN BE DETERMINED BY

$$\frac{t}{T} = \ln\left[\frac{h_1}{h_2}\right] = \ln\left[\frac{h_2}{h_3}\right] \text{ etc.}$$

AND THE STABILIZED PIEZOMETRIC LEVEL BY

$$H_0 = \frac{h_1^2}{h_1 - h_2}$$

$$H_1 = \frac{h_2^2}{h_2 - h_3}$$

CONSTANT INTAKE SHAPE FACTOR, NO GAS IN SOIL OR WELL POINT, ETC. ASSUMED.

GENERAL REQUIREMENT : $\quad \dfrac{h_1}{h_2} = \dfrac{h_2}{h_3} = \dfrac{h_3}{h_4}$ etc.

OBSERVATIONS AT EQUAL TIME INTERVALS

Fig. 49: Determination of time lag by observations at equal time intervals (Hvorslev [1951]).

The Hvorslev theory assumes isotropic soil conditions around the piezometer tip, no hydraulic loss in the piezometer system and no consolidation in the soil. The quantity of flow Q under a pressure difference p in time t is given, equation (3.6), by

$$Q = \frac{F\,k\,p}{t \cdot \gamma_w} \tag{3.15}$$

where k is the permeability of the soil and F is the piezometer shape factor, Figure 46, having the dimension of length. At time t = 0 let the error in piezometer reading be p_o and at time t the error in reading be p_t, then

$$\frac{P_o - P_t}{P_o} = 1 - e^{-\frac{F \cdot k \cdot t}{\gamma_w \cdot V}} \tag{3.16}$$

where V is the volume factor (volume of water entering the piezometer per unit pressure change). From this relationship it will be noted that F.k must be large in relation to V if equilibrium, i. e.

$$\frac{P_o - P_t}{P_o} \rightarrow 1.0, \text{ is to be achieved quickly.}$$

Appreciable errors are involved in assuming that the soil is incompressible (Penman [1960]) and the case of compressibility has been examined by Gibson (1963). He showed that the rate of flow Q from a piezometer of spherical shape and of radius r, when a pressure difference Δu is maintained between the water in the soil and that in the piezometer is

$$Q = 4\,\pi\,r \cdot \frac{k}{\gamma_w} \cdot \Delta u \cdot \left[1 + \frac{1}{\sqrt{\pi\,T_V}}\right] \tag{3.17}$$

where the time factor $\quad T_V = \frac{c_v \cdot t}{r^2}$, c_v being the coefficient of consolidation and k being the coefficient of permeability of the soil.

By plotting the flow rate Q against $\sqrt{\text{time}}$ for a constant head test, the coefficient of permeability of the soil may be obtained from the intercept on the Q axis (Gibson 1963). Practical examples are given by Bishop and Al-Dhahir (1970) and Al-Dhahir, Kennard and Morgenstern (1970).

In the case of piezometers embedded in partly saturated and fine grained soils high air entry ceramic tips are required (Bishop et al. [1960, 1961]) and their permeability may be equal to or even less than that of the soil in which they are in direct contact. In such circumstances care is required to ensure that the permeability of the ceramic stone is not measured! Gibson (1966) has concluded that the measured permeability will be in reasonable agreement with actual values if the piezometer ceramic is at least 10 times more permeable than the surrounding soil. Where the piezometer tip and surrounding soil are known to have comparable permeabilities, Gibson has presented a modified analysis.

3.2.3. Intake Factors

From equation (3.9) the computation of basic time lag T requires a value for the intake factor of the piezometer, F. Hvorslev (1951), by use of theoretical and empirical means, assembled intake factors for a range of intake shapes and boundary conditions. As stated by Hvorslev these factors are based on a number of simplifying assumptions few of which are fully obeyed under field conditions. They do, however, prove adequate for preliminary studies and the basic time lag can always be checked by field methods as explained in (3.2.2). Typical values of intake factor according to Hvorslev are given in Figure 46. Shape factors for various cylindrical piezometers are given by Al-Dhahir and Morgenstern (1969).

3.2 4 Calculation of Time Lag

Consider the case of the piezometer system shown in Figure 50. The flow of water to the piezometer is given by

$$q = \frac{2 \pi k L \cdot H}{\log\left[\frac{L}{D} + \sqrt{1 + \left(\frac{L}{D}\right)^2}\right]} \tag{3.18}$$

The total volume V for pressure equalization is $\frac{\pi}{4} d^2 H$. and the basic time lag T is V/q. For a coefficient of permeability $k = 10^{-5}$ cm/sec, the

TIME LAGS	FOR 90 PERCENT EQUALIZATION $= T_{90}$										BASIC TIME LAG T
APPROX. SOIL TYPE	SAND			SILT			CLAY				
COEFF. OF PERMEABILITY CM/SEC	10^{-1}	10^{-2}	10^{-3}	10^{-4}	10^{-5}	10^{-6}	10^{-7}	10^{-8}	10^{-9}	10^{-10}	
1 5CM CASING-SOIL IN CASING L=3D=15CM	6^m	1^h	10^h	4.2^d							193^d
2 5CM.CASING-SOIL FLUSH BOTTOM OF CASING	0.6^m	6^m	1^h	10^h	4.2^d						17^d
3 5CM.CASING-HOLE EXTENDED L=3D=15CM		1.5^m	15^m	2.5^h	25^h	10^d					4.5^d
4 5CM CASING-HOLE EXTENDED L=12D=60CM			6^m	1^h	10^h	4.2^d	42^d				47^h
5 10MM PIEZOMETER WITH WELL POINT DIA.=38MM LENGTH=45CM				3^m	30^m	5^h	50^h	21^d			130^m
6 10MM PIEZOMETER WITH WELL POINT AND SAND FILTER, D=15CM, L=1.08M					12^m	2^h	20^h	8.3^d	83^d		51^m
7 1.5MM MERCURY MANOMETER SINGLE TUBE WITH POROUS CUP POINT, D=32MM, L=62MM	ONE-HALF OF VALUES FOR 1.5 MM MERCURY U-TUBE MANOMETER OR 12CM BOURDON GAUGE					2^m	20^m	3.3^h	33^h	14^d	52^s
8 1.5MM.MERCURY MANOMETER SINGLE TUBE WITH WELL POINT, D=58MM, L=45 CM							6^m	1^h	10^h	4.2^d	16^s
9 7.5CM.W.E.S. HYDROSTATIC PRESSURE CELL IN DIRECT CONTACT WITH SOIL								16^m	2.6^h	26^h	4^s
10 7.5 CM. W.E.S. HYDROSTATIC PRESSURE CELL IN SAND FILTER, D=15CM, L=45CM									16^m	2.6^h	0.4^s

SYMBOLS s=SECONDS, m=MINUTES, h=HOURS, d=DAYS. – ASSUMPTIONS: CONSTANT GROUND WATER PRESSURE AND INTAKE SHAPE FACTOR, ISOTROPIC SOIL, STRESS ADJUSTMENT TIME LAG NEGLIGABLE, NO GAS. THE COMPUTED TIME LAGS HAVE BEEN ROUNDED OFF TO CONVENIENT VALUES

Fig. 51: Hydrostatic time lags (Hvorslev [1951]).

basic time lag is 13 minutes. Hvorslev computed time lags for a range
of piezometer systems and a summary of his data is given in Figure 51.

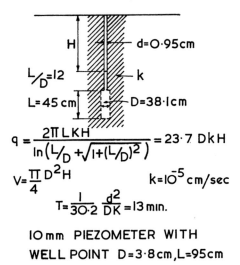

$$q = \frac{2\pi L K H}{\ln\left(L/D + \sqrt{1+(L/D)^2}\right)} = 23.7\ D k H$$

$$V = \frac{\pi}{4} D^2 H \qquad\qquad k = 10^{-5}\ cm/sec$$

$$T = \frac{1}{30.2} \frac{d^2}{DK} = 13\ min.$$

10 mm PIEZOMETER WITH
WELL POINT D=3·8cm, L=95cm

Fig. 50: Calculation of Basic Time Lag (Hvorslev [1951]).

3.2.5. Sources of Error

The principal sources of error in the determination of ground water pressures are summarized in Figure 52, (Hvorslev [1951]). The importance
of these errors and their control are reviewed by Hvorslev. Items 3 to 6
affect the value of the water level recorded while items 7 to 10 usually
modify the time lag value. For these reasons it is important that the
time lag of a piezometer system be determined in the field (Section
3.2.2.). In most installations it is possible to control the magnitude of the
errors by piezometer selection (Section 3.3.), by good methods of installation (Section 3.4.), by proper de-airing techniques (Section 3.5.) and by
reliable recording methods. It will be appreciated that in different
situations the accuracy and response requirements of a piezometer differ.
For example in earth dams the water pressure head may be in error by
0.5 m as a result of time lag. Such an error is unimportant in most cases
provided the piezometer is functioning properly. Thus a time lag of
several days may not be important because pore water pressures change
slowly. A mal functioning of the piezometer is extremely important
and the fact that the piezometer has the capacity to record pressure
changes of a few cm of water is of no importance in such a situation.

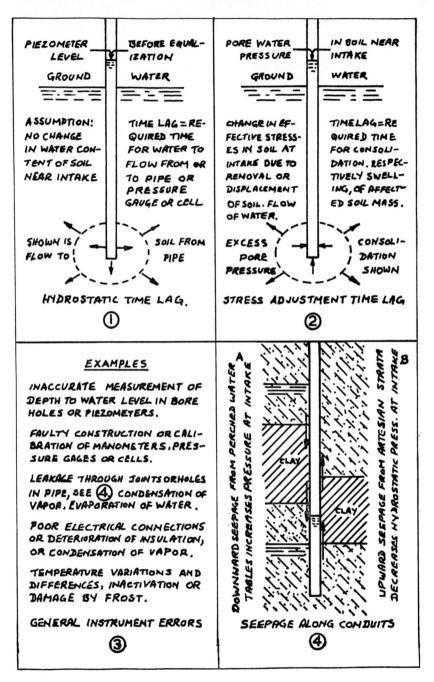

Fig. 52 a: Sources of error in ground water pressure measurement (Hvorslev [1951]).

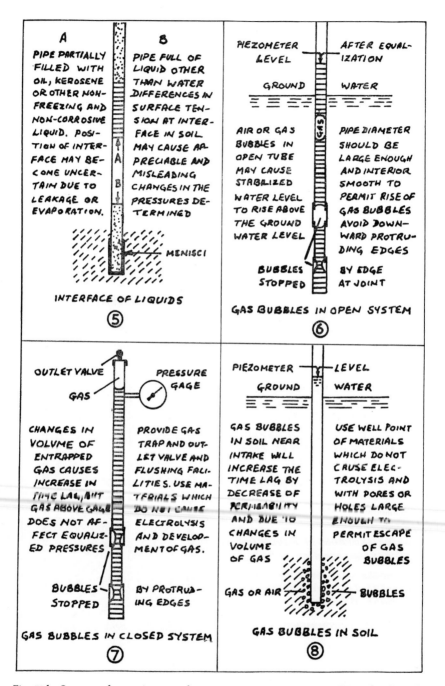

Fig. 52 b: Sources of error in ground water pressure measurement (Hvorslev [1951]).

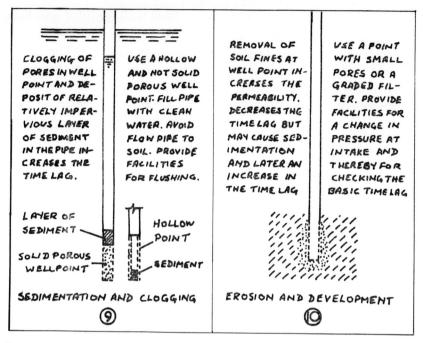

CLOGGING OF PORES IN WELL POINT AND DE-POSIT OF RELA-TIVELY IMPER-VIOUS LAYER OF SEDIMENT IN THE PIPE IN-CREASES THE TIME LAG.

USE A HOLLOW AND NOT SOLID POROUS WELL POINT. FILL PIPE WITH CLEAN WATER. AVOID FLOW PIPE TO SOIL. PROVIDE FACILITIES FOR FLUSHING.

REMOVAL OF SOIL FINES AT WELL POINT IN-CREASES THE PERMEABILITY. DECREASES THE TIME LAG BUT MAY CAUSE SED-IMENTATION AND LATER AN INCREASE IN THE TIME LAG

USE A POINT WITH SMALL PORES OR A GRADED FIL-TER. PROVIDE FACILITIES FOR A CHANGE IN PRESSURE AT INTAKE AND THEREBY FOR CHECKING THE BASIC TIME LAG

LAYER OF SEDIMENT

HOLLOW POINT

SOLID POROUS WELLPOINT

SEDIMENT

SEDIMENTATION AND CLOGGING ⑨

EROSION AND DEVELOPMENT ⑩

Fig. 52 c: Sources of error in ground water pressure measurement (Hvorslev [1951]).

3.3. Piezometer Types

All piezometer systems have a porous filter element which is placed in the ground. These elements may be classified according to their use, their method of operation and their method of recording. In the following sections the general features of a number of piezometers in use by the foundation engineer are considered. Piezometers specially made for research purposes are not considered in detail.

3.3.1. The Open Standpipe

The most common ground water recording technique is to observe the water level in an open borehole. Here the surface area through which the water enters is large and unless the soil is coarse grained a large time lag results. A particular disadvantage of this system is that different layers of soil, which may be under different water levels, are connected and consequently the value of the water table level recorded may have little, if any, significance. In most site investigation work the practice of recording the water level in the borehole each morning is still followed and in some cases a rough guide to the position of the ground water table results. A plumbline with measuring tape is used to determine the position of the water level with respect to the ground surface.

Some of the disadvantages of the open borehole may be overcome by the use of a casing which is extended to the level of water pressure measurement. The borehole is backfilled up to this level and sealed with a 0.3 m thickness of puddled clay backfill. The standpipe, about 5 cm diameter, is perforated over a length of about 1 m and surrounded by a sand or sand and gravel backfill. The test section is sealed, Figure 53, and the borehole backfilled to the ground surface. The top of the casing is protected by a screw cap or wooden plug. With this system a considerable volume of water must either flow into or out of the casing thus requiring a long time for pressure equalization. Also, leakage through the casing joints and seepage from adjacent strata may occur and obscure fluctuation in the static ground water table.

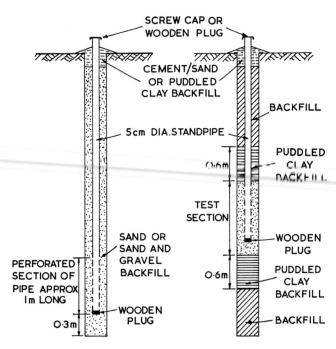

Fig. 53: Details of an open standpipe water level recorder.

3.3.2. Porous Tube Piezometer

To reduce the equalization time a riser pipe of small diameter is used and is connected to the perforated casing, the annulus between the riser pipe and the borehole being backfilled. A porous element, usually referred to as a tip or well point, is connected to the riser pipe and is placed in a layer of sand or gravel. This layout is referred to as a piezometer and, where the standpipe is open to the atmosphere, the piezometer system is an "open" one.

The porous tip is usually about 40 mm o. d. by 25 mm i. d. and up to 0.6 m in length. The most common tip is the nonmetallic ceramic stone (Norton stone) developed by Casagrande and illustrated in Figure 54. The main disadvantage of the ceramic tip is its susceptibility to damage and for this reason other types of tip but of the same overall dimension as the Casagrande tip are now in general use. The Terratest (Canada) piezometer comprises a porous sheath filled with a pea gravel. The pores are about 50 micron size and the tip can be used in direct contact with fine grained soils such as silts and clays.

Porous metallic tips are in extensive use and a detail of the porous bronze filter used by the Norwegain Geotechnical Institute (Geonor piezometer) is given in Figure 55. It comprises a 30 mm diameter filter

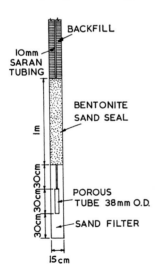

Fig. 54: Casagrande —
type borehole piezometer.

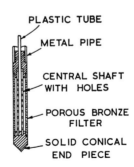

Fig. 55:
Geonor borehole piezometer tip.

cylinder connected to a central shaft by top and bottom end pieces. The bottom piece is cone-shaped, the top end being threaded to connect to standard drill rod. The piezometer element is fitted with a plastic riser pipe, usually nylon. In soft ground the piezometer can be installed by pushing or driving, or it may be driven from the bottom of a small diameter borehole in harder soil. If the drill rods are not removed it is possible to recover the piezometer after use.

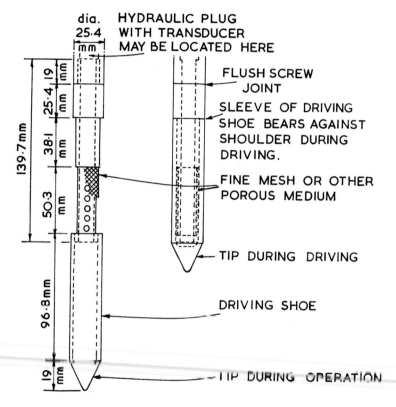

Fig. 56: Borehole piezometer tip (Parry [1971]).

A cheaper tip was developed by Parry (1971). It consists of a 25.4 mm o. d. mild steel tube, 12.7 mm i. d. Part of the tube is reduced to 15 mm o. d. and a number of 4.8 mm holes are drilled through the wall of the tube. Gauze mesh is wrapped around the perforated section. During installation the porous element is covered by a steel sleeve with a conical element, the outer diameter of which is flush with the outer diameter of the tip section and sealing tube, Figure 56. After the tip is driven to the required depth the porous element is uncovered by withdrawing the drill rods and leaving the driving shoe in the ground, or by insertion of a mandrel inside the rods and tapping the driving shoe further into the ground. Non-corrosive metal such as brass is recommended by Parry for long-term use. The tip may be used with a plastic riser pipe, or a hydraulic plug with pressure transducer can be screwed into the top end of the piezometer where a rapid response is required.

Where the porous tip is susceptible to damage it can be protected by a 25 mm o. d. rigid perforated p. v. c. tube. Where it is proposed to drive the piezometer through soft ground a perforated galvanised mild steel pipe is used. The lower end is conical-shaped, the top end being adapted to take the driving rods.

Because of the time lag associated with the flow of water from fine grained soils to the piezometer (Figure 51) it is common practice to provide the piezometer with twin lines or tubes. One of the lines passes to the bottom end of the piezometer, the other terminating at the top of the element. After installation, the piezometer is flushed through to remove air bubbles. This is achieved by pumping water down to the bottom of the piezometer tip and allowing it to escape via the other line. After de-airing, the de-airing line is closed and the pressure line is connected to a manometer or pressure gauge. The system is referred to as a hydraulic piezometer. Its chief advantages are: (i) the system can be de-aired during use, (ii) the time lag can be controlled by the selection of the tube diameter. The main disadvantage is that it is not possible to measure large suction pressures due to cavitation. Problems of freezing of the water in the lines have to be considered.

3.3.3. Electrical Piezometers

The principle of the electrical piezometer is that a diphragm is deflected by the water pressure acting against one face, the deflection of the diaphragm being proportional to the applied pressure. This pressure is measured by means of various electrical transducers. Such devices have very small time lags and are very sensitive. The most usual methods employed to measure the deflection of the diaphragm are vibrating wire gauges, resistance strain gauges or capacitance strain gauges.

The vibrating wire principle is well established and a high degree of success is reported by the Norwegian Geotechnical Institute. The B.R.S. piezometer is shown in section in Figure 57. The porous filter element is 50 mm diameter by 75 mm length and the method of recording the deflection of the diaphragm is clear from this figure. The Geonor vibrating wire piezometer essentially is similar to the B.R.S. piezometer in principle, Figure 58. The top end of the piezometer is connected to the ground surface by a plastic tube serving as a lead conduit and also maintaining atmospheric pressure on the top of the piezometer

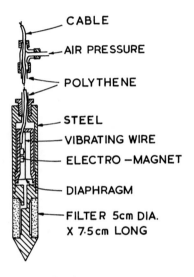

Fig. 57: B. R. S. — type vibrating wire piezometer (Penman [1960]).

diaphragm. The Maihak piezometer is shown in Figure 59. The chief differences between these piezometers are the dimensions and positioning of the porous element, the layout of the vibrating wire element and the mechanical means used to protect the instrument against moisture effects and damage. The Telemac cell also makes use of the vibrating wire principle and consists of a tube which acts as a spring. A vibrating wire stretched along it measures axial deformation under the action of external water pressure. The element is protected by a stainless steel cylinder terminating in a porous element which allows the pore water to enter the instrument. This piezometer has a very rapid response, temperature effects are negligible and it is easily installed.

The electrical resistance strain gauged transducer is not so widely used
as the vibrating wire system. The A.G.S. system makes use of a solid

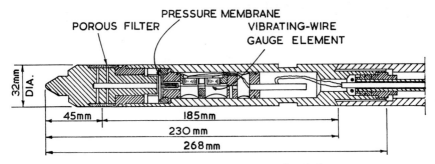

Fig. 58: Geonor electrical piezometer — borehole type.

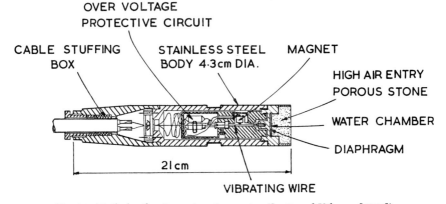

Fig. 59: Maihak vibrating wire piezometer (Scott and Kilgour [1967]).

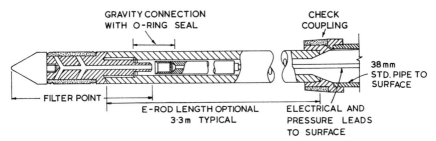

Fig. 60: Electric piezometer — Applied Geodata System Inc.

state semiconductor transducer and integrated circuit to produce a frequency modulated signal directly proportional to the pore water pressure
acting on the pressure sensing diaphragm. A line drawing of this piezometer tip is given in Figure 60. The piezometer is designed to be driven

into place. The transducer package is lowered into place after the piezometer tip is driven. Thus damage of the transducer during piezometer installation is prevented. It is possible to vacuum de-air the water within the porous filter point. Consequently a response time of a few milliseconds is possible and the measurement of rapidly changing pore pressures may be achieved. There are several other types of electrical piezometer and the main difference lies in the transducer package, the porous element and the arrangement of the body of the piezometer. Generally these piezometers are useful in situations requiring rapid response or dynamic readings (Lundgren [1966]).

3.3.4. Air-Pneumatic Piezometer

The pneumatic piezometer comprises a porous tip which contains a pressure-sensitive valve. The piezometer system consists of an air activated hydrostatic pressure cell, two air lines, an air supply and a pressure measuring gauge. In use a flow of compressed air is admitted into one of the air lines but is blocked by the pore water pressure acting on a thin flexible diaphragm. When the air pressure equals the pore

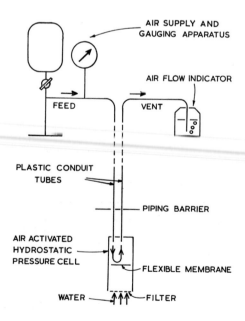

Fig. 61: Pneumatic piezometer — (Warlam and Thomas [1965]).

water pressure the membrane relaxes and allows excess air to pass into a flow indicating flask where air bubbles are visible. When further air supply is shut off the pressure in the air supply line is equal to the pore water pressure. This is the principle of operation of the Warlam and Thomas (1965) piezometer which is illustrated in Figure 61.

There are several advantages to the pneumatic piezometer: (i) a very small volume change is required to operate the air flow valve, consequently the time lag is small, (ii) the instrument is simple to operate and read, (iii) it has long term stability, (iv) inexpensive plastic tubing may be used to conduct the air to the piezometer, (v) the readings are direct, (vi) no de-airing of the lines is required.

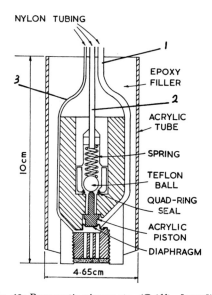

Fig. 62: Pneumatic piezometer (Griffin [1967]).

A somewhat similar pneumatic piezometer is described by Griffin (1967). The piezometer is read by measurement of the air pressure required to close a hydraulic balance system. Figure 62, shows a detail of the functioning of the piezometer. Air pressure from a control box is introduced into line 1. As the air pressure increases in line 1, and until the teflon ball check closes, each line records the same air pressure value. When the applied air pressure in line 1 equals the pore water pressure in the ground which acts on the diaphragm, the ball check closes. Because the pressure in line 1 can increase further, the pressure in line 2 which equals the balanced pore water pressure is read. Closure of the valve check causes a small displacement of water into or out of the soil and this can modify the value of the pore water pressure. To overcome this difficulty a third line (3) which is open to the atmosphere allows this volume change to occur without causing water to flow into the soil in the vicinity of the porous filter.

A very accurate pneumatic piezometer is the SINCO unit which is shown in Figure 63. Pressure changes as small as 1 cm of water can be recorded.

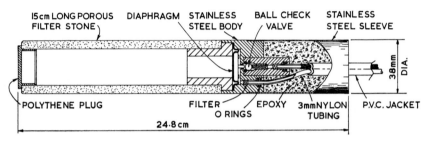

Fig. 63: Pneumatic piezometer — Slope Indicator Company.

3.3.5. Oil Pneumatic Piezometer

The Glötzl piezometer operates on the same principle as the air pneumatic piezometer but a hydraulic fluid (oil) is used instead of air. An oil-filled chamber leads to a diaphragm, pressure from the water being applied to the diaphragm by a piston. The diaphragm is held flat against a pressure plate. Two inlet ports in the pressure plate are connected to the readout station by a pressure line. The pore water pressure is recorded by pressurization of the inlet port until the diaphragm lifts off the pressure plate. When the diaphragm lifts, oil passes across the pressure plate and returns to the oil reservoir via the other line. Continuous pumping of oil will cause no further pressure change in the system. If the gauge pressure recorded is G and the pressure head at the inlet port is H, then the water pressure W is given by

$$W = G + H - S \qquad (3.19)$$

where S is the spring pressure used to hold the diaphragm against the pressure plate. The principle of the Glötzl measuring system is detailed in Figure 95 and Section 4.3.

3.3.6. Water Pressure Piezometer — Terrametrics

The Aquametric piezometer essentially is a pneumatic instrument, Figure 64. It comprises a porous filter stone set in a bubble chamber, the bubble chamber being connected to a co-axial tube. Water enters the bubble chamber and rises to a static level in the co-axial tube. A controlled gas pressure is introduced through the inner tube and slowly increased until the water in the inner tube is depressed to the level of the bubble chamber. The gas escapes to the outer tube thus preventing further increase in gas pressure. The water pressure acting in the bubble chamber is equal to the applied gas pressure in the inner tube. The advantages of this piezometer system are (i) the unit is of plastic and hence corrosion problems do not exist, (ii) it has no moving or electrical parts, (iii) a range of filter stone sizes can be chosen to match soils of different permeabilities, (iv) the water pressure is read directly.

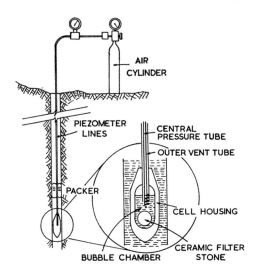

Fig. 64: Aquametric Water Pressure Cell — Terrametrics.

3.3.7. Piezometers for use in earth fill

Compacted earth fill is usually in a partly saturated state and consequently both air pressures and water pressures exist in the pore spaces as mentioned in (3.1.). There are certain difficulties associated with the measurement of pore water pressures in such soils. For example, if the pore water pressure u_w is measured, the effective stress in the soil will be greater than the correct value by $(1 - \chi)$ $(u_a - u_w)$, whereas if u_a is measured, the effective stress in the soil will be underestimated by χ $(u_a - u_w)$. The error in measurement therefore depends on the magnitude of $(u_a - u_w)$ and χ, both depending on the degree of saturation of the soil mass and the composition of the soil (clay content, plasticity, etc.).

Air will pass through the pores of the porous tip of a piezometer if the pores are too large. The size of the pores controls their air entry value. This is the difference between the air pressure on one side of a saturated porous filter and water pressure on the other side, at which blow-through of air occurs. In order that the piezometer will measure the pore water pressure, u_w, the air entry value of the piezometer must be greater than $(u_a - u_w)$. If this is not so the piezometer will record the pore air pressure value, a characteristic of nearly all embankment piezometers prior to about 1960. (see Bishop and Vaughan [1962]).

Two general types of piezometer have been used for the measurement of pore water pressure in earth fills. They are the twin line hydraulic piezometer and the electrical piezometer. Over the years the shapes of the piezometers have evolved and today several shapes are in use. Generally the shape is different from that of the borehole piezometer, being either disc-shaped or conical-shaped. The twin tube hydraulic piezometer was developed at the Building Research Station (Penman [1956]) and used by Little and Vail (1960) and others. Three main developments are responsible for the near universal use of this piezometer principle for measurement in rolled earth fill. They are (i) development in the porous tip particularly its air entry value, (ii) development in the tubing used to connect the piezometer tips to a gauge house, (iii) development in de-airing techniques to remove air bubbles from the system.

One of the first applications of high air entry piezometers was to measure suctions beneath road subgrades but the technique was not applied to rolled earth fill dams owing to the belief that positive and high pore water pressures developed. The relevance of compacted fill pore pressure characteristics was demonstrated by Bishop et al. (1961), who tested such soils under conditions where the pore air pressure was not atmospheric.

The early twin line hydraulic piezometers used copper tubes (Bassett [1959]). These were replaced by polythene tubes in later installations but Penman (1958) observed that polythene was permeable to air. For this reason nylon tubing was introduced about 1960. Saran tubing is widely used in U.S.A. and theoretically is preferable to nylon or polythene because of its lower permeability to air and water. It is, however, rather brittle and expensive. Nylon is strong and ductile and can sustain stretching of up to 100 % without tube closure or rupture. It is slightly permeable to water. This limitation has been overcome by coating nylon tubing with a polythene covering. In conjunction with the polythene-coated nylon tubing the amount of de-airing required was greatly reduced and details of typical de-airing systems are given in Section 3.5.

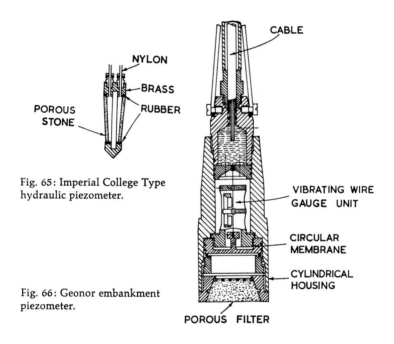

Fig. 65: Imperial College Type hydraulic piezometer.

Fig. 66: Geonor embankment piezometer.

The most successful and versatile high air entry value piezometer was that based on a design by Professor A. W. Bishop. The element is about 10 cm in length, and tapers from 5 cm to 3.8 cm in diameter. This is an ideal shape for placing in contact with a hole formed by a special mandrel. The ceramic can have any desired air entry value, the most usual being about 200 kN/m², the pore size about 1 micron and the permeability 2×10^{-6} cm/sec. The end fittings of the piezometer are either brass or a rigid p. v. c. material. Compression couplings connect the tubing to the piezometer as shown in Figure 65.

There are many other embankment piezometers which operate on an electronic recording principle. The Geonor electronic embankment piezometer uses a vibrating wire transducer element and a detail of this piezometer is given in Figure 66. The Maihak piezometer has also been used in earth fill and an excellent review of experiences with this instrument is given by Scott and Kilgour (1967).

3.3.8. Piezometer for use at a boundary

In situations such as retaining walls, piles and culverts it may be necessary to measure pore water pressures at the face of the structure. A number of commercially available piezometers are suitable, the primary requirement being that the porous disc of the piezometer should be located parallel to the face of the structure and of sufficient robustness that it will not sustain damage during installation or use. The Norwegian Geotechnical Institute design is, perhaps, the most simple and is very successful when used in the soft ground conditions of Norway. Figure 67

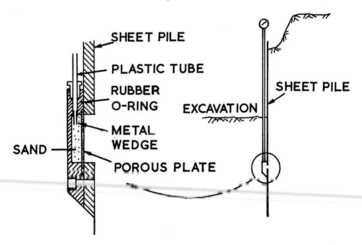

Fig. 67: Boundary piezometer — Bjerrum, Kenney, Kjaernsli (1965).

illustrates one of these special piezometers being used to measure pore water pressures adjacent to driven steel sheet piles (Bjerrum, Kenney and Kjaernsli [1965]). It consists of a box-shaped housing filled with sand, one face being porous metal. The box is attached to the pile by bolts so that the porous plate was opposite an opening in the steel sheet pile. A plastic tube fits into the top end of the piezometer and measurements of the height of water in the plastic tube were taken by an electrical probe or by the use of a Bourdon gauge. For more accurate work it should be possible to use a twin line hydraulic system and, if necessary, a high air entry value porous stone.

Warlam and Thomas (1965) describe the use of the pneumatic piezometer, Figure 61, for uplift pressure determination on the underside of a weir structure. The piezometers were set in 15 cm diameter by 20 cm deep holes cut into the chalk bedrock at the underside of the weir slab, the space around the piezometers being filled with a clean and saturated sand. The lines from the piezometer tips were passed through the slab and terminated in the spillway gallery. The nylon tubes were not protected in the concrete except at lift-joints where lengths of air hose pipe were used for protection. Seepage along the smooth nylon lines was prevented by the pipe joints and by the use of a neoprene rubber pad which was spread over the cell. Details of the layout of a piezometer and the method of sealing the lines are shown in Figure 68.

The measurement of pore water pressures behind walls which are backfilled subsequent to construction can be measured by the standard piezometer which is placed adjacent to the back of the wall as the backfill is placed. The piezometer type is selected in relation to the permeability of the backfill bearing in mind (i) that the backfill must be carefully packed around the piezometer and (ii) that the lines are protected from damage during the backfilling operations. Such an approach was followed by Adams and Hanna (1970) to record water pressures in a granular backfill behind a rigid wall. In cases where the backfill is not completely saturated, high air entry porous tips are required and a de-airing system should be incorporated in the layout (Section 3.5.).

Few attempts have been made to measure the pore water pressures set up in the ground due to pile driving. The works of Bjerrum and Johannsen (1961), Lo and Stermac (1965), Lambe and Horn (1965) have shown that it is possible to measure the magnitude of the static pore water pressure and its lateral extent from the side of the pile by the use of borehole-type piezometers. D'Appolonia (1971) has reviewed all available pore water pressure data pertaining to pile driving. There are several disadvantages to this technique of pore water pressure measurement due to the inexact knowledge of the exact position of the piezometer at depth with respect to the pile and the difficulty of protection of a piezometer in the middle of large pile cluster (Hanna [1967]).

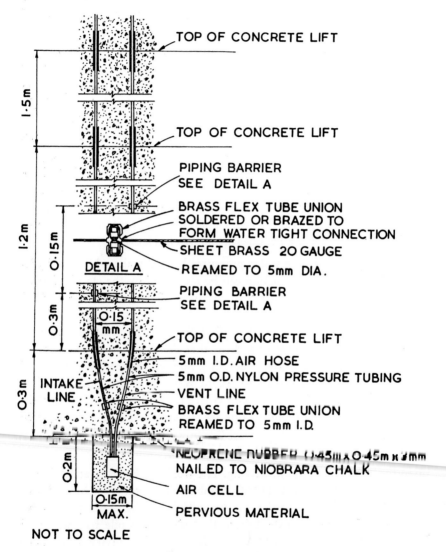

Fig. 68: Pneumatic piezometer installation in a weir slab —
(Warlam and Thomas [1965]).

To minimize some of these difficulties a special piezometer was designed and used by Hanna (1967) to measure static water pressure on a driven pile interface. The piezometer is welded to the face of the pile, Figure 69, and comprises a box 150 mm by 32 mm by 19 mm deep with a 3 mm thick porous bronze membrane. Twin hydraulic lines permit de-airing of the system. The space inside the piezometer box was filled with medium size sand, the nylon tubes being of 3 mm o. d. and 1.5 mm i. d. In use the piezometer is attached to the pile member by fillet weld as shown in Figure 70. Holding angles guide a 10 mm diameter conductor pipe along the pile and thus the nylon lines are protected from damage during the pile driving operation. This piezometer system was satisfactory even for the very hard driving conditions to which it was subjected. In its present form it is only suitable for recording static water pressures subsequent to pile driving but it should be possible, by the use of an electrical pressure transducer, to record dynamic pore water pressures. To date such a modification has not been attempted.

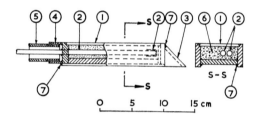

1 3mm DOVETAILED POROUS BRONZE MEMBRANE
2 6mm I.D. STAINLESS STEEL TUBE WITH END
   COVERED BY 200 MESH SCREEN
3 7.5cm CHANNEL SECTION PROTECTION TOE
4 19mm PIPE COUPLING
5 18mm PIPE
6 MEDIUM SAND
7 WELD

Fig. 69: Pile Piezometer (Hanna [1967]).

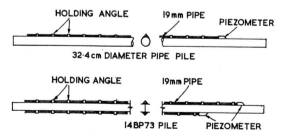

Fig. 70: Method of piezometer attachment to pile wall.

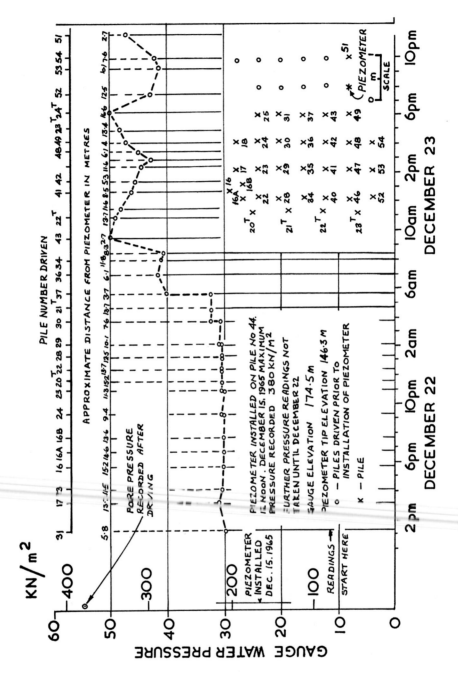

Fig. 71: Pore Water pressures due to pile driving (Hanna [1967]).

Test data typical of this piezometer are shown in Figures 71 and 72. Figure 71 refers to a piezometer on a 0.32 m diameter driven pipe pile of 32 m length, the piezometer being at 28 m depth. The data of Figure 72 were obtained from an H-section pile, 13.4 m long, which was the first pile of a cluster of 750 piles driven to form a nuclear reactor foundation. The change in pore water pressure with time as pile driving progressed was measured.

Other engineers have attempted to measure the water pressures at the base of a pile and the work of Adams and Radhakrishna (1971) shows that it is possible to measure suctions developed during a pulling test.

These examples show how the foundation engineer can either adopt existing piezometer systems or build special piezometers for measurement of pore water pressure at a boundary. This is a fairly recent departure from the traditional use of piezometers and consequently reported data are scarce. The same principles of piezometer selection apply as in the case of borehole or earth fill piezometers. The main factors which have to be considered in great detail are (i) the environment in which the piezometer will be used, in particular the installation problems and the construction operations, (ii) the problems of recording and (iii) the decision on where the piezometer is or should be located.

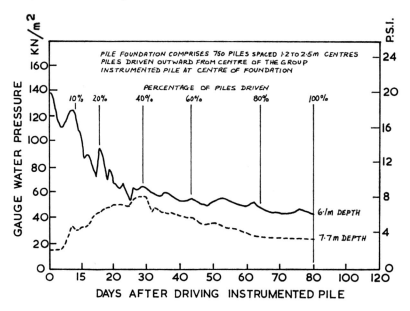

Fig. 72: Pore water pressures due to pile driving (Hanna [1967]).

3.4.   Piezometer Installation

3.4.1. Piezometer Installation in Boreholes

Most piezometers are installed within a permeable layer at the base of a borehole, the borehole above the permeable filter being sealed to isolate the point of water pressure measurement from adjacent soil layers. It is possible to install several piezometers at different levels in one borehole. A multiple piezometer is reported by Bjerrum, Kenney and Kjaernsli (1965). Several filter cylinders are fastened together by lengths of pipe, Figure 73, each filter being connected to a separate plastic tube. A multi-unit borehole piezometer is also reported by Vaughan (1969).

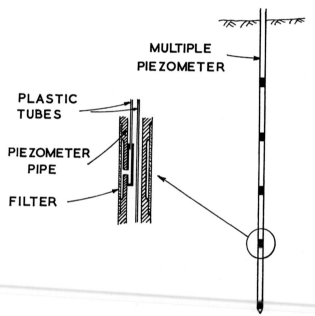

Fig. 73: Multiple piezometer — borehole type (Bjerrum, Kenney, Kjaernsli [1965]).

A standard type of piezometer installation is shown in Figure 74. In this case the piezometer is lowered to the bottom of the borehole, sand is placed around it and a seal is placed above it to prevent water from flowing towards it from the upper zones of ground. The seal usually comprises grout which may be cement, clay cement, dry bentonite powder which swells in contact with moisture, or clay balls (Casagrande [1949]). The seal produced should have a permeability less than that of the surrounding soil mass. This is easily achieved in coarse grained soils

(e. g. sands) but in cases where the in-situ permeability of the soil is very low then difficulty in forming a plug of grout of permeability less than that of the surrounding soil may occur. This topic is reviewed in Section 3.4.3. Details of installation of several piezometers in a borehole are given by Vaughan (1969).

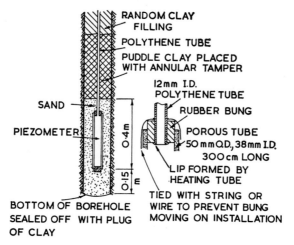

Fig. 74: Detail of borehole piezometer installation.

3.4.2. Piezometer Installation in rolled earth fill

These piezometers are usually installed during earth fill placement when the fill has reached the required elevation. A trench about 0.8 m deep is dug from the positions of the boreholes to the recording station (gauge house). The lines from the piezometer are placed in this trench. The piezometers are placed near this main trench in small side trenches. A tapered hole, if the Bishop type piezometer is used, is formed in the base of the hand-dug trench, with a special mandrel. The tubes are laid from the gauge house to the piezometer location. The piezometer elements are carefully saturated with de-aired water and taken on site under water. The connecting tubes, which have been carefully de-aired from the gauge house by flushing with de-aired water, are connected to the piezometer tip under water. At this stage a check or zero reading is taken in the gauge house. The piezometer tip is lifted out of the water and carefully pressed into the special hole formed for it in the rolled fill. Readings are taken to establish the minimum piezometer reading and several checks are made during trench backfilling and during placement of about 1 m of fill for accidental damage to the tips. Valuable information on the specialized techniques and precautions necessary during piezometer installation are given in the Pore Pressure and Suction in Soils Conference (1960), and in several publications on earth dam design and construction as well as in the various manuals e. g. U.S.B.R. (1963).

3.4.3. Piezometer Sealing.

Vaughan (1969) examined the problems of sealing a piezometer in a borehole in some detail and a summary of his findings follows. Figure 75 refers to sealing into a permeable layer. Vaughan shows that the piezometer error, ε, is related to the permeability of the grout, k_g, the length of the grout zone, H, the permeability of the soil layer, k, the area of the borehole grout plug, a, and the piezometer intake factor, F, by the expression,

$$\varepsilon = \varepsilon_0 - N\,P'_H \qquad\qquad (3.20)$$

where $\varepsilon_0 = H/(B\,H + 1)$, $N = 1/(B\,H + 1)$, $B = F\,k/(a_1\,k_g)$ and P'_H is the pore water pressure in the permeable layer.

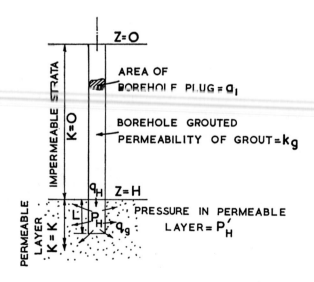

Fig. 75: Piezometer sealing into a permeable layer (Vaughan [1969]).

For the piezometer to record without significant error, ε_0 must be small and Vaughan states ". . . for a typical installation the permeability of the borehole plug can be significantly greater than the permeability of the permeable strata without significant error resulting".

Sealing a piezometer in a homogeneous soil is illustrated in Figure 76. The piezometer error ε is related by the expression

$$\varepsilon = \varepsilon_0 \left[1 - a - b \sqrt{A} \, e^{-\sqrt{A} \cdot H} \left(\frac{H \, \text{Tan h} \, (\sqrt{A} \cdot H)}{\text{Tan h} \, (\sqrt{A} \cdot H)} \right) \right] \qquad (3.21)$$

where

$$\varepsilon_0 = \text{Tan h} \, (\sqrt{A} \, H) / [\sqrt{A} + B \, \text{Tan H} \, (\sqrt{A} \cdot H)]$$

$$A = f \cdot k / (a_1 \, k_g)$$

$$f = 2 \, \pi / \log \, (r_0 / r_b)$$

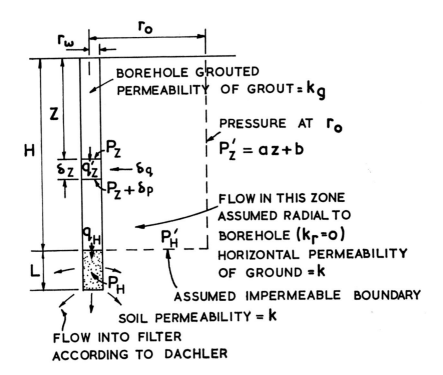

Fig. 76: Piezometer sealing into a homogeneous soil (Vaughan [1969]).

Typical errors of piezometers are computed by Vaughan and he shows that the errors are small and unlikely to exceed the likely error in reading the piezometer by indirect means. For example, a 5 m deep borehole with a 15 cm diameter filter in an overconsolidated soil, k = 5 x 10^{-9} cm/sec plugged with a grout, k_g = 5 x 10^{-8} cm/sec, would have an error of only 7 cm. In certain cases the permeability of the grout can be several orders of magnitude greater than that of the soil without significant error resulting (Vaughan [1969]).

3.5. De-airing of Piezometers and Piezometer Lines

Air can enter the piezometer system through the walls of the tubing if it is slightly permeable to air, or through the porous tip if the soil is partly saturated. The first-mentioned source may be eliminated by the use of a nylon tube coated with a polythene cover. The second source of air entry is much more difficult to control and can never be eliminated completely. As mentioned above, during the installation of piezometers in rolled earth fill great care is exercised in ensuring that the piezometer system is completely de-aired. With such a condition fulfilled it is still possible for air to enter the system in the following manner. The initial suction pressures in the soil may be sufficiently large so that tensions in the water in the piezometer tip occur. Even with the system completely de-aired, cavitation and loss of water to the soil will occur. In this manner air from the soil will slowly diffuse through the ceramic stone. To control the entry of air into the piezometer tip it is necessary to flush out the system periodically.

The standard method is to connect each twin-tubed piezometer to the instrument house and to circulate air-free water to remove any gas which may have accumulated. The technique of achieving this is to use a pressure tank containing a rubber bladder which is pressurized from an air supply source. The return water is collected in a second cylinder. In practice three tanks of the same size are used (Penman [1972]), two of them fitted with scales to measure the volume of water flowing into or out of the tanks. Air is pumped into the top of tank A causing a flow into the rubber bladder in the second tank and this forces air-free water into the piezometer system. The flow is measured by the fall of water into tank A and this is checked by the scale on tank C where the return water is collected. The water in cylinder B which circulates through the piezometer lines must be de-aired. This is achieved by boiling under vacuum. The water is heated and a vacuum is applied to cause boiling. Boiling is continued for a period of about 15 minutes. The air-free water is then drawn off and into cylinder B of the de-airing apparatus. With a large number of piezometer tips served by one de-airing unit, a constant pressure pump is used to circulate the water. Figure 77 shows the layout of a de-airing unit, the cylinders having a capacity of 5 l which is sufficient to de-air 800 m of tubing.

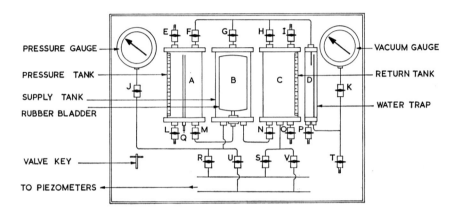

PANEL MOUNTED DE-AIRING UNIT

Fig. 77: De-Airing Unit — Soil Instruments Ltd.

Details of de-airing systems are given by Little and Vail (1960), and Bishop, Kennard and Penman (1960). It should be noted that with the use of the high air-entry porous tip and polythene-coated nylon tubes, the entry of air into piezometers is small and the need to circulate air-free water after the initial de-airing during installation seldom arises (Penman [1972]).

During the installation of electrical and pneumatic piezometers similar precautions must be taken to ensure that the piezometer tip is completely de-aired. With most of these piezometers it is impossible to de-air subsequent to installation and hence care is required in selecting the air entry value if the instrument is to be used in a partly saturated soil.

3.6. Methods of Recording

There are three standard methods of piezometer recording. They are (i) mechanical methods, (ii) electrical methods and (iii) manometers.

With the borehole piezometer which uses a single line the most usual method of water level determination is a plumbline which is lowered until it makes contact with the water surface. The most satisfactory system is a co-axial cable kept on a drum and fitted with slip rings which are connected to a milliammeter with variable resistance and battery. Immersion of the tip of the coaxial cable in water closes the electrical circuit and this is recorded on the milliammeter. The tip of the

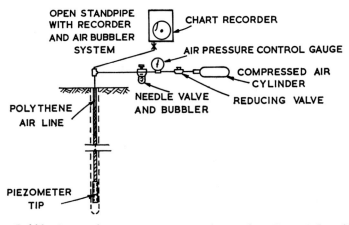

Fig. 78: Bubbler System for piezometer automatic recording (Penman [1972]).

"dipper" is designed so that drops of water clinging to the walls of the standpipe or to the dipper will not close the electrical circuit. This recording system is used where the water table is below ground level.

Where the water table rises above ground level, the stick-up standpipe is capped and the water pressure at this level is recorded by a Bourdon gauge. Bourdon pressure gauges have several disadvantages in field use. Their accuracy is not high and small changes in a high pressure value may be difficult to detect. They are susceptible to corrosion and frost damage (Section 3.7.) and the gauges may jam in a moist environment. Over long periods of use they require to be recalibrated.

Automatic recording of an open piezometer is achieved by use of a bubbler system (Penman [1972]). A small air line, Figure 78, is passed down the piezometer standpipe and a very small flow of gas passed down it to produce several bubbles per minute. The pressure of the gas is equal to the height of the water in the standpipe above the end of the bubbler tube. This pressure is automatically recorded by a chart recorder which may be mechanically or electrically powered. Gas is supplied through a regulator from a cylinder of compressed air or nitrogen.

The electrical transducer is a relatively expensive method of recording. It is not always reliable under field conditions, especially under long-term use because it is impossible to recalibrate once the piezometer is in the ground, (Cooling [1962]). It has the advantage that the elevation of the piezometer tip does not control the position of the instrument station. Hosking and Hilton (1963) report on the use of the Maihak gauge while Scott and Kilgour (1967) conclude from an extensive survey that the leads from their vibrating wire piezometers to the reading station were the weakest link in the system. These authors examined the strength and flexibility of Maihak conductor cables, the use of high air entry porous tips, temperature variation effects, and piezometer stability over a period of 2 years. The chief merit of the electrical piezometer is its ability to take automatic readings. Despite this great advantage there are several major limitations and Wilson (1967) concludes ". . . Because of severe environmental problems and long-term stability, the use of electrical piezometers is not generally recommended for installations in embankments where reliable readings are required over an extended period of time". Examples of studies of the behaviour of electrical piezometers are to be found in the works of Muhs and Campbell-Allen (1955), Pinkerton and McConnell (1964), Silva (1966) and Olivieria and Ferrari (1970).

The most reliable method of recording is the mercury manometer system and the design produced by Soil Instruments (U.K.) Ltd. is shown in Figure 79. Twin tubes from each piezometer are connected to the triple valve units and the upper end of each manometer unit is connected to a separate water header tank. The manometer scales are calibrated directly in metres head of water and five units are mounted on a panel 125 cm in width. The height of the panel is determined by the maximum pore water pressure to be recorded. For example, a head of 15 m of water requires a 1.4 m high panel. Where high pressure values are to be used the manometers are connected to a back pressure from a static

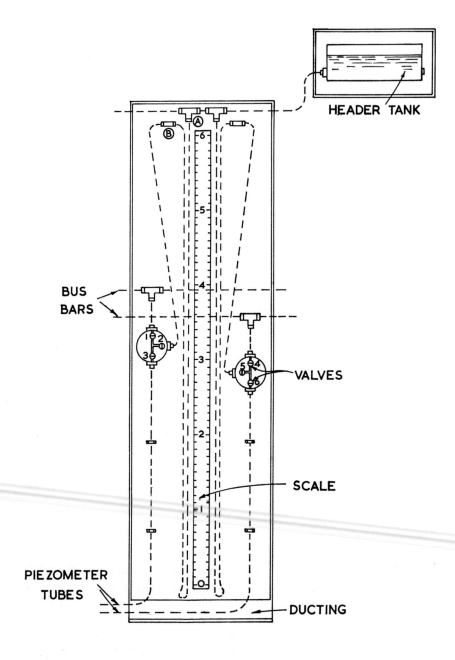

HEADER TANK

BUS
BARS

VALVES

SCALE

PIEZOMETER
TUBES

DUCTING

Fig. 79: Mercury Manometer Unit — Soil Instruments Ltd.

head of water to reduce their length as shown in Figure 80. Here the pore water pressure at the piezometer is

$$u = H + A + B \qquad (3.22)$$

where A + B = an elevation constant for each piezometer tip and H is the mercury manometer reading.

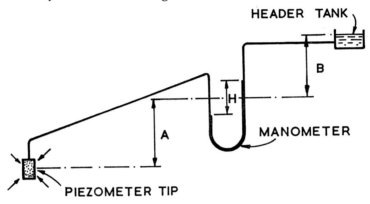

Fig. 80: Header Tank with Mercury Manometer Unit.

Where a number of piezometers are to be read, the back pressure unit usually comprises a mercury pot compensated system as shown in Figure 81. This unit can be used with up to 20 units and the pore water pressure at the piezometer tip is

$$u = H_1 + H_2 + A + B \qquad (3.23)$$

De-aired water is introduced into this system from the de-airing panel (Figure 77). The chief advantages of the mercury manometers are that they do not require calibration or zero correction, and their sensitivity does not alter with pressure range. With Bourdon gauges, which could be used in place of the manometers, their sensitivity decreases with pressure range increase because their scale length does not change with pressure change. They have several other limitations as mentioned above.

It should be noted that with twin line hydraulic piezometers the gauge house must be at an elevation equal to or greater than that of the lowest piezometer, because if the water in the piezometer lines is in tension air bubbles will tend to form and cause errors in readings.

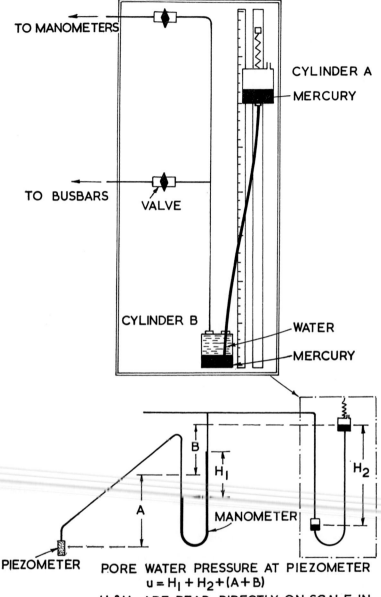

TO MANOMETERS

TO BUSBARS

VALVE

CYLINDER A

MERCURY

CYLINDER B

WATER

MERCURY

B

H_1

A

H_2

MANOMETER

PIEZOMETER

PORE WATER PRESSURE AT PIEZOMETER
$$u = H_1 + H_2 + (A + B)$$
H_1 & H_2 ARE READ DIRECTLY ON SCALE IN
METRES OF WATER PRESSURE, AND (A + B)
IS A CONSTANT IN METRES FOR EACH
PIEZOMETER

Fig. 81: Constant Head Back Pressure Unit — Soil Instruments Ltd.

3.7. Winterizing Piezometers

An advantage of the mercury manometer is that it will not freeze. However with other methods of recording and in particular with borehole piezometers it may be necessary to use an antifreeze. For use with Geonor piezometers the manufacturers recommend a liquid comprising 5.5 l of glycerence, 5.5 l of alcohol, 10 l of water and 4 cm^3 of concentrated sulphur acid. They recommend that where the specific gravity is more or less than 0.99 it can be corrected by the addition of glycerence or alcohol. This solution will not freeze until temperatures below -27° C are reached.

Problems occur with the sealing of piezometers in frozen ground. Guther (1972) recommends a seal of bentonite, water and methanol. The purpose of the methanol is to depress the freezing temperature of the bentonite without appreciably altering its swelling potential.

3.8. Protection of Piezometers

The protection of piezometers in rolled earth fill is simple after the first 1 to 2 m of fill has been placed over the piezometer tip and lines (Hoskings [1968]). With borehole piezometers the top end of the piezometer should terminate in a protective cap which is either flush with the ground surface and covered by a metal screw cap which protects the instrument against vandalism, or should be carried some distance above ground level. Again the top end should have a protective cover and the stick-up clearly marked to warn site traffic and personnel.

Most piezometer suppliers provide advice on protective measures to be taken and many examples of good practice are to be found in the literature already cited.

An excellent example of piezometer top protection is given by Holden (1968) in connection with a foundation instrumentation for the pre-loading of an overpass approach embankment. A detail of the method of installation is shown in Figure 82. The brass rod on top of the piezometer line was to measure the settlement of the piezometer tip. All the lines were directed to a box culvert cast in the base of the fill and allowances were made for settlement by coiling the top ends of the lines.

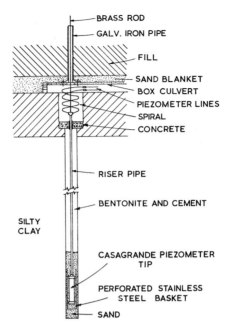

Fig. 82: Detail of piezometer protection (Holden [1968]).

3.9. Accuracies and Performance of Piezometers

The accuracy of a particular piezometer is controlled by (i) the type of piezometer used, (ii) the method of recording employed and (iii) the ground conditions in which it is installed. In section 3.2.5. sources of error were considered. Provided that all joints in piezometer lines are perfectly sealed, the system is completely de-aired and the elevation of the piezometer tip is known, then a high degree of accuracy can be achieved. With the open tube borehole piezometer the water level can be measured to 1 cm of water or better accuracy. The accuracies of the mercury manometer and Bourdon gauges have been discussed. The equipment suppliers'brochures quote accuracies from 0.1 % of the full range of reading with a sensitivity of 0.01 % of full range to about 2 % of full range for electrical and pneumatic piezometers. These accuracies may not be real because they do not necessarily allow for errors caused by air in the piezometer tip and other errors. Hence it is prudent to carry out with great care all the operations necessary to minimize errors in reading.

Several evaluations of piezometer performance have been reported. None cover all piezometer types but there are three very useful comparisons. The work of Penman (1972) compared the performance of a high air-entry hydraulic piezometer with a vibrating wire electrical piezometer. The hydraulic piezometer measured the pore water pressure while the electric piezometer, having a relatively coarse filter, measured the pore air pressure. As the height of the embankment fill increased, Figure 83, both piezometers showed a rise in pore water pressure and, had the

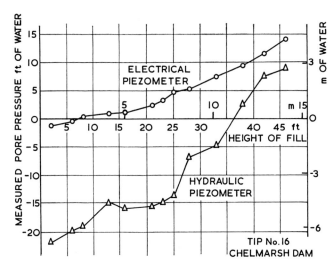

Fig. 83: Pore pressures at Chelmarsh Dam (Penman [1972]).

height of the fill been such that all the air was forced into solution, both piezometers would have recorded the same pore water pressure value. Earlier work by Penman (1960) on dams in the U.K. has shown the importance of high air-entry tips and a summary of the early work on this subject is given in the Proceedings of the Conference on Pore Pressures and Suction in Soils. The treatment by Scott and Kilgour (1967) of the performance of vibrating wire piezometers is excellent and most of the practical limitations in their use have been evaluated.

In conclusion it would appear that the most satisfactory all purpose piezometer may be the pneumatic type owing to (i) its small volume change and time lag characteristics, (ii) its simplicity of operation, (iii) its minimum interference with construction and long term stability. Olivieria and Ferrari (1970) compare the performances of Maihak and Warlam pneumatic piezometers.

3.10. Measurement of Soil Moisture Stresses

Gray (1969) described the use of a maximum recording piezometer used for studying the influence of forest cutting on the stability of natural clay slopes. The piezometer (Swanston [1967]) operates on the principle that as the water level rose in the outer piezometer tube it carried up with it, in an inner tube, powdered cork. As the water level fell the powdered cork adhered to the walls of the inner tube thus indicating the maximum water level. This is done by pulling out the inner recording

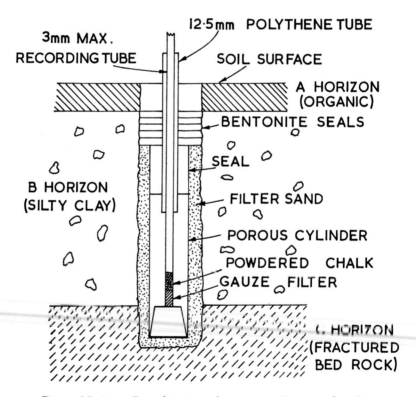

Fig. 84: Maximum Recording type of piezometer (Swanston [1967]).

tube. An illustration of this simple piezometer is given in Figure 84. Gray also describes the use of tensiometers which have the advantage of being able to record automatically, over a period of time, soil suction changes in the ground both during and after a storm (Watson [1967]).

References

ADAMS, J. I., and HANNA, T. H., (1970), "Ground movements due to pile driving", Proceedings Conference on the behaviour of Piles, Institution of Civil Engineers, London, 127—133.

ADAMS, J. I., and RADHAKRISHNA, H. S., "Uplift resistance of augered footings in fissured clay". Canadian Geotechnical Journal, Vol. 8, No. 3, 452—462.

AL-DHAHIR, Z. A., KENNARD, M. F., and MORGENSTERN, N. R., (1970), "Observations on pore pressures beneath the ash lagoon embankments at Fiddler's Ferry Power Station", Proceedings Conference on In situ Investigations in Soils and Rocks, Institution of Civil Engineers, London, 265—276.

AL-DHAHIR, Z. A., and MORGENSTERN, N. R., (1969), "Intake factors for cylindrical piezometer tips". Soil Science, Vol. 107.

BASSETT, D. J., (1959), "Field Measurement of Pore Water Pressures", Proceedings Twelfth Canadian Soil Mechanics Conference, Ottawa, 2—15.

BISHOP, A. W., and ELDIN, G., (1950), "Undrained triaxial tests on saturated sands and their significance in the general theory of shear strength", Geotechnique, Vol. 2, 13—32.

BISHOP, A. W., and HENKEL, D. J., (1962), "The measurement of soil properties in the triaxial test", Edward Arnold, London.

BISHOP, A. W., (1960), "The measurement of pore pressure in the triaxial test", Proceedings Conference on Pore Pressure and Suction in Soils. Institution of Civil Engineers, London, 38—46.

BISHOP, A. W., KENNARD, M. F., and PENMAN, A. D. M., (1960), "Pore pressure observations at Selset dam", Proceedings Conference on Pore Pressure and Suction in Soils, Institution of Civil Engineers, London, 91—102.

BISHOP, A. W., and BJERRUM, L., (1969), "The relevance of the triaxial test to the solution of stability problems". Norwegian Geotechnical Institute, Publication No. 34.

BISHOP, A. W., ALPAN, I., BLIGHT, G. E., and DONALD, I., (1961), "Factors controlling the strength of partly saturated cohesive soils", Proceedings Conference on Shear Strength of Cohesive Soils, American Society of Civil Engineers, 503—532.

BISHOP, A. W., and VAUGHAN, P. R., (1962), "Selset Reservoir: Design and Performance of the Embankment", Proceedings, Institution of Civil Engineers, London, Vol. 21, 305—346.

BISHOP, A. W., and AL-DHAHIR, Z. A., (1970), "Some comparisons between laboratory tests, in-situ tests and full scale performance, with special reference to permeability and coefficient of consolidation", Proceedings Conference on In Situ Investigations in Soils and Rocks, Institution of Civil Engineers, London, 251—264.

BJERRUM, L., and JOHANNESSEN, I., (1960), "Pore pressures resulting from pile driving in soft clays", Proceedings, Conference on Pore Pressure and Suction in Soils, Institution of Civil Engineers, London, 108—111.

BJERRUM, L., KENNEY, T. C., and KJAERNSLI, B., (1965), "Measuring instruments for strutted excavations", Proceedings, American Society of Civil Engineers, Vol. 91, SM 1, 111—141.

CASAGRANDE, A., (1949), "Soil Mechanics in the design and construction of Logan airport", Contributions to Soil Mechanics 1941—53, Boston Society of Civil Engineers.

COOLING, L. F., (1962), "Field Measurements in Soil Mechanics", Geotechnique Vol. 12, No. 2, 75—104.

CRONEY, D., COLEMAN, J. D., and BLACK, W. P. H., (1958). "The movement and distribution of water in soil in relation to highway design and performance". Highway Research Board, Special Report No. 40, Washington, D.C.

D'APPOLONIA, D. J., (1971), "Effects of Foundation construction on nearby structures", Proceedings Fourth Pan American Conference on Soil Mechanics and Foundation Engineering, Puerto Rico, Vol. 1, 189—236.

GIBSON, R. E., (1963), "An analysis of the system flexibility and its effect on time lag in pore water pressure measurements". Geotechnique, Vol. 13, No. 1, 1—11.

GIBSON, R. E., (1966), "A note on the constant head test to measure soil permeability in-situ", Geotechnique, Vol. 16, No. 3, 256—259.

GRAY, H., (1969), "Effects of forest clear cutting on the stability of natural slopes", Reprint, Slope Indicator Company, Seattle, U.S.A.

GRIFFIN, W. H., (1967), "Piezometers monitor waterfront fill", Civil Engineering (New York), June, 41—43.

GUTHER, H. H., (1972), "Bentonite seals for piezometers in frozen soils". Canadian Geotechnical Journal, Vol. 9, No. 1, 115—116.

HANNA, T. H., (1967), "The measurement of pore water pressure adjacent to a driven pile". Canadian Geotechnical Journal, Vol. 4, No. 3, 313—325.

HOLDEN, J. C., (1968), "Field measurements to evaluate the performance of sand drains at Dynon road overpass, Melbourne", Proceedings, Field Measurement Symposium, Australian Road Research Board, Vol. 4, Part 2, 1878—1895.

HOSKINGS, A. D., (1968), "Subsurface Testing with particular reference to embedded instruments", Proceedings, Field Measurement Symposium, Australian Road Research Board, Vol. 4, Part 2, 1698—1722.

HOSKINGS, A. D., and HILTON, J. I., (1963), "Instrumentation of earth dams on the Snowy Mountains scheme", Proceedings, Fourth Australian New Zealand Conference on Soil Mechanics and Foundation Engineering, 251.

HVORSLEV, M. J., (1951), "Time lag and soil permeability in groundwater observations", Bulletin No. 36, Waterways Experimental Station, Corps of Engineers, U.S. Army.

KALLSTENIUS, T., and WAALGREN, A., (1956), "Pore Water Pressure Measurement in Field Investigations", Proceedings No. 13, Royal Swedish Geotechnical Institute.

LAMBE, T. W., (1959), "Sealing the Casagrande Piezometer", Civil Engineering (New York), April.

LAMBE, T. W., (1962), "Pore pressures in a foundation clay", Proceedings, American Society of Civil Engineers, Design of Foundations for control of Settlement, Vol. 90, No. 5, 47—72.

LAMBE, T. W., and HORN, H. M., (1965), "The influence on an adjacent building of pile driving for the M.I.T. Materials Center", Proceedings Sixth International Conference on Soil Mechanics and Foundation Engineering, Montreal, Vol. 2, 280—284.

LITTLE, A. L., and VAIL, A. J., (1960), "Some developments in the measurement of Pore Pressure", Proceedings, Conference on Pore Pressure and Suction in Soils, Institution of Civil Engineers, London, 75—80.

LO, K. Y., and STERMAC, A. G., (1965), "Induced pore pressures during pile driving operations", Proceedings Sixth International Conference on Soil Mechanics and Foundation Engineering, Montreal, Vol. 2, 285—289.

LUNDGREN, R., (1966), "Electric piezometer for field installation", Civil Engineering (New York), Vol. 36, No. 8, 52—53.

MATYAS, E. L., (1963), "Compressibility and shear strength of compacted soils", Ph. D. Thesis, University of London (Unpublished).

MUHS, H., and CAMPBELL-ALLEN, D., (1955), "A laboratory examination of an electrical pore pressure gauge for use in earth dams". Journal, Australian Institute of Engineers, September, 241—245.

OLIVIERIA, G., and FERRARI, I., (1970), "Field Measurements on Rio Jaguari Dam, Brazil", Proceedings Fourth Congress Brazilian Society of Soil Mechanics and Foundation Engineering, Rio de Janeiro, Vol. 1, No. 2, 43—65.

PARRY, R. H. G., (1971), "A simple driven piezometer", Geotechnique, Vol. 21, No. 2, 163—167.

PENMAN, A. D. M., (1956), "A field piezometer apparatus", Geotechnique, Vol. 6, No. 2, 57—65.

PENMAN, A. D. M., (1958), Correspondence, Geotechnique, Vol. 8, No. 3, 136.

PENMAN, A. D. M., (1960), "A study of the response time of various types of piezometer", Proceedings Conference on Pore Pressure and Suction in Soils, Institution of Civil Engineers, London, 53—58.

PENMAN, A. D. M., (1972), "Instrumentation for embankment dams subjected to rapid drawdown", Building Research Station (England), Current Paper CP 1/72.

PINKERTON, I. L., and McCONNELL, A. D., (1964), "Behaviour of Tooma Dam", Transactions, Eighth Congress on Large Dams, Edinburgh, Vol. 2, 351—375.

SILVA, F. P., (1966), "Neutral pressures in compacted cohesive soils", Proceedings American Society of Civil Engineers, Vol. 92, SM1, 105—120.

SKEMPTON, A. W., (1954), "Pore Pressure Coefficients A and B", Geotechnique, Vol. 4, 143—147.

SKEMPTON, A. W., (1960), "Effective Stress in Soils, Concrete and Rocks", Proceedings, Conference on Pore Pressure and Suction in Soils, Institution of Civil Engineers, London, 4—16.

SWANSTON, D. N., (1967), "Soil water piezometry in a Southeast Alaska landslide area", U.S. Forest Service, Publication No. 52, 1—15.

SCOTT, J. D., and KILGOUR, J., (1967), "Experience with some vibrating wire instruments", Canadian Geotechnical Journal, Vol. 4, No. 1, 100—123.

TERZAGHI, K., (1923), "Die Berechnung der Durchlässigkeitsziffer des Tones aus dem Verlauf der hydrodynamischen Spannungserscheinungen", Sitz. Akad. Wissen. Wien Math.-naturw. K1. Abt. IIa, 132, 105—124.

VAUGHAN, P. R., (1969), "A note on sealing piezometers in boreholes". Geotechnique, Vol. 19, No. 3, 405—413.

U.S.B.R., (1963), "Earth Manual", U.S. Government Printing Office Washington, D. C.

WARLAM, A. A., and THOMAS, E. W., (1965), "Measurement of hydrostatic uplift pressure on spillway weir with air piezometers". Instruments and Apparatus for Soil and Rock Mechanics, ASTM, Special Technical Publication No. 392, 143—151.

WATSON, K. K., (1967), "A recording field tensiometer with rapid response characteristics", Journal of Hydrology, Vol. 5, 33—39.

WILSON, S. D., (1967), "Investigation of embankment performance". Proceedings American Society of Civil Engineers, Vol. 93, SM4, 135—156.

4 | Earth
Pressure
Measurement

4.1. The General Principle

In Chapter 3 the principle of effective stress was mentioned and methods of measuring the water pressure component were reviewed. Because the total stress component must also be known before the effective stress component can be calculated, this chapter is concerned with the measurement of total earth pressures. Two general types of measurement arise in foundation engineering — stresses in a soil mass and stresses on a boundary at a soil-structure interface. For convenience of measurement, the stress vector at a "point" on a boundary or in a soil mass is resolved into normal and shear "average" components. In traditional civil engineering structures such as raft foundations, the design of the foundation is controlled by the distribution of normal stresses along the contact surface and in the underlying stressed soil mass. The influence of boundary shear stresses usually is not critical. This approach applies to many foundation structures such as a bulkhead, but in cases where overall stability considerations arise shear stresses may be critical. The gravity retaining wall is a good example and in the instrumentation of such a structure the shear stress distribution on the base of the wall may also be required.

Many problems arise when making earth pressure measurements. The main problem is to ensure that the earth pressure measuring device (the cell) measures the average stress acting. If the design is faulty then an erroneous reading results. For this reason the general requirements of an earth pressure cell are considered in Section 4.2. and this is followed in the later sections by details of some of the earth pressure cells which are available and how they may be used by the civil engineer.

4.2. Earth Pressure Cell Design Requirements

When an earth pressure cell is introduced into a mass of soil the stress field in the vicinity of the cell is modified owing to redistribution of stresses. It is this modified stress field which is recorded by the cell. The basic problem in earth pressure cell design is to obtain a measure of the stress which would have existed in the ground had the pressure cell not been inserted. In the following study the case of normal pressure measurement is considered.

To allow for the upset of stress distribution caused by the inclusion of a cell in a soil, Taylor (1947) proposed a cell action factor. Taylor showed that the additional pressure recorded by the cell, p_e, due to its rigidity (relative) was of the form:

$$\frac{p_e}{p} = \frac{B/D \left[\dfrac{N}{E_s} - \dfrac{N}{E_c} \right]}{1 + \dfrac{B}{D}\dfrac{N}{E_c}} \qquad (4.1)$$

where

        p is the field stress existing at the plane of the cell in the absence of the cell

        E_s is the stress/strain modulus of the soil

        E_c is the stress/strain modulus of the cell

        D is the diameter of the cell

        B is the half thickness of the cell

        N is a property of the soil such that N/D is analogous to the coefficient of subgrade reaction

This expression was simplified by the introduction of a cell action factor, C_A, so that

$$p_e/p = C_A \cdot B/D \qquad (4.2)$$

and the cell error variation with cell geometry and cell to soil stiffness, E_c/E_s, is shown in Figure 85 according to this relation. This diagram shows that the pressure cell reading error depends on the geometry of the instrument, the stiffness of the soil and the stiffness of the cell. This work was verified experimentally by Peattie and Sparrow (1945) and they concluded that a stiff guard ring around the cell diaphragm was essential (Figure 86). In the use of such a cell the outer ring is rigid and the diaphragm deflects. Tory and Sparrow (1967) examined the behaviour of such a cell and they showed that the best performance occurs when the cell diaphragm is very stiff relative to the soil and when the cell is as flat as possible. They defined a flexibility factor, F, as $E_s d^3 / (E_c t^3)$ and Figure 87 shows how the earth pressure measured

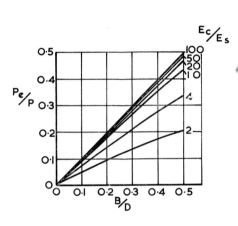

Fig. 85: Variation of cell error with cell thickness and compressibility (Peattie and Sparrow [1954]).

Fig: 86: Variation of C_A with sensitive area of pressure cell (Peattie and Sparrow [1954]).

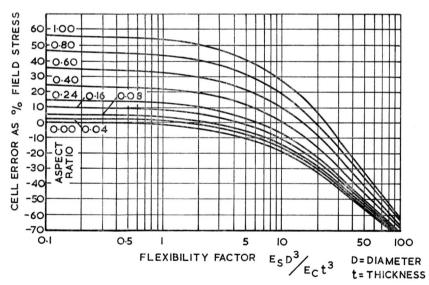

Fig. 87: Variation of cell error with flexibility factor (Tory and Sparrow [1967]).

errs with flexibility factor F and cell aspect ratio B/D. It will be noted, for a particular B/D ratio, that for small values of flexibility factor the graph is almost horizontal. Use of this portion allows the cell to cater for changes in the soil stiffness without appreciable error in measured pressure.

Monfore (1950) showed theoretically that the error in pressure measurement was directly proportional to B/D ratio while the W.E.S. (1944) suggested that $B/D \leq 0.1$ was necessary. The stress distribution across the face of a buried earth pressure cell is non-uniform and, according to Monfore (1950), has a minimum value at the centre and a large value at the edge. By recording the pressures on a central sensitive area which is about $\frac{1}{2}$ to $\frac{1}{3}$ of the total area of the cell face, the error due to high edge stresses is reduced to acceptable levels and this principle is used in most cells, apart from cells of the Glötzl type.

A number of researchers have recommended that the deflection of the cell diaphragm should not exceed certain values. The W.E.S. (1944) recommend $\delta/D \leq 1/2000$ and this is a value often quoted for cell design, δ being the central deflection and D being the diameter. Other, and more recent work suggests that this ratio should be 1/5000 or greater.

If the diaphragm thickness is chosen so that its central deflection does not exceed the diameter/2000 ratio, then the pressure p required to cause a central deflection δ is

$$p = \frac{\delta \cdot 96 \, E t^3}{D^4} \qquad (4.3)$$

where t is the diaphragm thickness, D the diameter and E the Young's modulus of the cell material. For $\delta = D/2000$, the maximum allowable pressure is

$$p_{max} = \frac{96 \, E}{2000} \left(\frac{t}{D} \right)^3 \qquad (4.4)$$

The maximum skin stress in the diaphragm, f_d, is

$$f_d = \frac{3}{16} p \left(\frac{D}{t} \right)^2 \qquad (4.5)$$

Combining with equation (4.4.) this gives

$$f_d = \frac{288}{32000} E \cdot \left(\frac{t}{D}\right) \tag{4.6}$$

This expression indicates that for high earth pressures the diaphragm must be thick, the allowable stress in the cell material should be high and its modulus of elasticity should be low.

4.3. Types of Earth Pressure Cell

Over the last decade or so the most popular cell has been that consisting of a diaphragm. Some other cells rely on a rigid piston sensing element while a very flexible cell unit is also used (e. g. the Glötzl type cell). Most cells are designed to measure static or very slowly varying normal stresses. Special cells have been developed to record dynamic stresses (e. g. Whiffin and Morris [1962]).

4.3.1. Electrical earth pressure cell

With the diaphragm type total earth pressure cell, the deflection of the diaphragm is measured and by calibration, usually in water, the pressure (average) can be related to the diaphragm deflection. As mentioned above, the central deflection of the diaphragm is usually limited to less than 1/2000 times the diameter. Two methods are used to measure deflection, strain gauges (electrical resistance) and vibrating wire gauges. The strain gauge system is illustrated by Figure 88. With this cell error

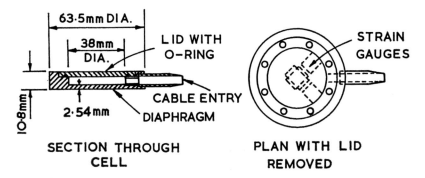

Fig. 88: Electrical Strain gauged earth pressure cell (Sparrow and Tory [1966]).

occurs due to cross-sensitivity. By cross-stress is meant a stress acting in the plane of the diaphragm, e. g. an earth pressure cell measuring the horizontal stress beneath a loaded foundation (Figure 89). Even where the outer ring is very stiff the cell may still be sensitive to cross-stresses because the cross-stress causes the diaphragm to be loaded in compression. The error is a maximum when the cross-stress acts in the direction of measurement of the strain gauge. The error due to cross-sensitivity can be minimized by the arrangement of the strain gauges. Brown and Pell (1967) show how this may be achieved by use of the arrangement given in Figure 90.

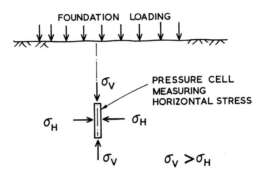

Fig. 89: Earth pressure cell in a situation where cross-sensitivity is likely to be important.

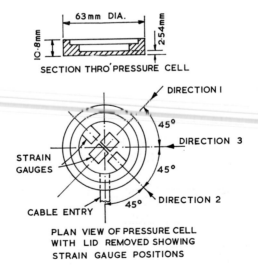

Fig. 90: Strain gauge arrangement on cell diaphragm to minimize cross-sensitivity (Brown and Pell [1967]).

There are several reports dealing with the use of electrical resistance strain gauges for measuring diaphragm deflection. Brown and Pell (1967) review their work for the measurement of subgrade pressures and Lee (1968) and Trollope and Lee (1961) consider measurements on foundation structures.

The vibrating wire principle of diaphragm deflection measurement is used in a number of earth pressure cells. The NGI total earth pressure cell Oien (1958) originally developed for the measurement of earth pressure at a boundary has been used with sheet piles, retaining walls, tunnels and in earth dams. The cell comprises a rigid housing and a circular membrane. The membrane has two protruding arms between which the gauge wire is stretched. When an external pressure is applied to the membrane, the protruding arms rotate slightly and cause an increase of stress in the gauge wire. Thus a change in frequency of the

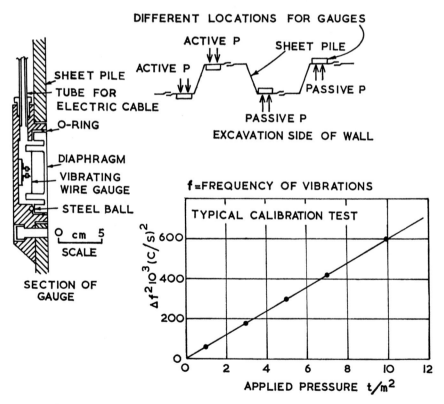

Fig. 91: Vibrating Wire Earth Pressure Cell for sheet pile wall measurement (Bjerrum, Kenny and Kjaernsli [1965]).

gauge wire is caused and by calibration a measure in change of the average earth pressure acting on the membrane is obtained. A section through a gauge in use on a sheet pile wall is shown in Figure 91. It will be noted that the cell is mounted so that the membrane is flush with the surface of the sheet pile. For the measurement of stress in earth fill the cell is attached to a steel plate so that the membrane is flush with one side of the steel plate.

The type P-100 pressure cell is 94 mm diameter and is supplied in standard sizes for pressures up to 2500 kN/m². There are other much larger pressure cells supplied by Geonor which are used for measurement in coarse grained materials. The P-150 cell has a circular rigid plate supported on three vibrating wire gauge load cells. Thus the total

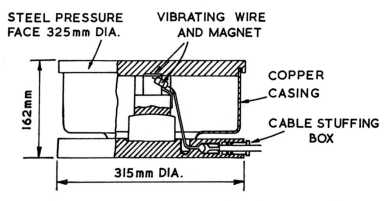

Fig. 92: Cross section through a Maihak earth pressure cell
(Scott and Kilgour [1967]).

force acting on the circular plate is measured. The membrane is 250 mm diameter and the pressure range is 0 to 1000 kN/m².

An earth pressure gauge of a similar type to the Geonor P-100 is referred to by Cooling (1962).

The Maihak vibrating wire cell is of interest and has been used widely. Figure 92 illustrates the principal features of this cell. The earth pressure is transmitted to the cell casing which deforms. To ensure that casing is free to deform, cotton is stuffed between the casing and the bottom plate and wrapped around the casing. A protective wrapping is placed around the circumference of the cell to keep out dirt. The cell is fairly heavy to handle.

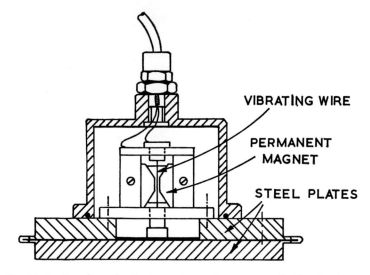

Fig. 93: Section through vibrating wire earth pressure cell (Shepherd [1967]).

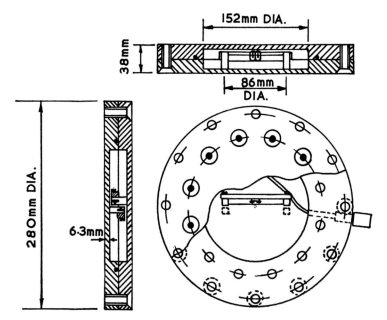

Fig. 94: Vibrating wire earth pressure cell (Thomas and Ward [1969]).

Shepherd (1967), describes a vibrating wire pressure cell consisting of two 15 cm diameter steel plates, Figure 93, between which oil is injected. The plates are connected by a weld around the thin flanges which project radially from the plates. One plate is of reduced thickness over its central zone and the vibrating wire is connected to this diaphragm, the other end being anchored to the body of the cell. The supporting frame and the vibrating wire are temperature compensating. When a pressure change occurs on the steel plate the wire gauge tension changes and by calibration the pressure acting is obtained.

One of the most versatile cells is that developed by Ward and Thomas (1969). It consists of two metal discs, each recessed to form a flexible diaphragm, Figure 94. When bolted together a load capsule results. In use the deflection of the diaphragm is measured by a vibrating wire strain gauge stretched between posts located $1/2.\sqrt{3}$ of the diameter of the diaphragm either side of the centre. At these positions the angular rotation due to uniform pressure on the diaphragm is greatest. The posts are 23 mm high and the 0.25 mm diameter high tensile steel wire is excited into transverse vibration by an electromagnet. The change in average normal pressure across the diaphragm is proportional to the square of the frequency of vibration. The cell is ventilated by an air line, thus the cell joints are sealed only against water pressures and the pressure inside the cell is atmospheric.

By matching of the coefficient of thermal expansion of the diaphragm and the vibrating wire element, temperature change effects can be virtually eliminated. Thomas and Ward (1969) quote apparent pressure changes of less than 0.5 kN/m²/°C.

The cell has a half thickness/diameter ratio of 0.07 and the ratio of the sensitive area to the full area of the cell face is 0.34. The maximum diameter/deflection ratio is about 2000. According to the method of Monfore (1950), the average excess pressure on the sensitive surface, P_e, is about 40 kN/m². The cell is designed for an average pressure of up to 2500 kN/m².

The B.R.S. type cell can be used either as a boundary cell or for earth fill pressure measurement. For use as a boundary cell the back face and the periphery of the cell are coated with a 6 mm thickness of rubber compound. This is then mounted in the structure so that the uncovered diaphragm is flush with the surface of the structure. This technique ensures that the cell is loaded symmetrically and the cell is not distorted by movement of the structure in which it is embedded.

Thomas and Ward draw attention to the use of earth pressure cells in fully saturated soil subject to large changes of pore water pressure such as tidal variations. Under increasing water pressure the diaphragm deflects and tends to move away from the soil. Thus, even if the pore water pressure is measured independently, the soil pressure measured may be in error. For these reasons they suggest that fluctuating or reversing pressures would generally be better measured by a rigid type of cell. They also state that the cell may be modified to work as an effective pressure cell by pressurization of the interior of the cell to match the external pore water pressure.

Thomas and Ward give details on cell manufacture, calibration, performance and connections required for use. The chief advantages of the cell are: (i) the cell being a double diaphragm type can detect errors due to bedding in the soil by the difference of reading on the two faces of the cell; (ii) the cell has a linear calibration with no hysteresis, (iii) long term problems of corrosion are overcome by use of nitrogen circulation.

4.3.2. Hydraulic Cells — Glötzl

The principle of the Glötzl cell is illustrated in Figure 95. A hydraulic sensing pad is embedded within the soil. The stress in the soil surrounding the sensing pad applies pressure to the pad and this pressure is measured by a mechanical technique. The sensing pad, which may be circular or rectangular-shaped, has a large area to thickness ratio. Thus

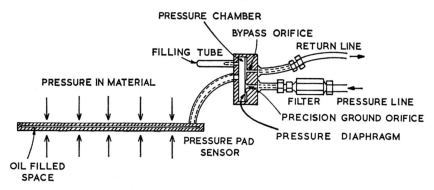

Fig. 95: Principle of the Glötzl earth pressure cell.

it is a very thin disc and consequently stress distortion effects due to variations in the modulus of the sensor pad and the soil are very small.

In use the unknown stress acting on the cell boundary or in the soil mass is measured by determining the hydraulic pressure in the connecting tubing. A small and constant volume of oil is pumped through the cell and when the line pressure equals the pressure in the fluid in the cell, the pressure diaphragm in the pressure chamber deflects and thus permits oil to flow through the bypass orifice and into the return line. The pressure in the supply line cannot increase further and hence the cell pressure is equal to the line pressure at the entrance to the bypass chamber. Because the pump may be at a very different elevation to the cell unit a gauge elevation correction, equal to the difference in elevation of the cell and the pressure measuring transducer times the specific gravity of the oil, must be applied. The oil in the cell is pressurized. Thus the resultant earth pressure is equal to the bypass gauge pressure plus gauge elevation correction minus the zero gauge reading (prestress value in the cell plus gauge elevation correction).

The Glötzl cell has been used for pressure measurements in concrete, pressure at a joint (rock/concrete interface, earth/concrete interface) and for earth pressure measurement. The principle of measurement is similar to that of the Glötzl piezometer (Section 3.3.5.). For an installation comprising several cells a switching block is required. The oil may be supplied by manual or power pumps. The oil pressure is recorded by a precision pressure gauge. Where a wide range of pressure values is to be recorded, a range of pressure gauges is provided. If required, automatic recording is possible.

The main advantages of this cell are (i) the system is simple and contains no delicate parts, (ii) long term reliable measurements are possible, (iii) corrections are simple to determine and apply, (iv) the gauge unit is cheap, (v) the return line may be common to several cells.

In some situations where there is likely to be a change in temperature (e. g. beneath a concrete raft which is cast on top of the pressure cells), it is necessary to record the temperature of the cell and apply a temperature correction to the readings. The temperature correction may be determined by laboratory testing.

While it is claimed that the cell has a very small cell action factor, it is prudent to check the response of the cell to loading in contact with the soil. For example, where the cell is used to record contact pressure beneath a slab or adjacent to a retaining wall, a load test may be carried out under field conditions and the gauge pressure compared with the applied pressure to give the cell action factor.

Details of cell use are given by Adams and Hanna (1970) for earth pressure measurement behind a rigid retaining wall.

They placed the cells just behind the wall and packed around them with a layer of sand by hand techniques as the backfill level behind the wall was brought up. For the measurement of contact stress beneath slabs the earth pressure cell may be placed in contact with the soil and the slab cast on top. This is most easily achieved by digging small pits about 30 to 40 cm square to which the pressure lines to and from the cell to the gauge house are installed. When the cell is to be installed, the bottoms of these pits are carefully levelled to make contact with the soil. In clays this can be achieved by a scraping action whereas in coarse materials a layer of fine sand is used. The concrete slab is then placed on top of the cells.

In some installations piezometer tips are installed adjacent to the total earth pressure cells to give a measure of the pore water pressure in the ground. Where there is a Glötzl installation the Glötzl piezometer (Section 3.3.5.) is attractive because of the availability of the pressure return line and the pressure recording equipment.

The Glötzl cell is a cheap instrument and is particularly useful for the measurement of contact pressure gradients owing to its small diameter. It is thus a suitable cell for contact pressure measurement beneath slabs supported by piles or anchors and behind walls as well as in earth fills. Few comprehensive publications dealing with the use of the Glötzl earth pressure cell are available.

4.3.3. Carlson Stress Meter

This cell was used as far back as 1916. The principle of operation is that a thin film of mercury, when pressurized, causes a diaphragm to deflect. Figure 96 shows a section through a Carlson stress meter. When the diaphragm is flexed by the film of mercury under pressure, the strain meter unit gives a change in output which can be recorded by a suitable bridge. Details of the cell are given by Carlson and Pritz (1951). The cell is used for the measurement of stress at a boundary.

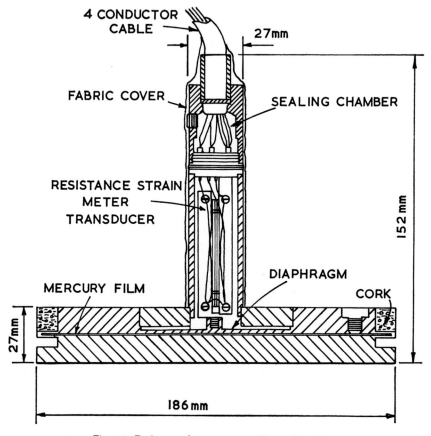

Fig. 96: Carlson soil stress meter (Kruse [1967]).

4.3.4. W. E. S. Cell

The Waterways Experimental Station pressure cell is similar in principle to the Carlson cell but the flexure of the diaphragm is recorded by means of four resistance strain gauges, two in the tensile and two in the compressive zones of the diaphragm to give a full bridge circuit thus minimizing temperature change effects. The chief limitation of this cell lies in the problems of creep under long term use. Because the cells are disc shaped they can be used in earth fill.

4.3.5. Other Cells

Over the years many other types of earth pressure cell have been used. Kallstenius and Bergau (1956) describe a hydraulic — type cell used by the Royal Swedish Geotechnical Institute for earth pressure measurement behind rigid structures. The Goldbeck cell operates on a piston principle. Magnusson (1948) reports on the use of a hydraulic cell for pressure measurements in earth dams. There are also reports by Plantema (1953) on the use of an electrical type cell.

4.4. Measurement of Dynamic Pressures

The civil engineer on occasions may have to measure dynamic pressures on structures or in a soil mass and, although this is a much neglected field of study, a number of earth pressure cells are available. Ingram (1965) considers the use of piezoresistive strain gauges which have a much greater sensitivity than the conventional strain gauge. Thus the deflection of the cell diaphragm can be very small yet a large electrical output must result if a high degree of resolution is required. As mentioned in Section 4.1. the side walls must be very rigid to prevent bending effects. The cell should be density matched to the soil for proper dynamic response.

The S. E. gauge reported by Ingram (1965) is shown in Figure 97. Each diaphragm has two silicon solid state strain gauges attached, one in the centre and the other near the edge. The strain gauges, connected as a full Wheatstone bridge circuit, are waterproofed and insulated. Details of the calibration and use of this cell are given by Ingram.

Abbott, Simmons, Reiff and Mitchell (1967) survey the literature on the subject up to 1967 and review the behaviour of identical tests on four different cells: the W.E.S. SE-type; the IITRI piezoresistive cell; the UNM gauge and the rigid spool gauge. These authors conclude that the most popular gauges are the rigid spool gauge and the W.E.S. SE-type diaphragm gauge. For field use they conclude that these gauges are too small and that larger and more robust gauges are in need of development.

Comprehensive information on the problems associated with the measurement of earth pressure due to dynamic loading is given in the

Proceedings of the International Symposium on Wave Propagation and Dynamic Properties of Earth Materials (1967) especially the papers by Abbott et al., Selig and Tobin, Hadala, Rogers and Truesdale, and Truesdale and Schwab.

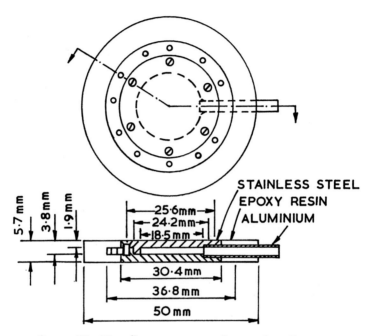

Fig. 97: The SE earth pressure gauge (Ingram [1965]).

4.5. Measurement of Normal and Shear Stresses

For directions other than the principal direction, shear stresses occur in addition to normal stresses and these can be of particular significance in embankments and on soil/structure interfaces such as piles and retaining walls. Agarwal and Venkatesan (1965) discuss the measurement of normal and shear stresses on piles. Their instrument consists of three parts; a casing (1), a cantilever (2) and a pressure cell (3) as shown in the line drawing, Figure 98. The casing is a protective device. The pressure cell comprise a diaphragm (6) and an electrical resistance strain gauge is bonded to the inside centre of the diaphragm, the leads being taken through a water tight plug in the back plate (13). The fixed end (4) of

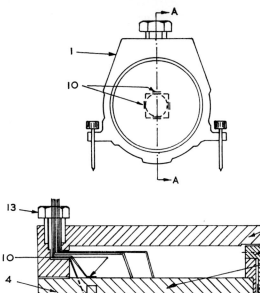

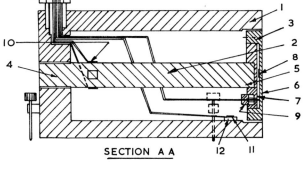

SECTION A A

1	HOLLOW CASING CLOSED AT THE REAR AND MACHINED 105 mm I.D. AT THE FRONT – CAST IRON
2	CANTILEVER 24 mm SQUARE SECTION – NICKEL PLATED
3	PRESSURE CELL 100 mm DIA. STEEL — NICKEL PLATED
4	FIXED END OF CANTILEVER
5	FREE END OF CANTILEVER
6	DIAPHRAGM OF THE PRESSURE CELL EFFECTIVE DIA. 80 mm AND 0·8m THICK
7	BACK PLATE OF PRESSURE CELL
8	STRAIN GAUGE OF DIAPHRAGM
9	WATER TIGHT PLUG
10	STRAIN GAUGES OF THE CANTILEVER
11	COMPENSATING GAUGE
12	STEEL PLATE
13	WATER TIGHT CABLE OUTLET

Fig. 98: Cell for measurement of normal and shear stresses on a soil-pile interface (Agarwal and Venkatesan [1965]).

the cantilever, with four strain gauges (8) attached, is screwed into the rear end of the casing. A temperature compensating strain gauge (10) is bonded to the inside of the casing.

When a uniform pressure is acting normal to the face of the cell, the diaphragm deflects. The cantilever does not deflect but when there is a vertical shear force the cantilever deflects. The pair of strain gauges on the horizontal sides of the cantilever record this force. The other pair of strain gauges on the vertical sides of the cantilever record the frictional force in the horizontal direction.

Deflection of the cantilever causes the face of the cell to rotate but the error caused by this rotation is very small. Similarly the effects of normal stress eccentricity on the cell are small. The authors conclude that the working principle of the instrument is sound but also believe that further improvements are possible to increase reliability and make the cell easier to use.

Perhaps the ultimate in normal and shear stress measurement is to be found in the cells developed at Cambridge by Arthur and Roscoe (1961). Figure 99 illustrates the principle of operation. Normal and shear forces, P and Q, applied to the active face of the cell, aa, are transmitted through thin webs to the rigidly held base. Foil strain gauges are attached to the webs, connected in three separate circuits to record simultaneously P and Q and the eccentricity, e, of P. The effects of any interaction between the circuits is automatically accounted for during calibration.

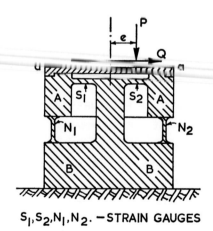

$S_1, S_2, N_1, N_2.$ —STRAIN GAUGES

Fig. 99: Cross-section of contact stress transducer (Arthur and Roscoe [1961]).

Two transducers can be bolted together as shown in Figure 100 so that the shear webs are mutually perpendicular. The unit will then measure simultaneously (i) normal force P, (ii) components of eccentricity, e_1 and e_2, (iii) components of shear force Q_1 and Q_2. To date this pressure cell is a laboratory instrument but it has potential for use in the field.

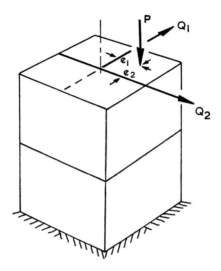

Fig. 100: Use of contact stress transducer for measurement of shear and eccentricity in two directions.

Earth pressure cells, capable of measuring normal and shear stresses, but which work on a telemetric principle, are reviewed by Prange (1972) but to date have not been used extensively in the field.

Thorley et al. (1970) describe an interfacial friction device which is used to determine the shaft friction on piles. While strictly it is not an instrument but more of a field testing device, the principle of operation may be used in the future in an instrument for stress determination on the face of a deep foundation. It consists of two horizontal double-acting pistons each carrying a pair of contact plates. Two vertical pistons are also connected to the contact plates. The equipment is used down a borehole and at the required elevation a radial jacking pressure is applied which expands the plates against the borehole sides. The lower plates are then jacked downwards and thus the shear stress as a function of displacement and normal pressure is obtained.

4.6. Indirect Methods of Earth Pressure Measurement

In some foundation situations it may not be possible to use the conventional earth pressure cell for pressure determination. In some cases indirect methods may be employed to give average values (deduced) of pressure. Several examples are given to illustrate the use of the indirect method.

Golder (1948) describes a 1.8 m long strain gauge for timber strut load measurement. He used these strut load values to calculate the earth pressure distribution on the wall based on simplifying assumptions concerning the equivalent length of waling supported by each strut and the length of runner supported by each waling.

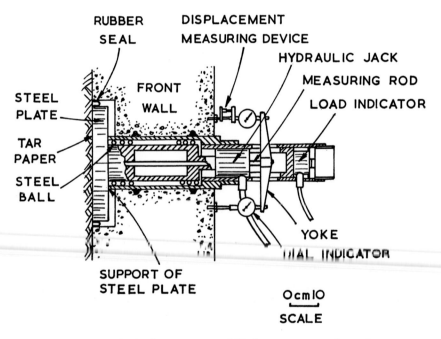

Fig. 101: The load measuring and displacement measuring unit
(Broms and Ingleson [1971]).

The loads acting on timber sheeting may be determined by the instrumentation of the contact clips with strain gauges. Thus the average load acting on a sheet is known and the average pressure is obtained.

Broms and Ingleson (1971) describe earth pressure measurements made during the compaction of backfill behind the abutments of a rigid frame bridge. The earth pressures were measured by rigid steel plates of 0.4 m diameter which were placed in recesses in the back side of the front wall as shown in Figure 101. An elevation showing the arrangement of the cells is given in Figure 102. The force acting on the steel plate was measured by a system comprising a hydraulic jack and load indicator and a displacement measuring device. With this set-up the steel plate could be pushed against the fill by the hydraulic jack, the applied load being recorded by the load cell. Thus the load and the deflection of the plate were recorded.

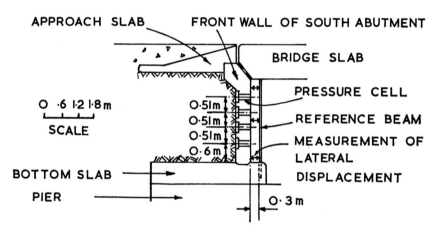

Fig. 102: Location of earth pressure cell units (Broms and Ingleson [1971]).

A typical load-displacement curve is given in Figure 103 and Broms and Ingleson (1971) interpret the earth pressure in the following manner. By drawing a tangent to the straight portion of the diagram and projecting until it intersected the load axis the initial earth pressure on the steel plate was obtained. From the slope of the diagram between I and II the equivalent modulus of deformation of the earth fill was determined as follows:

$$E = \frac{P\,(1 - \mu^2)}{2\,a \cdot \delta} \tag{4.7}$$

where P is the applied load, a is the radius of the steel plate, δ the lateral displacement of the plate and μ is Poisson's ratio of the fill material.

Attempts have been made to infer the bending moment diagram and the earth pressure distribution on steel sheet pile bulkheads by measurement of the deflected shape of the bulkhead using a slope indicator. Thompson and Maitich (1961) discuss some of the problems associated with this technique. Many of these limitations may be no longer valid thanks to the power of the finite element technique of analysis.

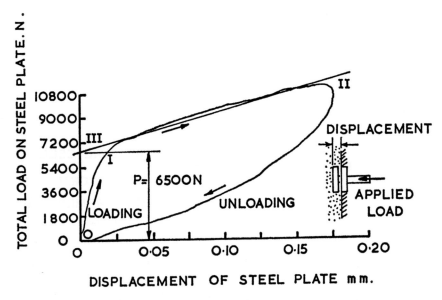

Fig. 103: Typical load-displacement relationship illustrating method of earth pressure determination (Broms and Ingleson [1971]).

4.7. State of Stress in a Soil Mass

In many foundation problems the size of the cell is small compared with the mass of soil under study and hence the cell is assumed to measure the stress at a "point". In earth dam studies, for example, it is possible, due to the two dimensional nature of the problem, to arrange the earth pressure cells in one plane with one or more cells at right angles to this plane. By arrangement of four cells to form an equivalent 45° rosette, the stress state in the soil can be measured as discussed by

Thomas and Ward (1969). Figure 104 (a) shows an end elevation of the earth pressure cell array used at Balderhead dam. Figure 104 (b) shows normals to the cells forming a 45° rosette and figure 104 (c) shows the Mohr Circle of stress.

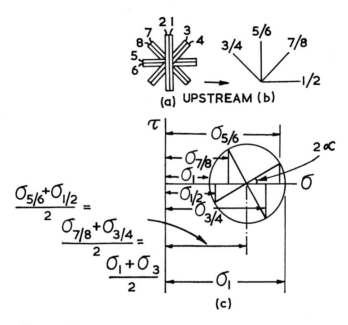

Fig. 104: (a) Layout of cell cluster showing number of cell faces
(b) Normals to cells forming 45° rosette
(c) Mohr circle of stress (Thomas and Ward [1969]).

When cells are oriented in directions which are not principal directions the cell action factor may depend on stress direction as shown by Buck (1961). He found the cell action factor for cells oriented to measure the major principal stress σ_1, the minor principal stress σ_3 and the stress at 45° to the principal planes to be

Stress measured	σ_1	σ_3	σ_{45}
Cell action factor	1.08	0.91	0.92

Care and experience are required in the use of earth pressure cells for the determination of stress state in a soil mass. The review by Thomas and Ward (1969) mentions the factors which are important.

Normally the earth pressure cell clusters are used with piezometer tips and they may be located at several levels. At the Scammonden dam (Penman and Mitchell [1970]) five total pressure cells were arranged along the axis of the core with piezometers in the middle and at the ends of the group. A layout of these earth pressure cells and piezometers is given in Figure 105.

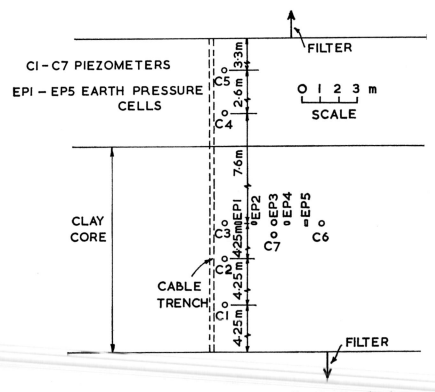

Fig. 105: Layout of earth pressure and piezometer cells at Scammonden dam (Penman and Mitchell [1970]).

4.8. Comment

In addition to the factors mentioned above, many other factors should be considered when selecting an earth pressure cell. In the search for the best possible measurement the importance of accuracy must not obscure the importance of applicability. As a general rule each part of an instrumentation programme should be designed to measure a specific quantity. The ideal instrument may be considered as having the following:

1. Simple principle of design and operation
2. Durability in the field environment
3. Accuracy both for long and short term measurements
4. A proven record in the field
5. Ease of calibration and re-calibration
6. Non-sensitive to environmental changes
7. Minimum interference due to installation in the ground
8. Simple installation procedures
9. Minimum overall cost

None of the earth pressure measuring devices fulfills all of these characteristics. In all cases comparative studies have not been carried out to compare the performances of different cells. For this reason alone the foundation engineer has to rely heavily on equipment manufacturers and suppliers for information on performance and guidance on installation techniques. Much useful data are given in the literature produced by equipment manufacturers and in the references quoted. An excellent review of stress and strain measurement in soil is given by Selig (1964).

The techniques for earth pressure determination in the field are now established and cells are available. The work of the Building Research Station in England and the Norwegian Geotechnical Institute has made the main contributions to earth pressure measurements during the last twenty years.

A useful review on earth pressure cells, design, calibration and performance is given by Hamilton (1960), while Morgan and Gerrard (1968) and Lee (1968) report on Australian experiences.

References

ABBOTT, P. A., SIMMONS, K. B., REIFF, C. M., and MITCHELL, S., (1967), "Recent Soil Stress Gauge Research" Proceedings, International Symposium on Wave Propagation and Dynamic Properties of Earth Materials, University of New Mexico Press, 221—238.

ADAMS, J. I., and HANNA, T. H., (1971), "Ground movements due to pile driving", Proceedings Conference on Behaviour of Piles, Institution of Civil Engineers, London, 127—134.

AGARWAL, S. L., and VENKATESAN, S., (1965), "An instrument to measure skin friction and normal earth pressure on deep foundations". ASTM STP No. 392, Instruments and apparatus for soil and rock mechanics, 152—169.

ARTHUR, J. R. F., and ROSCOE, K. H., (1961), "An earth pressure cell for the measurement of normal and shear stresses". Civil Engineering and Public Works Review, Vol. 56, No. 659, 765—770.

BJERRUM, L., KENNY, T. C., and KJAERNSLI, B., (1965), "Measuring instruments for strutted excavations", Proceedings, American Society of Civil Engineers, Vol. 91, SM1, 111—141.

BROMS, B. B., and INGLESON, I., (1971), "Earth pressure against the abutments of a rigid frame bridge", Geotechnique, Vol. 21, No. 1, 15—28.

BROWN, S. F., and PELL, P. S., (1967), "Subgrade stress and deformation under dynamic load", Proceedings, American Society of Civil Engineers, Vol. 93, No. SM1, 17—46.

BUCK, G. F., (1961), "An interim research report on cell action studies connected with research on pressure measurements in sands", Proceedings, Midlands Soil Mechanics Society (England), Vol. 4, 96—105.

CARLSON, R. W., and PRITZ, D., (1951), "Development of a device for the direct measurement of compressive stress", Journal, American Concrete Institute,

COOLING, L. F., (1962), "Field measurements in soil mechanics". Geotechnique Vol. 12, No. 2, 75—104.

GOLDER, H. Q., (1948), "Measurement of pressure in timbering of a trench in clay", Proceedings, Second International Conference on Soil Mechanics and Foundation Engineering, Rotterdam, Vol. 2, 76—81.

HADALA, P. F., (1967), "The effect of placement method on the response of soil stress gauges", Proceedings, International Symposium on Wave Propagation and Dynamic Properties of Earth Materials, University of New Mexico, 255—264.

HAMILTON, J. J., (1960), "Earth pressure cells — design, calibration and performance". Technical Paper No. 109, Division of Building Research of National Research Council of Canada.

INGRAM, J. K., (1965), "The development of a free-field soil stress gauge for static and dynamic measurements", ASTM. STP 392. Instruments and apparatus for soil and rock mechanics, 20—35.

KALLSTENIUS, T., and BERGAU, W., (1968), "Investigations of soil pressure measuring by means of cells". Proceedings, Royal Swedish Geotechnical Institute, Vol. 12.

KRUSE, G. H., (1965), "Measurement of embankment Stresses on a hundred foot high retaining wall", American Society for Testing and Materials, Special Technical Publication No. 392 — Instruments and Apparatus for Soil and Rock Mechanics, 131—142.

LEE, I. K., (1968), "Field measurements at a soil structure interface", Field Measurement Symposium, Proceedings, Australian Road Research Board, Vol. 4, Part 2, 1785—1805.

MAGNUSSON, G., (1948), "Research methods and instruments for the measurement of stresses and deformations in earth dams". Transactions, 3rd Congress on Large Dams, International Commission on Large Dams of the World Power Conference, Vol. 1, 493—499.

MONFORE, G. E., (1950), "An analysis of the stress distributions in and near stress gauges embedded in elastic solids", U. S. Bureau of Reclamation, Report SP26.

MORGAN, J. R., and GERRARD, C. M., (1968), "Free field measurements of stresses and strains in soils", Field Measurement Symposium, Australian Road Research Board, Vol. 4, Part 2, 1743—1760.

OIEN, K., (1958), "An earth pressure cell for use on sheet piles, Oslo subway", Proceedings, Conference on Earth Pressure Problems, Brussels, Vol. 2, 118—126.

PEATTIE, K. R., and SPARROW, R. W., (1954), "The fundamental action of earth pressure cells", Journal of the Mechanics and Physics of Solids, Vol. 2, 141—155.

PENMAN, A. D. M., (1972), "Instrumentation for embankment dams subjected to rapid drawdown", Building Research Station (England) Current Papers CP1/72.

PENMAN, A. D. M., and MITCHELL, P. B., (1970), "Initial behaviour of Scammonden Dam", Proceedings 10th Conference of the International Commission on Large Dams, Montreal, 723—747.

PLANTEMA, G., (1953), "A soil pressure cell and calibration equipment". Proceedings, 3rd International Conference on Soil Mechanics and Foundation Engineering, Vol. 1, 283—288.

PRANGE, B., (1972), "The state of telemetry in soil mechanics", Proceedings, Roscoe Memorial Symposium, Foulis, 476—488.

ROGERS, E. J., (1967), "Transducer for dynamic soil pressure", Proceedings, International Symposium on Wave Propagation and Dynamic Properties of Earth Materials, University of New Mexico, 921—930.

SELING, E. T., (1964), "A review of stress and strain measurements in soils", Proceedings, Symposium Soil-Structure Interaction, University of Arizona, 172—188.

SELIG, E. T., and TOBIN, H. G., (1967), "Investigation of piezoresistive soil stress gauges", Proceedings, International Symposium on Wave Propagation and Dynamic Properties of Earth Materials, University of New Mexico, 239—254.

SHEPHERD, R., (1967), "Some measurements of foundation bearing pressures", Journal of Strain, Vol. 3, 32—35.

SPARROW, R. W., and TORY, A. C., (1966), "Behaviour of soil mass under dynamic loading", Proceedings, American Society of Civil Engineers, Vol. 92, SM3, 59—86.

TAYLOR, D. W., (1947), "Pressure distribution in soils", Soil Mechanics fact finding survey, Waterways Experimental Station (U.S.A.).

THOMPSON, P. J., and MATICH, M. A. J., (1961), "The performance of some steel sheet pile bulkheads", Proceedings, 15th Canadian Soil Mechanics Conference, 80—114.

THORLEY, A., CALHOON, M. L., ZEMAN, Z. P., WATT, W. G., (1970), "Borehole instruments for economical strength and deformation in-situ testing". Proceedings, In Situ Investigations in Soils and Rocks, British Geotechnical Society, 155—165.

TORY, A. C., and SPARROW, R. W., (1967), "The influence of diaphragm flexibility on the performance of an earth pressure cell". Journal of Scientific Instruments, Vol. 44, 781—785.

TROLLOPE, D. H., and LEE, I. K., (1965), "The measurement of soil pressures". Proceedings, 5th International Conference on Soil Mechanics and Foundation Engineering, Vol. 2, 493—499.

TRUESDALE, W. B., and SCHWAB, R. B., (1967), "Soil strain gauge instrumentation", Proceedings, International Symposium on Wave Propagation and Dynamic Properties of Earth Materials, University of New Mexico, 931—942.

THOMAS, H. S. H., and WARD, W. H., (1969), "The design construction and performance of a vibrating-wire earth pressure cell". Geotechnique, Vol. 19, No. 1, 39—51.

U.S. Waterways Experimental Station, (1944), "Soil pressure cell investigation". Technical Memorandum, No. 21D—1.

WHIFFIN, A. C., and MORRIS, S. A. H., (1962), "Piezoelectric gauge for measuring dynamic stresses under roads". Engineering (London) Vol, 203, April, 27, 741—746.

<table>
<tr><td>5</td><td>Measurement
of
Ground
Movements</td></tr>
</table>

5.1. General

The measurement of foundation and ground movements is concerned with the accurate determination of settlements (and heaves), lateral movements, change of position, change of dimension as well as the change in length of foundation elements. During the last 10 years techniques of field measurement, which rely on both conventional surveying and special equipment, have been developed for soil and foundation engineering. In this chapter a review is given of a range of devices and techniques which are in use. No attempt is made to comment on the advantages and disadvantages of competing proprietary equipment but it will be apparent that many factors other than accuracy control the choice of an instrument for field use.

5.2. Measurements by conventional survey techniques

In most foundation instrumentation projects simplicity and reliability are essential because of the pressures of finance and time limitations. In the great majority of foundations most, if not all, of the required data can be obtained by simple surveying techniques (see Cole and Burland [1972], for example). The most common uses of the conventional survey technique are for the determination of elevation and change in elevation, the determination of lateral displacement by offset measurement from a line of sight; the determination of distance and distance change by tape measurement between observation pillars; and the determination of change of position by triangulation.

5.2.1. Elevation Determination

The order of survey accuracy used is determined by the type of reference points and the datum to which the measurements are referred. For absolute movement determination it is essential that the datum benchmark be located well away from the zone of ground movement otherwise it may also be affected by the ground movements. A permanent

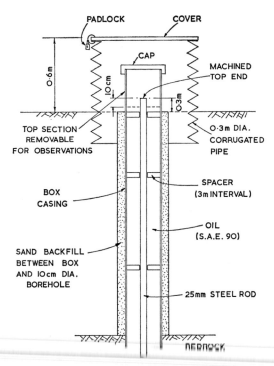

Fig. 106: Rock benchmark installation.

benchmark is used if available. Where this is not available, a benchmark or a number of benchmarks, depending on the size of the project, are formed. The degree of sophistication of benchmark construction depends on the accuracy required, the ground and environmental conditions, and the permanency of the installation. It is essential in all cases that the benchmark is isolated from ground which is subject to movement due to load changes or water content changes. For these reasons the most usual practice is to locate the benchmark in sound bedrock. A sketch of a typical benchmark installation is shown in Figure 106. Features of importance in this installation are the isolation of the reference rod from the borehole by means of the casing, spacers and oil filling; the access at the top end to the specially machined reference; and the very robust protective vandalproof cover. Some designs isolate the top 5 to 10 m and locate the benchmark rod about 3 m further into the overburden usually with a driving shoe attached. Other and more sophisticated benchmarks are available for special cases (Burland, Moore and Smith [1972]).

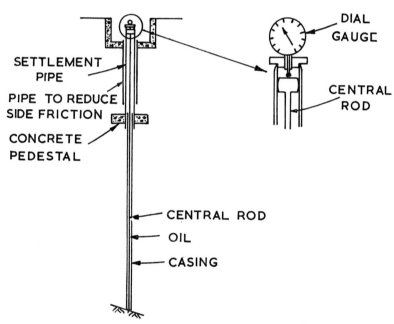

Fig. 107: Precise settlement gauge and benchmark (Bjerrum et al. [1965]).

Details of benchmarks for precise survey work are given by Bozozuk et al. (1962) and Kjellman et al. (1955). There are special cases where a benchmark may be used for direct settlement readings. The method (Bjerrum et al. [1965]) is illustrated in Figure 107. Here the steel casing is connected to a settlement plate and the differential movement between the plate and the benchmark is recorded by a dial gauge. An accuracy of ± 0.1 mm is reported.

Settlement points may be classed in two groups: those used for ground surface settlement measurement and those attached to foundation structures. First, the ground settlement devices are considered. The simplest device is a block of concrete surrounding a reinforcing bar. The device is very simple and cheap. It is susceptible to damage from construction activity and frost heave. The latter limitation may be overcome by isolation of the measuring reference bar by means of a concentric tube. The more common approach is to install a pipe or rod in a small diameter (10 cm or less) hole, the rod being isolated from the ground by means of a casing. There are several types of point available. The Borros point (Bjerrum et al. [1965]) comprises a rod fixed into the ground by flexible metal anchors, an outer pipe being used to eliminate friction. The point is installed by placing in the ground, by driving or by using a prebored hole, at the required depth the assembled inner rod, the tip and the outer isolation tube. The outer tube is held and the inner rod is driven thus forcing the flexible anchors into the soil. The outer pipe is then screwed free from the end piece and raised about 30 cm.

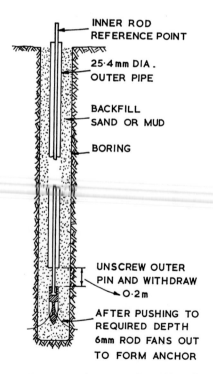

INNER ROD
REFERENCE POINT

25·4 mm DIA.
OUTER PIPE

BACKFILL
SAND OR MUD

BORING

UNSCREW OUTER
PIN AND WITHDRAW
0·2 m

AFTER PUSHING TO
REQUIRED DEPTH
6mm ROD FANS OUT
TO FORM ANCHOR

Fig. 108: Geonor settlement probe (Wilson [1967]).

Figure 108 shows a sketch of a Borros point. A settlement point may be made up by joining a 25 mm steel bar to a 60 cm length of 50 mm diameter auger, the unit being screwed into the base of a small diameter cased borehole. With both systems measurements can be taken at almost any depth, it being cheap to install and reliable in use provided the top end is protected.

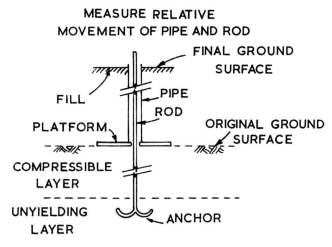

Fig. 109: Settlement platform with anchor post (Dunnicliff [1971]).

An extension of the above-mentioned point is a settlement plate used with an anchor post. Figure 109 illustrates the principle. The plate is placed on top of the compressible layer, and fill placed on top up to ground surface. The anchor post is then installed. The movement of the plate relative to the top of the anchor rod is measured by dial gauge thus eliminating the need for a survey crew. In practice there are severe limitations to this system of measurement. The placing of the plate interferes with the filling operations and the riser pipe is susceptible to damage.

All levelling points installed in the ground are susceptible to damage. It is, therefore, advisable to protect the top end by means of a metal concentric box with lockable cover cap. Taylor (1967) recommends that having selected the number of settlement points required one should double them to allow for loss during construction and post-construction. The reference points on foundation structures are either rigidly attached to the structure by bolting or welding, or special demountable points are employed. A detail of a reference pin and socket commonly used for survey of foundation settlements is shown in Figure 110. It comprises a steel or brass socket grouted into a hole in the side of the foundation. The reference pin screws into the socket. When not in use the socket is protected with a cover plate. The levelling staff is placed on top of the reference pin. On steel structures such as oil tanks, lugs may be welded to the outside of the tank about 0.3 m above ground level. Each lug, which has a protective cover, has a steel ball bearing about 25 mm diameter welded to it. This forms the reference mark for the survey. Reference points on structures such as retaining walls may be the top of the wall member (e .g. a pile) but, because such points are susceptible to damage from construction works, it is more usual to attach brackets to the wall near the top. These brackets support the reference points.

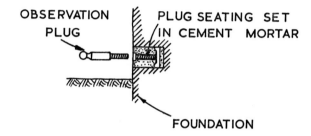

Fig. 110: Reference pin and socket for foundation settlement measurement.

Where settlement measurements are to be taken on a road or access to a site, it is impossible to maintain the reference points if they project above ground surface. In such cases a special reference head, similar to that shown by Figure 111, may be used. It consists of a steel tube about 25 mm diameter which is placed in the ground so that the top end, with the special fitting plug, is about 20 mm below ground surface. The plug has a central hole about 15 mm deep into which an extension rod about 150 mm in length fits. The top end of the extension rod is cone-shaped. Each rod is numbered for the corresponding reference point. When not in use the extension pieces are removed.

The Road Research Laboratory has developed methods of settlement measurement behind bridge abutments and details of the reference points used are given by Margason and Cross (1966), Margason (1970) and Cross (1970).

For the measurement of ground heave due to the formation of an excavation, the movement points referred to above are unacceptable due to their vulnerability on site. This problem may be overcome by the use of a method first suggested by Bozozuk (1963). The heave points are made from four 6 mm thick steel fins welded together to form a

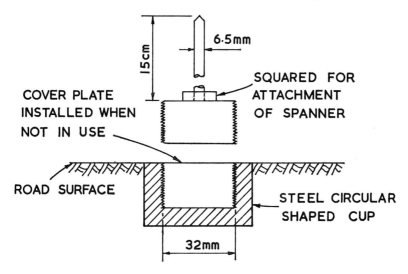

Fig. 111: Settlement point for use on road and pavement surface.

vane 90 mm in diameter and 0.3 m in length, Figure 112. A plate 19 mm thick, welded to the top ends of the point and with a 12 mm diameter tapped hole in the centre aids installation. To install a heave gauge, a 100 mm diameter borehole is drilled to the required depth. The heave gauge is lowered on a string of drill rods and forced into the bottom of the borehole until the top plate is flush with the bottom of the borehole. The drill rods are then removed and the hole back-filled with a red bentonite slurry as shown in Figure 112. The bentonite is placed at a water content of about 900 per cent and coloured with Erythrosine dye. The bentonite protects the borehole from cave-in and the red dye facilitates location of the boreholes while excavation is in progress. By sounding through the bentonite with stainless steel flush-jointed rods of about 10 mm diameter, the top plate is located and its elevation is determined by levelling techniques. It is essential that the sounding rods are carefully machined and numbered if high accuracy measurements are to be made. Hanna and Adams (1968) refer to the use of this heave point.

Dunnicliff (1971) gives details of various other types of heave points and the special precise extensometer of Burland et al. (1972) may also be used as a heave gauge in certain circumstances.

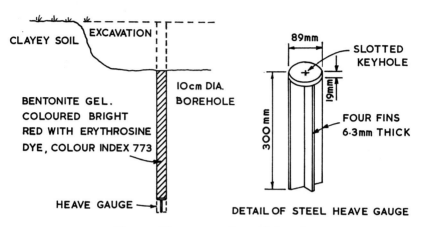

Fig. 112: Heave gauge (Bozozuk [1963]).

Having established the necessary benchmarks and references points, optical levelling techniques are used to determine elevation. Usually second or third order accuracy is used and errors of up to 0.8 mm are reported by Kjellman et al. (1955). By the limiting of sight lengths, balancing back and foresight distances, plumbing the staff and using a clearly marked staff as well as selecting stable staff turning points, where necessary, this accuracy can be improved. This is especially so if the levelling circuit is always closed on a benchmark and the measured closing error distributed in proportion to the square root of the distance from the starting point (usually a benchmark). Today the use of parallel plate micrometer instruments is common and closing errors of ± 0.5 mm or less are possible. First order levelling may be required where a high degree of accuracy is needed, e. g. the measurement of settlement and tilting of turbine foundations (Fitzherbert and Barnett [1967]). On congested construction sites this may prove to be very difficult due to the time required to complete a set of readings.

Special equipment in the form of staves capable of being used in limited headroom such as for levelling in basement ducts, may be required.

Bolgov (1967) summarizes measurement accuracy relative to the choice of levelling instrument chosen.

5.2.2. Lateral Movement from Offsets

By locating permanent targets at the two ends of a line of sight, the line of sight is defined. Errors may arise during the setting up of the theodolite over the station and also sighting on to the target at the other end of the line of sight. In most survey work the end stations are of a temporary nature but may be of a permanent form as used in dam instrumentation, for example (Oberti [1964]).

When the movement reference points have been established either in the ground or on the structure foundation, the line of sight defined by the theodolite and the permanent foresight target is dropped in turn on to a steel tape or scale held at right angles across the line of sight and zeroed on the reference mark on top of the reference point. The reference mark is usually a line scribed on the top of the reference point. In some cases permanent scales are attached to the reference points. Where possible the reference points should be set in line between the stable end references. In such cases where the offset is small (less than 1 m), the accuracy of measurement should be less than $\pm$ 2.0 mm.

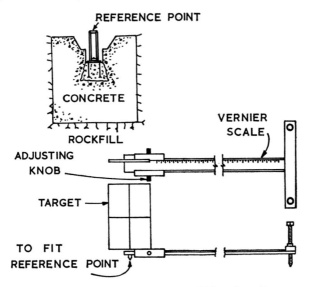

Fig. 113: Vernier target gauge (Wilson [1967]).

Wilson (1967) refers to specially designed vernier gauges with targets which were employed at Infernillo Dam. A detail of the vernier target is given in Figure 113. On many building sites in built-up areas, lines of sight are of very limited length and the targets at the end of the lines of sight may be located on existing buildings which are assumed to be fixed. Cole and Burland (1972) used six lines of sight to define the lateral movements of the top of a diaphragm wall in London. The theodolite stations were reinforced concrete plinths with built-in theodolite mountings, the reference targets being on buildings outside the site boundary. The reference points comprised observation brackets bolted to the top of the diaphragm wall at 5.18 m centres. The zero line was scribed onto a brass plate fixed to each bracket. All subsequent readings were made by measuring the offset from the "zero" line to a moveable target enscribed with a 'V' notch. Figure 114 shows a plan view of the reference points and lines of sight in relation to the buildings surrounding the site.

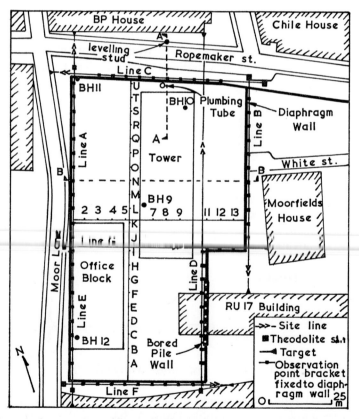

Fig. 114: Arrangement of lines of sight, settlement points and targets used by
Cole and Burland (1972).

If the line of the reference points is not straight but curved (e. g. the crest of an arch dam), precise movement measurements are best obtained by triangulation methods (Section 5.2.4.).

Care is required to ensure that the lateral movements are real, especially where lines of sight are long ($>$ 100 m). This is because the line of sight may bend in the lateral direction due to changes in air temperature and humidity. Environments, such as a line of foundations being concreted when the air temperature is very low, can give rise to serious error unless reciprocal sightings are taken. Similar troubles may be encountered along the top edge of a retaining wall.

Theodolites with a resolution of 1 second of arc are in common use for offset measurements. The sensitivity of the theodolite required depends to a large extent on the target being used and on the length of sight involved. Cole and Burland (1972) used a one second instrument for their observations.

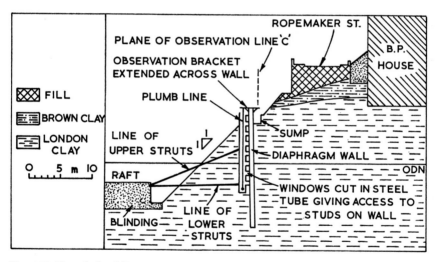

Fig. 115: Use of plumbline in measuring wall translation (Cole and Burland [1972]).

Bjerrum et al. (1965) describe the use of fine wires pulled tightly by heavy weights. These wires were strung out at the same level as the reference points on the sheet piles, and they were aligned with the plane of a base line by theodolite. The distances between the reference points and the reference wire were measured by a scale. Offsets to reference points located in vertical lines down the sheet piles were measured with a scale and plumbline. Accuracies of better than ± 1 mm are quoted. A similar technique was employed by Cole and Burland (1972) and Figure 115 shows the plumbline in relation to the plane of observation.

5.2.3. Tape measurement between observation points

Steel tapes are normally used along the ground surface and give an accuracy of about 5 mm in 30 m. When corrections are applied for tape sag, tension, temperature and ground slope an accuracy of about ± 1 mm in 30 m can be achieved. Milner (1969) discusses sources of error in tape measurement.

The principle of tape measurement in movement determination is that a reference monument located well away from the zone of ground movement is used as the datum and the distances between it and all other reference monuments are measured. It is essential that the monuments are in line. The monuments have a reference line scribed on top normal to the direction of measurement. The accuracy of a reading depends on the tape corrections referred to, but also on the quality of the monument. The monument must be located so that it is not influenced by climatic factors and the reference mark is protected against damage. It is usual to use the same monument or reference pin for settlement and lateral movement measurements.

Adams and Hanna (1970) describe the use of taping techniques to record the radial displacements away from the edge of a circular-shaped group of 750 piles as the piles were progressively driven from the centre outwards. The readings were taken during a period of very low air temperature ($+5°$ C to $-24°$ C).

5.2.4. Triangulation

The principle used in triangulation is that the angles subtended between the ends of a fixed base line and the observation point are measured. The reference base line must be located outside the area affected by ground movements. The accuracy of a triangulation survey depends on the length of base line and its accuracy and the length of the line of sight. For routine work with base lines up to 200 m long, an accuracy of about ± 10 mm results. A much higher degree of accuracy is possible and Reynolds and Dearinger (1970) using a base line of about 30 m obtained building movements to an accuracy of ± 0.3 mm in the horizontal direction and ± 0.6 mm in the vertical direction. These authors give details of the targets and monuments used and discuss the sources of error involved.

Precise triangulation is used in dam movement measurement especially in concrete arches where the movements are very small. Mendes et al. (1970) refer to the work on the Manicouagan Dam in Quebec, while Kobold (1961) discusses displacement and deformation measurement by geodetic methods.

5.2.5. Electronic Distance Measurement

An electro-optical distance measuring instrument developed at the National Physical Laboratory has a range of 15 to 3000 m and an accuracy of 3 in 1,000,000. The instrument is described by Froome and Bradsell (1966, 1968) and has been used by Penman and Mitchell (1970), and Penman et al. (1971) to relate the movement reference points on the downstream face of Scammonden dam to an immovable pillar located 210 m away. The immovable pillar, founded on bedrock, is shown in relation to the dam section in Figure 116.

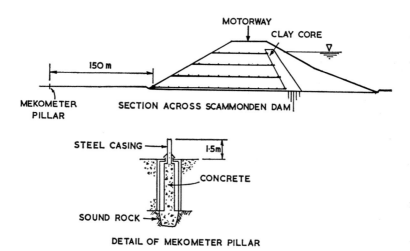

Fig. 116: Detail of Mekometer pillar (Penman [1969]).

The principle of the electronic distance meter is that the unknown distance is compared to a multiple of calibrated distances where the calibrated distance is the wavelength of the modulation on a carrier. In use an intensity modulated infra-red beam is transmitted from the meter to a reflector at the other end of the line. The beam reflected back to the meter is converted to an electronic signal and compared with an international reference signal. The reflected beam, owing to the time required to traverse the distance to the reflector and back, has a phase delay relative to the reference signal and, by comparison of the reflected signal, with the reference signal the phase delay is converted to distance. General details of Electronic Distance Measurement devices are given by Gort (1970), Moffitt (1970), Tomlinson (1970) and Romaniello (1970).

5.2.6. The Laser

The laser beam may be used to define a reference line for offset measurement to monuments. The beam of light usually has a diameter of 6 mm increasing to 12 mm in a length of 300 m. It should be possible to take offsets to this line to an accuracy of $\pm$ 3 mm. To date this technique has not been used although the laser is extensively used for tunnel alignment and other setting out work, see for example Hudswell Badger Ltd. (1971).

5.2.7. Photogrammetric method of movement measurement

This method of movement measurement requires the use of a photo-theodolite or some other precise camera which is used to take a series of successive photographs from a fixed station along a fixed camera axis. Where the movements are in a plane parallel to the image plane of the camera, one camera station is sufficient to record the movements. To measure three-dimensional movement it is necessary to photograph from two camera stations with the lines of sight convergent. Movement in two image planes is then resolved by intersection into movement in the object plane for successive photographic plates from each of the two camera stations.

In practice the observations are complicated by small errors in the alignment of the photographic plates in the stereocomparator; by small errors in the setting up of the camera at the fixed camera station; by differences in flatness of pairs of photographic plates. It is for these reasons that the quality of a photogrammetric displacement survey is dependent on the adjustment procedure followed in the correction of data. Some comments on the procedure to be followed in the design of a photogrammetric movement measurement project are given by Borchers (1968), who quotes examples of measurements on structures. The photogrammetric technique can be used for recording movements in engineering structures. It has also been used for recording the movements of dams. Vasilenko (1968) refers to work on rock-fill dams in Russia where use of a 30 m base line gave accuracies of about ± 5 mm in movement measurement. Using a base line of 200 m Planicka and Nosek (1970), report accuracies of ± 5 mm to ± 10 mm depending on weather conditions, terrain and the number of camera stations used. Their observations also refer to rock fill dams.

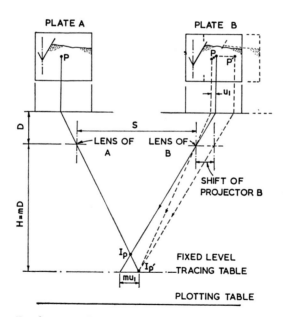

Fig. 117: Displacement Contouring (Butterfield and Andrawes [1972]).

The great advantage of the photogrammetric technique is that a permanent record is taken of a very large number of potential movements, thus enabling displacement contours to be drawn at any subsequent time. To date the technique has only been used to record the displacement of large rock-fill dams. Perhaps this is due to the necessity of having access to very expensive cameras and expensive plotting machines. The photogrammetric method is more widely used for recording displacements in the vicinity of laboratory scale foundation structures (Butterfield, Harkness and Andrawes [1970]) and is discussed further in Chapter 8.

The principle of displacement measurement from pairs of photographs is shown in Figure 117 and examples are given by Butterfield and Andrawes (1972).

5.3. Single Point Settlement Gauges (Remote)

There are many situations where it is not practicable to carry a vertical reference rod through to the ground surface, e. g. the vertical settlement of a point beneath a road. Terzaghi (1938) introduced a "hose level" manometer and this has led to a number of more accurate and more versatile instruments which rely on the manometer principle being developed. All remote settlement gauges rely on the determination of the elevation of one point with respect to a benchmark by optical levelling. The elevation of the other point is obtained by relative elevation addition to the known elevation. Thus accuracy of measurement is controlled by the accuracy of optical levelling as well as the factors common to the manometer system, namely temperature differential along the water-filled tube and the presence of air bubbles in the manometer tube.

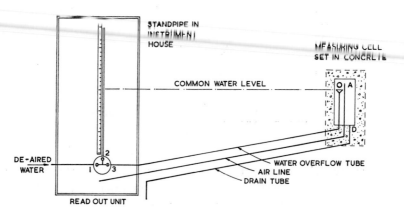

Fig. 118: Single Point Hydraulic Settlement Gauge (Soil Instruments Ltd.).

Figure 118 illustrates the principle of the water manometer tube gauge. A measuring cell is buried in the fill and connected to a remote read-out unit comprising a drain tube and air tube connected to the cell and a vertical scale alongside a standpipe. The cell is at the same elevation as the read-out unit. In use de-aired water is pumped into the vertical standpipe which causes overflow in the cell buried in the fill. The overflow returns from the cell via the drain tube. The elevation of the overflow level in the cell is then read on the scale attached to the vertical standpipe. The height of the standpipe must be sufficient to cover the elevation of the cell unit and its anticipated settlement.

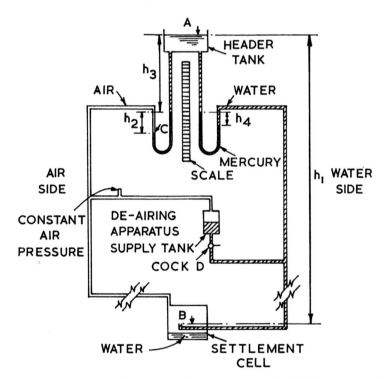

Fig. 119: Arrangement of hydraulic settlement gauge with cell below the read-out unit (Dunnicliff [1968]).

There are several sources of error which may be of importance. Because tap and distilled water contain about 10 p.p.m. of dissolved oxygen, it is necessary to circulate water through the full length of the polythene coated nylon tubing. With this procedure an accuracy in elevation reading of ± 0.5 mm is possible. To overcome this problem Little and Vail (1960) used de-aired water. For water flushing to be effective the tube diameter must not be too large otherwise the water can pass a bubble of air without carrying it along the tube. Inside diameters of 2.5 to 4.0 mm are used. The drain pipe from the cell must be on a continuous slope away from the cell, otherwise back-up in the drain will give rise to false readings in elevation. Difference in atmospheric pressure between the water surfaces in the cell and at the read-out unit can arise through omission of the air tube or by use of too small an air pipe. The air pipe should be 12.5 mm i. d. or greater. Temperature variation in the water line is overcome by flushing with water before each measurement is taken.

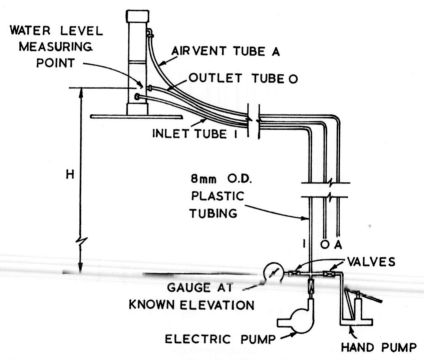

Fig. 120: Operation of hydraulic settlement gauge with cell above the read-out unit (Wilson [1967]).

With careful procedures accuracies of about ± 10 mm are possible and Penman and Mitchell (1970) refer to repeatabilities of ± 6 mm at Scammonden dam using 230 m length of tubing.

The overflow cell may be located above or below the level of the read-out unit. Where the cell is below the read-out unit, an air back-pressure is applied inside the cell and details of the settlement gauge arrangement are given by Dunnicliff (1968), Figure 119. When the cell is located above the read-out unit, a pressure gauge on the water line measures the difference in elevation between the cell and read-out unit. The principle is shown in the schematic diagram, Figure 120, according to Wilson (1967). Corrections to the pressure gauge reading are made for water temperature in the line and for barometric pressure differences between the cell and read-out unit. Wilson states that "... measurements of elevation difference are repeatable to ± 9 mm". A total of 34 of these cells has been used at the Oroville Dam (Department of Water Resources [1968]) but the survival record has not been good owing to the very large movements causing damage to the air vent tubes.

A settlement gauge with the cell below read-out was developed at the Road Research Laboratory (U. K.) and uses a mercury manometer (Irwin [1964]). Nitrogen pressure is applied to the cell unit, Figure 121, until an electrical contact between the base of the cell and the mercury is made.

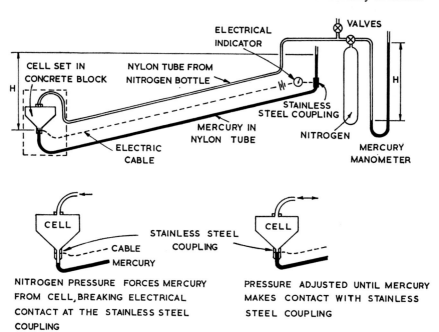

Fig. 121: Mercury Settlement Gauge (Irwin [1964]).

The elevation of the contact is determined from the measured nitrogen pressure with knowledge of the elevation of the mercury surface at the read-out unit. Corrections for temperature difference along the manometer tube are required. Accuracy is about $\pm$ 2 mm. A mercury manometer gauge in which the cell may be above or below the read-out unit is referenced by Dunnicliff (1971), who quotes an accuracy of $\pm$ 3 mm for a 3.6 m elevation difference using 300 m of tubing.

Other single point remote settlement devices are described by Cermak and Stepansky (1970) and Russell (1960). Venes (1967) describes a water level gauge used for turbine-block settlement measurement.

5.4. Multiple Point Settlement Gauges (Remote)

The principle of the multiple point gauge is that several additional cells are installed in the manometer tube. Ward et al. (1968) used a multipoint water level gauge to record settlement in the vicinity of a loaded water tank. A plan of the site showing the location of the water level gauges is given in Figure 122. The gauge consists of a series of interconnected water pots. Each pot is a brass cylinder 28 mm i. d. and sealed at the

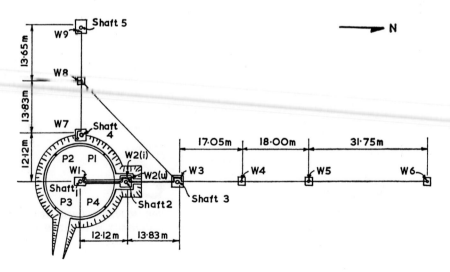

Fig. 122: Layout of water level gauges near test tank (Ward et al. [1968]).

top with a brass lid. A flexible hose, Figure 123, connects the bottom of the pots to water and the top of the pots to an air supply. The pots are mounted on three footscrews for levelling purposes. A hollow stainless steel float with conical shaped top bears on a lever which actuates a

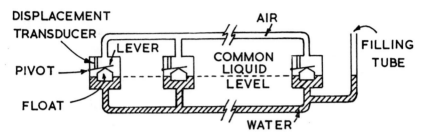

TRANSDUCER READINGS CALIBRATED IN PLACE TO RELATIVE ELEVATIONS OF INTERCONNECTED CELLS. SETTLEMENT OF A CELL CAUSES MOVEMENT OF FLOAT LEVER AND TRANSDUCER

Fig. 123: Multi-point settlement gauge (Ward et al. [1968]).

displacement transducer. Relative movement of the brass pots changes the elevations of the water surface and hence the transducer readings. Accuracies of $\pm$ 0.1 mm are quoted.

The Road Research Laboratory mercury settlement gauge (Irwin [1964]) can be used as a multi-point instrument. Additional cells, each with a separate electrical contact and cable, are installed in the manometer tube, Figure 124. Readings of elevation are taken by increasing the nitrogen pressure to lift the mercury column and break contact between the cell base and the mercury column in each cell in turn.

A simple but precise multiple point settlement gauge was developed at the Building Reserarch Station (Burland et al. [1972]). Two basic components, a permanent circular magnet axially magnetized which acts as a marker in the ground and a sensor, form the system. As the sensor, a reed switch, moves axially into the field of the magnet, it closes and activates an indicator light or buzzer. The equipment is used down a 100 mm diameter hole and the magnet holders are short lengths of

76 mm diameter p.v.c. pipe. Special springs grip the side of the borehole to fix the magnet at the required elevation. Thus a number of magnets may be installed in a borehole from the bottom upwards and where the bottom magnet is located in sound rock, it can be used as a benchmark.

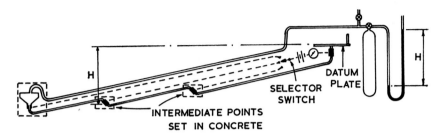

Fig. 124: Multi-point mercury settlement gauge (Irwin [1964]).

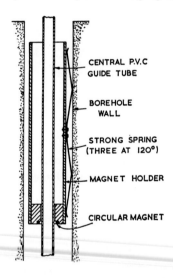

Fig. 125: Precise borehole extensometer — section through magnet holder
(Burland et al. [1972]).

A central p.v.c. guide tube is used for lowering a tape attached to the sensor head. Figure 125 shows a section through a magnet holder. Typical results, uses and details of installation are given by Burland et al. (1972). This instrument, while designed as a multiple position settlement device, can also be used in a horizontal or an inclined borehole. At present the instrument cannot be operated remotely. Accuracies as high as 0.02 mm can be achieved with special measuring rods.

Prange (1972) describes the telemetric settlement gauge. The principle of operation is that when a coil is placed in the centre of a metal ring or plate, the inductivity is altered and, by moving a transmitter containing the coil along an axis perpendicular to the metal plate, its position can be located. The metal plates or rings are installed around a plastic pipe. Locating accuracies of $\pm$ 1 mm are quoted.

5.5. Vertical Tube Settlement Gauges

All gauges rely on a string of telescoping tubes to which a series of plates are attached. The settlements of these plates are measured and hence average strain in the ground can be determined.

In the Building Research Station electrical gauge, rigid p.v.c. telescopic tubing is placed in the fill during construction. The measurement points comprise 0.3 m square steel plates placed around the plastic tube at about 3 m vertical interval. The steel plates can move independent of the tube, Figure 126. A probe which contains a coil forming the active arm

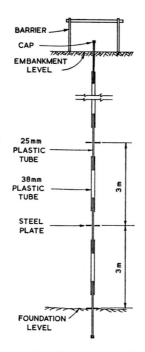

BARRIER

CAP

EMBANKMENT
LEVEL

25mm
PLASTIC
TUBE

38mm
PLASTIC
TUBE

3 m

STEEL
PLATE

3 m

FOUNDATION
LEVEL

Fig. 126: Electrical vertical settlement gauge (Soil Instruments Ltd.).

of a parallel resonance bridge is lowered on the end of a graduated cable down the inside of the plastic pipe. When the coil is central in each steel plate a maximum imbalance is read. With this system the steel plate can be located to about ± 3 mm although Penman (1969) describes a method of achieving accuracies of about ± 2 mm. This gauge may also be installed in a boring when the steel plate is replaced by an expanding device. The device comprises two arrow heads attached to pistons in two small cylinders. The arrows are driven into the wall of the borehole by application of hydraulic pressure to the cylinders.

The "cross-arm" type of gauge is the oldest being developed by the U.S. Bureau of Reclamation. A 38 mm pipe is attached to a short length of channel. A spacer of 50 mm pipe is carried up to the next channel section cross-arm. The cross-arms ensure that the 38 mm diameter pipe moves together a distance equal to the compression of the soil between the cross-arms. When each cross-arm is installed, the elevation of a reference point on the top pipe section is determined by levelling. Depths to the measuring point at the lower end of the 38 mm pipe are sounded by a special torpedo. Figure 127 shows the principal features of this gauge.

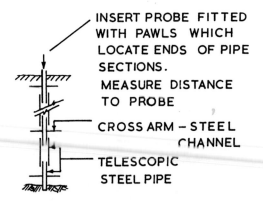

INSERT PROBE FITTED WITH PAWLS WHICH LOCATE ENDS OF PIPE SECTIONS.
MEASURE DISTANCE TO PROBE

CROSS ARM – STEEL CHANNEL

TELESCOPIC STEEL PIPE

Fig. 127: Cross-arm vertical settlement gauge (Dunnicliff [1971]).

During installation most of the soil surrounding the pipes is excavated and subsequently replaced by hand compaction. Corrosion of the steel pipes has occurred in some of the older installations; but this difficulty can be overcome with the use of a plastic pipe. Further details on the use of this gauge are given by Gould (1954).

5.6. Full Profile Gauges (Remote)

The principle of operation of these devices is that the cell unit is pulled along a buried flexible pipe laid in a trench, usually horizontal, and the distance from the fixed measuring unit is measured by a tape. The movable cell unit is referred to as a torpedo. The elevation of the torpedo may be made at any position within the pipe thus giving a vertical profile of the pipe with respect to the fixed measuring unit.

There are several types of full profile gauge. In the overflow type the torpedo consists of an overflow gauge (see Figure 118) and was developed by Lauffer and Schober (1964). Penman and Mitchell (1970) used this gauge at the Scammonden dam and report an accuracy of $\pm$ 2.5 mm. The set-up was used to measure both vertical and horizontal movements and comprised rigid p.v.c. pipes laid in the fill to a fall of 1 in 40 from the core of the dam to the gauge house on the downstream face. Steel plates with central holes which fit over the pipe were spaced at 15 m intervals and their horizontal movements were related to a reference plate fixed to the instrument house. This was achieved by use of an induction coil (see Section 5.7.) which can be passed through the pipe by a duct motor (Deadman and Slight [1965]) driven by compressed air. The horizontal position of each steel plate is indicated by the lack of balance of a inductance bridge as the coil passes through the plate. The water level device (torpedo) is also pulled through the duct by the motor and the elevation of the pipe at predetermined positions determined with respect to the elevation of the instrument house.

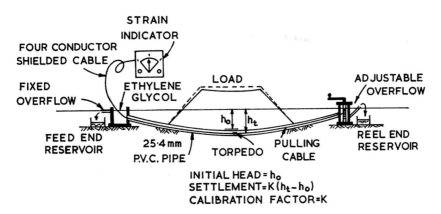

Fig. 128: Fluid settlement gauge (Bozozuk [1969]).

In the profile gauge described by Bozozuk (1969), the torpedo consists of a strain gauge pressure transducer. With this instrument the pressure transducer measures the liquid (ethylene glycol) head between the torpedo and the free liquid surface, Figure 128. Temperature corrections are necessary and Bozozuk reports a measurement accuracy of ± 2.5 mm. The gauge is particularly useful for the monitoring of vertical settlement profiles beneath foundations on compressible soils, e. g. road embankments.

Bergdahl and Broms (1967) describe the Swedish Geotechnical Institute gauge. A flexible hose is placed on the ground or in a trench before placement of the embankment fill and the vertical movement of this stationary hose is measured with respect to a reference point. The principle of the system is illustrated by Figure 129 while Figure 130 gives details of the measuring unit. The reference point may be a rock benchmark or it is a monument referenced to a benchmark. Two plastic tubes of different diameters form the unit. The inner tube is air-filled and is connected to a rubber balloon. The other end is connected to an air-sensitive manometer and an air pressure regulator. The annular space

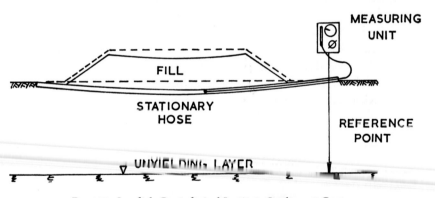

Fig. 129: Swedish Geotechnical Institute Settlement Gauge
(Bergdahl and Broms [1967]).

between the outer and inner tubes is filled with water and at the balloon end a plastic container is attached to the outer tube. Thus the balloon is completely surrounded with water. The water level in the standpipe, h, with respect to the reference point is measured by a scale. The hydrostatic pressure acting on the rubber balloon is proportional to the difference in height, h_2, between the free water surface in the standpipe and the measuring cell. Details of gauge use are given by Bergdahl and Broms (1967). For maximum accuracy with this cell, corrections for temperature and barometric pressure are required.

A modified version of the Swedish Geotechnical Institute gauge is reported by Dunnicliff (1971) and it has been used on several sites in the U.S.A. with success.

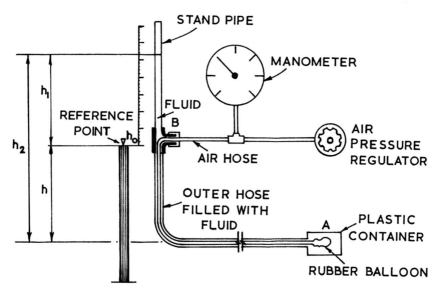

Fig. 130: Measuring Unit (Bergdahl and Broms [1967]).

5.7. Horizontal Movement Gauges

The measurement of lateral movement within a soil mass requires the installation of devices such as telescoping tubes, tensioned wires and transverse extensometers as well as the conventional surface monuments already referred to in Section 5.2.

5.7.1. Telescoping Tubes

This technique is also used for vertical movement recording and the principle of operation is that a telescoping tube with 30 cm square steel plates attached at predetermined intervals has an electrical torpedo passed through it to locate the positions of the plates with respect to one end. The torpedo is pulled through either by a pulley and wire system (Wilson [1967]) or by a special motor (see Section 5.6.). Accuracies in location of the embedded plates of ± 2 mm are given by Penman and Mitchell (1970); but this may be an exceptional case and a lower order of accuracy is to be expected. Crisp (1970) discusses the use of telescoping tubes and draws attention to the necessitiy for correction of the measured length to allow for the effect of bends in the tube, the profile of the tubing being determined as discussed in Section 5.6. Penman et al. (1971) describe the horizontal plate gauge used at Scammonden dam and give details of the torpedoes used for horizontal and vertical position measurements.

5.7.2. Tensioned Wire Devices

The tensioned wire device consists of steel wires or cables, attached to anchor zones and conducted through guide pipes to a measuring point where the movement of a point on a cable is observed relative to a fixed reference, the tension in the wire being held constant. The multiple point extensometer (Terrametrics System) measures the relative displacement of the wires which are fixed in the ground along the axis of a borehole as shown in Figure 131. During installation each measuring

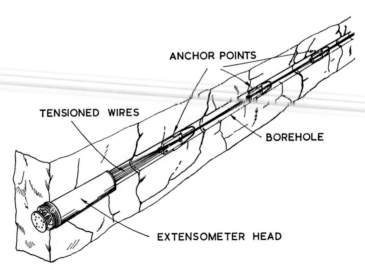

Fig. 131: Multiple point extensometer (Terrametrics System).

wire is tensioned by spring cantilevers in the measuring head. As the ground adjacent to the borehole deforms, the distance between the sensor head and each fixed point changes resulting in positive or negative cantilever deflections which are sensed by a manual or automatic trans- ducer. This extensometer may also be used for vertical measurements as well as in inclined directions.

The Interfels extensometer depends on a similar principle of operation but either a tensioned wire or a rigid rod is used to measure relative move- ments from one measuring point to another. The instrument may be a single or multiple unit. Accuracies are in the range 0.01 to 0.1 mm depending on the extensometer length. Figure 132 shows a layout of a triple rod extensometer and a detail of one rod and measuring device is

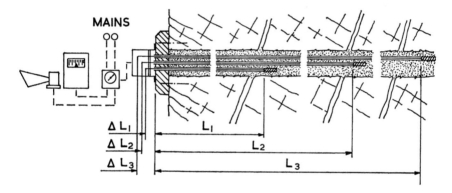

Fig. 132: Triple rod extensometer with alarm device (Interfels System).

given in Figure 133. The rods are assembled on site to the required length and at the end of an installation most parts of the extensometer can be recovered for use elsewhere. The measuring device is a special dial gauge which fits into an opening on the sensing head and allows the plunger to bear on the end of the protruding movement rod (Figure 21). For remote reading the extensometers are equipped with electric measurement transmitters. An alarm system may be built into the system to go off when a pre-set displacement occurs.

A simple and cheaper form of multiple point extensometer was used by Shannon and Strazer (1968). They used tensioned wires attached to anchor plates in the ground. A detail of a similar system is given in Figure 134.

McRostie et al. (1972) report on the use of single movement gauges to record soil lateral movement behind an anchored retaining wall. The gauges were made from two concentric steel pipes with a short length of auger attached to the inner one. After installation the inner pipe was advanced 0.6 m into undisturbed ground by rotation of the inner pipe relative to the outer pipe. Readings of the relative movement between the wall and the inner pipe were obtained with a dial gauge bearing on a machined ring welded to the wall. Reproducibility of readings is quoted as 0.05 mm.

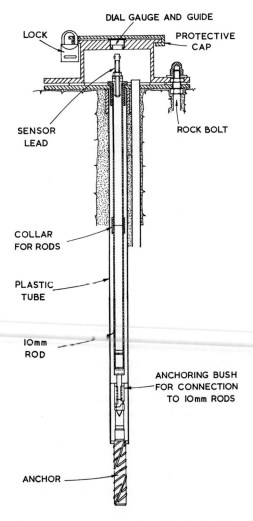

Fig. 133: Detail of rod extensometer and reading device (Interfels System).

A tensioned wire gauge is also described by Mezhnev (1970).

The transverse extensometer has been used for measuring precisely the profile of earth retaining structures (Dunnicliff [1971]). A vertical tensioned wire fixed between two anchor plates, Figure 135, makes contact with resistance elements. The resistance elements move with the adjacent structure, the wire being held by the end anchors. The horizontal movement of each resistance element is measured with respect to the steel wire by a Wheatstone bridge. Dunnicliff (1971) reports repeatability of $\pm$ 0.5 mm.

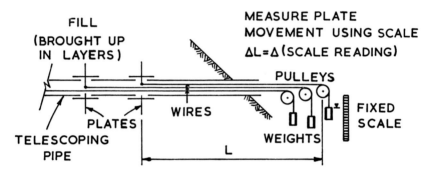

Fig. 134: Tensioned wire gauge (Shannon and Strazer [1968]).

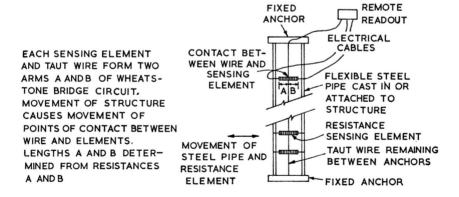

Fig. 135: Transverse extensometer (Dunnicliff [1971]).

The deflectometer is also a tensioned wire device used for measuring movements normal to the axis of a borehole in soil or rock. In this instrument, Figure 136, the tensioned wire passes over knife edges at various points along its length and transducers measure the angular change in direction of the wire at each knife edge. Thus relative deflections are measured. Müller and Müller (1970) discuss the use of the deflectometer for earth dam instrumentation and quote an accuracy of ± 0.04 mm with a knife edge spacing of about 5 m.

Wilson (1967) describes the horizontal movement gauges installed in the Gespatch and Oroville dams. There are several other devices of this working principle.

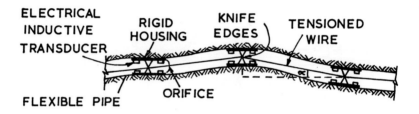

TRANSDUCERS SENSE ANGULAR VARIATION α OF WIRE WITHIN ORIFICE . HENCE CONTINUOUS ANGULAR TRAVERSE ALONG PIPE

H = L sin. α

Fig. 136: Deflectometer (Dunnicliff [1972]).

5.8. Strain Meters

There are several groups of strain meter used by the foundation engineer. The most common is the portable extensometer used for the measurement of distance between two points, e. g. the change in shape of a tunnel. To achieve this, bolts are fixed to the walls of the tunnel or opening and a telescoping rod or tube, on which is mounted a micrometer or a tensioned steel tape, is used to measure distance. The Interfels convergence measuring device, Figure 137, uses a perforated steel tape and a tensioning device. Length changes in relation to the initial reading are read by a dial gauge which is calibrated in a calibration frame before and after each measurement. The range of the instrument is from 1.5 to 30 m with a sensititivity of $1 \cdot 10^{-5}$ of the range. The Terrametrics tape extensometer is a similar type of gauge.

Fig. 137: Convergence Measuring Device (Interfels System).

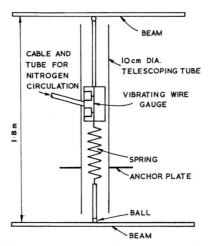

Fig. 138: Vibrating Wire Strain Gauge Soil Extensometer (Kennard et al. [1967]).

There are many other portable extensometers such as an invar rod or tube, although aluminium has also been used with success (Ward and Thomas [1965]). Invar wire extensometers are reported by Terzaghi and Peck (1967) and Burke (1957).

Several embedded soil extensometers are available. They comprise a strain measuring device on an element connecting two anchor plates. The vibrating wire strain gauges, Figure 138, developed in England

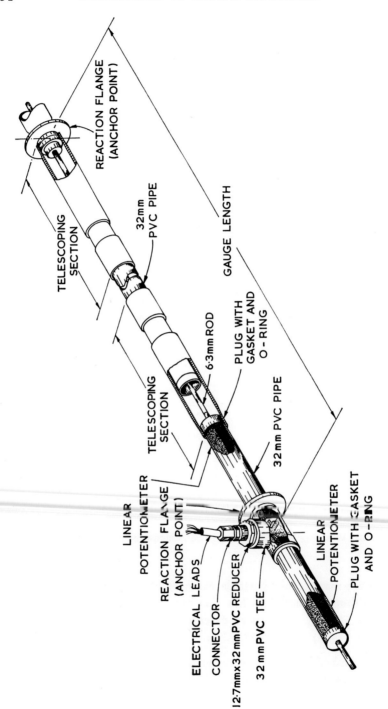

REACTION FLANGE
(ANCHOR POINT)

TELESCOPING
SECTION

32mm
PVC PIPE

GAUGE LENGTH

6·3mm ROD

PLUG WITH
GASKET AND
O - RING

TELESCOPING
SECTION

32mm PVC PIPE

LINEAR
POTENTIOMETER

REACTION FLANGE
(ANCHOR POINT)

ELECTRICAL LEADS

CONNECTOR

12·7mm x 32mm PVC REDUCER

32mm PVC TEE

LINEAR
POTENTIOMETER

PLUG WITH GASKET
AND O - RING

Fig. 139: Soil Strain Meter (Slope Indicator Co.).

makes use of a helical spring and a vibrating wire unit in a frame. When
the beam arms of the gauge move, the tension in the helical spring
changes thus causing a change in the frequency of vibration of the
tensioned wire element. The vibrating wire element is kept at atmospheric pressure by a nitrogen line through which the gas is slowly passed.
This also keeps the gauge dry and thus prevents corrosion. The extensometer spans 1.8 m and has a movement range of 0.15 m to an accuracy
of ± 0.5 mm. This instrument has been used in a number of earth dams
and details on performance are given by Kennard et al. (1967), Penman
and Mitchell (1970) and Penman et al. (1971).

For the extensometers embedded in the El Infernillo Dam (Marsal and
Ramirez [1967]) a potentiometer strain measuring principle was used.
Two plate anchors are connected to a linear potentiometer by stainless
rods protected by telescoping tubes. The Slope Indicator Company
manufactures a strain meter which operates on this principle. Aluminium
flanges are clamped to the pipe at the anchor points, Figure 139. The
gauge length is about 1.8 m with a displacement measuring range up
to 0.15 m. The cable from the meter to terminal station is conducted
within a polythene tube.

The strain meters referred to above are for use in soil masses. In some
cases it is necessary to measure surface tensile or compressive movements over short lengths. Wilson (1967) refers to spring loaded wires

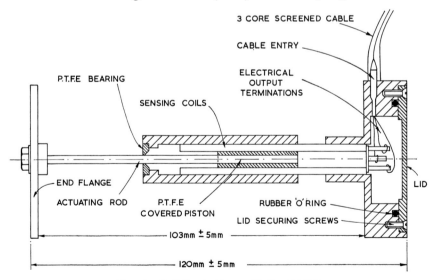

Fig. 140: Soil Strain Gauge (Potter [1969]).

used by the Corps of Engineers for this purpose. For the measurement of dynamic and long term strains in soils beneath road pavements the Road Research Laboratory (England) have developed a soil strain gauge (Potter [1969]) and a displacement gauge (Lister and Mayo [1970]). The soil strain gauge, Figure 140, consists of two aluminium end plates, 64 mm diameter, attached to a differential transformer. The two coils of the transformer are wired to form a half bridge circuit and the change of inductance of the coils as the core moves is measured by a carrier amplifying system connected to an ultra violet recorder or magnetic tape recorder via a filter. Details of the operations involved in the use of this gauge are given by Potter. The gauge is capable of recording tensile and compressive dynamic strains in the range 10 to 25,000 microstrain and long term strain in the range 20 to 1,000,000 microstrain.

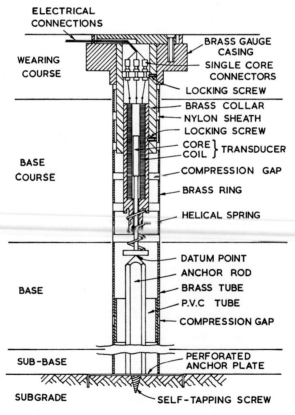

Fig. 141: Transient and Long Term Displacement Gauge (Lister and Mayo [1970]).

The transient displacement gauge is shown in section view in Figure 141 and comprises three components: (i) a casing fixed in the road surface, (ii) a rod anchored at its lower end at the elevation where the movement is to be measured and (iii) a displacement transducer to measure the movement of the datum rod relative to the casing.

5.9. Inclinometers

Inclinometers are used extensively to monitor movements in earth fills, deflections of bulkheads, soil and ice creep, and the bending of piles during driving. Most of these instruments consist of a pendulum actuated transducer enclosed in a watertight torpedo. The torpedo is lowered down a near-vertical guide casing installed in the ground or attached to a structure. The inclination of the casing from the vertical is measured at predetermined intervals and the profile of the vertical shape of the casing is obtained by integration of the observed slope values from the bottom. The bottom of the casing is usually keyed into rock and is assumed to be free from translation. Where this is not so, the top of the casing, whose position is fixed by survey methods, can be used as the datum. There are six basic types of inclinometer and within each type there are a number of proprietory instruments.

5.9.1. Inclonometer Types

One of the crudest devices is the flexible tube installed in a borehole. Steel rods of increasing length are lowered inside the tubing in turn and the rod length which is just able to pass a given point gives a measure of the curvature of the tubing in the vicinity of that point. Toms and Bartlett (1962) describe the use of this technique for the location of slip surfaces in unstable slopes.

The most successful inclinometer is the Wheatstone bridge type developed Wilson (1962). The pendulum, Figure 142, contacts a special precision-wound resistance coil and divides it into two resistances which form one half of the bridge circuit. The other half of the bridge is contained in the control box. The instrument is so designed that the component of inclination in the plane defined by four wheels on the pendulum container is directly proportional to the potentiometer reading when the circuit is in balance. Thus the inclinometer measures the slope of the chord joining the two points of contact between the wheels and the guide casing. The azimuth and relative position in the ground are controlled by the pairs of wheels which are guided in vertical slots formed in the walls of specially extruded casing of either aluminium or plastic. The multi wire cable has a stranded steel cable in the centre and this cable is used to support the weight of the instrument while it is lowered down the casing. Readings of slope are taken in two perpendicular directions, and thus the two components of horizontal movement can be determined. This instrument has a long record of successful use and accuracies of up to 25 mm in 300 m have been achieved. Some examples of the use of this instrument for movement measurement in rock fill are given by Wilson and Hancock (1965) while Hanna (1968) discusses its use for pile bending measurement.

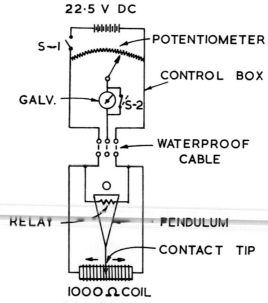

Fig. 142: Circuit diagram of slope indicator instrument.

Vibrating wire strain gauge transducers have also been used to measure the tilt of the inclinometer, but these instruments are sensitive to temperature effects and zero drift (Dunnicliff [1971]). Bonded electrical resistance strain gauges are used and the instrument developed by Soil

Instruments Ltd. is given as an example. The probe consists of a semi-rigid pendulum housed in an oil-filled metal tube. A beryllium-copper strip rigidly fixed at its upper end and attached to a conical weight at its lower end forms the pendulum. Changes in strain in this strip occur when the pendulum acts as a cantilever loaded at its free end and the strains are detected by pairs of electrical resistance strain gauges bonded on to the strip. These gauges produce a voltage which is proportional to the angle of inclination of the probe and, by means of a meter with a centre zero scale, angles of inclination with respect to the vertical direction are determined. The cross-sensitivity (Section 4.3.1.) of the instrument is quoted as 6 minutes of arc for a $20°$ inclination. The plastic casing has four guide ridges on the inner wall which enable the pendulum to be located on a selected guide. Spring-loaded feet on the pendulum probe ensure that it is lightly held in the plastic casing. The connecting cable to the indicator unit has a high tensile steel straining wire which supports the self weight of the probe when raising and lowering in the casing. The performance of this inclinometer is reported by Murray and Irwin (1970) and they conclude (i) that the instrument is sound but requires frequent calibration, (ii) that measurements are generally within 7 mm over a vertical distance of 6 m for angles of inclination in the range $\pm 10°$ (iii) the system provides a reasonably accurate assessment of the movements of the plastic casing, but the ability of the casing to follow the movements taking place in compressible soils has not been ascertained.

For higher precision work the tilt of the pendulum can be measured by a pair of servo-accelerometers and the Digitilt instrument (Slope Indicator Company) is used as an example. The sensor unit is 42.8 mm o. d. by 0.927 m in length with two fixed wheels which roll on the inner surface of the casing and a third wheel (spring-loaded) which tracks in a guide groove. The 0.5 g servo-accelerometers are energized by an applied voltage and provide a very quick stabilized response to tilt by a change of current flow. The resulting voltage output is proportional to the sine of the angle of inclination of the casing from the vertical. The standard instrument has a range of $\pm 30°$ but with special accelerometers this range can be increased to $\pm 90°$. During operation the instrument is lowered to the bottom of the casing and a reading taken. The instrument is then raised in increments of 0.6 m and further readings taken. After the instrument is raised, it is rotated through 180 degrees and the procedure repeated. A 30 m hole can be surveyed in

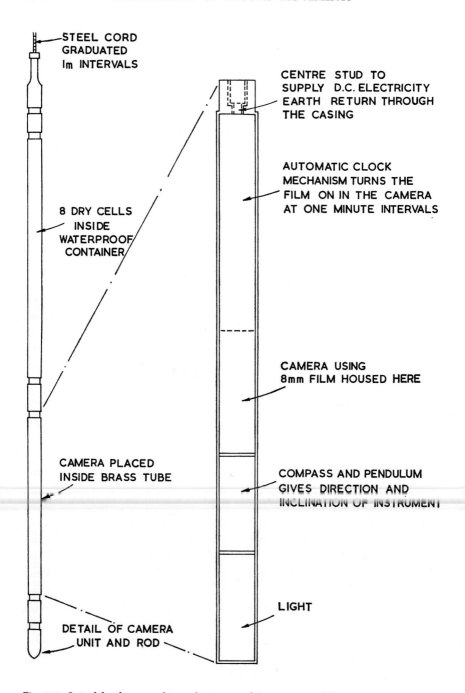

Fig. 143: Interfels photographic inclinometer showing general features of operation.

approximately 30 minutes. An automatic recording facility is available with choice of paper punch or magnetic tape recording. A sensitivity of 1 in 10,000 is quoted, this being 10 times more sensitive than the original slope indicator developed by Parsons and Wilson (1956).

Bromwell et al. (1971) describe an automatic recording inclinometer which makes use of the accelerometer principle for slope measurement. They quote an overall accuracy in locating the absolute position of a 30 m long tube to be about 6 mm and changes in position along this tube can be measured with confidence to about 2.5 mm.

A photographic method of tilt recording makes use of the Eastman Multishot System (Interfels). The borehole inclination and direction is measured by the following procedure.

  (i) A steel cable is attached to the top of a brass container, Figure 143, and the cable and container marked at 1 m vertical intervals.

 (ii) The camera is then removed and loaded with 8 mm film. When connected to the d. c. power supply, an automatic clock starts the camera taking photographs at 1 minute intervals. When connecting the camera, the operator also starts a stop watch.

(iii) The container is then lowered down the borehole 1 m at a time with a time interval of 1 minute between each increment of depth.

 (iv) The camera records a photograph of a pendulum and compass face thus giving the inclination of the hole and direction. Figure 144 gives a sketch of a typical photograph.

  (v) The film strip is removed and processed in the field to ensure that the camera was correctly synchronized with the lowering of the probe.

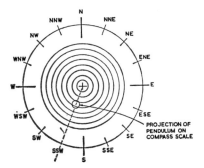

Fig. 144: View of pendulum and compass recording by camera (Interfels System).

Fairly lengthy and complicated calculations are involved but the system is very reliable and relatively cheap. An accuracy in the order of $\pm$ 25 mm in 25 m is possible.

5.9.2. Errors in Inclinometer Use

Several factors can affect the results of an inclinometer survey. First, the precision of the pendulum system is controlled to a large extent by the principle of tilt measurement employed and maintenance and calibration carried out during use. There are a number of references dealing with this subject. Wilson and Hancock (1965) refer to a precision of 3×10^{-4} radians in inclination change between successive readings while Hakman and Buser (1962) suggest that a single slope reading may be in error by up to 3×10^{-3} radians due to imperfections in the casing and instrument malfunctions. For a similar inclinometer, inclination precision of $\pm 1 \times 10^{-4}$ radians is given by Lambe (1968) and others. Dunnicliff and Gould (1971) discuss in detail accuracies obtained from inclinometer observations and their general conclusion is that the precision of the measurement may differ significantly from the precision of the inclinometer system. There are a number of factors responsible which include;

(i) spiralling of the casing with the result that the grooves at depth do not have the same orientation as at the ground surface. A spiral of 1 degree in 3 m is common,

(ii) lack of repeatability of the reading position with the result that the inclinometer is at a different depth for each set of readings,

(iii) sensitivity of the inclinometer to temperature and humidity change. These changes have no effect on the resistance element inclinometer using a Wheatstone bridge circuit and the accelerometer types, but the bonded-resistance strain gauge type is affected and with this instrument temperature equalization is required before starting a set of measurements. This may be achieved by leaving the instrument down the hole for at least 30 minutes,

(iv) the skill of the observer. For a high degree of accuracy the reading depth interval must be equal to the spacing of the inclinometer wheels, otherwise the deflections of the casing are not composed of straight lines between the measuring points. Quantitative data on this detail are given by Bromwell et al. (1971). Checks can be made in the field by taking two sets of inclinometer readings in one vertical plane but separated by 180 degrees. The sum of these two readings should be a constant value, otherwise an error exists. Use of this procedure in the field can detect faulty equipment, gross errrors and poor technique.

Further details on errors in inclinometer use are given by Murray and Irwin (1970), Bromwell et al. (1971), Kallstenuis and Bergau (1961), Simons et al. (1968) and others.

5.9.3. Some uses of inclinometers

Inclinometers have been used for many types of measurement although their main use is in the determination of lateral displacement in a mass of soil or rock fill due to load change (e. g. movements in embankments, lateral movements near to excavations). Gray (1969) refers to the use of inclinometers for the monitoring of soil creep while Wilson (1970) shows applications in snow and ice movement measurement as well as in natural and artificial slopes. Hanna (1968) and Fellenius (1970) discuss the use of inclinometers for pile bending determination.

One of the earliest applications of inclinometer reading for bending moment determination in sheet pile walls was by Tschebotarioff and Ward (1957) and this work has been followed by a number of others e. g. Bailly et al. (1969), Thompson and Maitich (1961) and Dunnicliff (1971).

Examples of embankment studies with inclinometer instruments are given by Rico et al. (1969), Wilson and Hancock (1965), Kaufmann and Weaver (1967), Bourges et al. (1969), Marsal and Ramirez (1967) and many others.

References

ADAMS, J. I., and HANNA, T. H., (1970), "Ground Movements due to Pile Driving", Proceedings, Conference on Behaviour of Piles, Institution of Civil Engineers, London, 127—134.

BAILLY, J. P., BASSAL, J. L., PILOT, G., and SCHLOSSER, F., (1969), "Experimentation sur le batardeau d'une excavation", Proceedings, Seventh International Conference on Soil Mechanics and Foundation Engineering, Mexico City, Vol. 2, 407—415.

BERGDAHL, U., and BROMS, B. B., (1967), "New Method of Measuring in-situ Settlements", Proceedings, American Society of Civil Engineers, Vol. 93, SM5, 51—58.

BJERRUM, L., KENNY, T. C., and KJARENSLI, B., (1965), "Measuring Instruments for Strutted Excavations", Proceedings American Society of Civil Engineers, Vol. 91, SM1, 111—141.

BOLGOV, I. F., (1967), "Settlement Measurements of Structures", Soil Mechanics and Foundation Engineering, No. 2, March-April, 128—130.

BORCHERS, P. E., (1968), "Photogrammetric Measurement of Structural Movements", Proceedings, American Society of Civil Engineers, Vol. 94, SU1, 67—80.

BOURGES, F., CARRISAN, M., CHIAPPA, J., LEGRAND, J., and PAUTE, J. L., (1969), "Etude du tassement des vases supportant des remblais", Proceedings, Seventh International Conference on Soil Mechanics and Foundation Engineering, Mexico City, Vol. 2, 35—43.

BOZOZUK, M., JOHNSTON, J. H., and HAMILTON, J. J., (1962), "Deep Benchmarks in Clay and Permafrost Regions", National Research Council of Canada, Paper 86-C.

BOZOZUK, M., (1963), "The Modulus of Elasticity of Leda Clay from Field Measurements", Canadian Geotechnical Journal, Vol. 1, No. 1, 43—51.

BOZOZUK, M., (1969), " A Fluid Settlement Gauge", Canadian Geotechnical Journal, Vol. 6, No. 3, 362—364.

BROMWELL, L. G., RYAN, C. R., and TOTH, W. E., (1971), "Recording inclinometer for measuring soil movement". Proceedings, Fourth Pan American Conference on Soil Mechanics and Foundation Engineering, Puerto Rico, Vol 2, 333—343.

BURKE, H. H., (1957), "Garrison Dam-Tunnel Test Section Investigation", Proceedings, American Society of Civil Engineers, Vol. 83, SM4, 1438-1 to 1438-50.

BURLAND, J. B., MOORE, J. F. A., and SMITH, P. D. K., (1972), "A Simple and Precise Borehole Extensometer", Geotechnique, Vol. 22, No. 1, 174—177.

BUTTERFIELD, R., ILARIQIECS, R M and ANDRAWES, (1970), "A Stereophotogrammetric method for measuring displacement fields", Geotechnique, Vol 20, No. 3, 308—314.

BUTTERFIELD, R., and ANDRAWES, K. Z., (1971), "The Visualization of Planar Displacement Fields", Proceedings, Roscoe Memorial Symposium, Cambridge University, 467—475.

CERMAK, Z., and STEPANSKY, M., (1970), "Deformation Measurements on Earth and Rockfill Dams in Moravia", Transactions, Tenth International Congress on Large Dams, Montreal, Vol. 3, 197—205.

COLE, K. W., and BURLAND, J. B., (1972), "Observations of Retaining Wall Movements associated with a large Excavation", Proceedings Fifth European Conference on Soil Mechanics and Foundation Engineering, Madrid, Vol. 1, 445—453.

CRISP, R. L., (1970), "Instrumentation and Results of Measurements of Earth and Pore Pressures, Lateral Deformation and Settlement in a Rockfill Dam", Transactions, Tenth International Congress on Large Dams, Montreal, Vol. 3, 371—387.

CROSS, J. E., (1970), "Settlement Behind Bridge Abutments", Road Research Laboratory Report LR. 310.

DEADMAN, D. J., and SLIGHT, J. R., (1965), "A New Approach to the Duct Rodding Problem — Ductmotor No. 1", Post Office Electrical Engineers Journal, Vol. 58, Part 2, 91—92.

Department of Water Resources, (1968), "Performance Report No. 1 — Oroville Dam", Sacramento, California, April.

DUNNICLIFF, C. J., (1968), "Instrumentation of the Plover Cove Main Dam", Geotechnique, Vol. 18, No. 3, 283—300.

DUNNICLIFF, C. J., (1971), "Equipment for Field Deformation Measurements", Proceedings, Fourth Pan American Conference on Soil Mechanics and Foundation Engineering, Puerto Rico, Vol. 2, 319—332.

FELLENIUS, B. H., (1971), Contribution to Session E, Proceedings, Conference on the Behaviour of Piles, Institution of Civil Engineers, London, 202, 203.

FITZHERBERT, W. A., and BARNETT, J. H., (1967), "Causes of Movement in Reinforced Concrete Turbo Blocks and Developments in Turbo Block Design and Construction", Proceedings, Institution of Civil Engineers, London, Vol. 36, 351—394.

FROOME, K. D., and BRADSELL, R. H., (1966), "A New Method for the Measurement of Distances up to 5000 ft. by Means of a Modulated Light Beam", Journal of Scientific Instruments, Vol. 43, 129—133.

FROOME, K. D., and BRADSELL, R. H., (1968), "NPL Mekometer III", Allgemeine Vermessungs-Nachrichten, Vol. 4, 159—163.

GORT, A. F., (1970), "Electronic Distance Measurements with the Hewlett-Packard Model 3800", (Hewlett Packard).

GOULD, J. P., (1954), "Compression Characteristics of Rolled Fill Materials in Earth Dams", U.S. Bureau of Reclamation, Technical Memorandum 684.

GOULD, J. D., and DUNNICLIFF, C. J., (1971), "Accuracy of Field Deformation Measurements", Proceedings, Fourth Pan American Conference on Soil Mechanics and Foundation Engineering, Puerto Rico, Vol. 1, 313—366.

GRAY, H., (1969), "Effects of Forest Clear Cutting on the Stability of Natural Slopes", Reprint, Slope Indicator Company, Seattle, U.S.A.

HAKMAN, P. A., and BUSER, W. M., (1962), "Bulkhead Test Program at Port of Toledo, Ohio", Proceedings, American Society of Civil Engineers, Vol. 88, SM3, 151—184.

HANNA, T. H., (1968), "The Bending of Long H-Section Piles", Canadian Geotechnical Journal, Vol. 5, No. 3, 150—172.

HANNA, T. H., and ADAMS, J. I., (1968), "Comparison of Field and Laboratory Measurements of Modulus of Deformation of a Clay", Soil Properties from In-Situ Measurement. Highway Research Record No. 243, Highway Research Board, 12—22.

Hudswell Badger Ltd., (1971), "Optical Guidance Unit".

IRWIN, M. J., (1964), "A Mercury-filled Gauge for the Measurement of the Settlement of Foundations", Civil Engineering and Public Works Review, March, 358—360.

KALLSTENUIS, T., and BERGAU, W., (1961), "In-situ Determination of Horizontal Ground Movements", Proceedings, Fifth International Conference on Soil Mechanics and Foundation Engineering, Paris, Vol. 1, 481—485.

KAUFMAN, R. I., and WEAVER, F. J., (1966), "Stability of Atchafalaya Levees", Proceedings, American Society of Civil Engineers, Vol. 93, SM4, 157—176.

KENNARD, M. F., PENMAN, A. D. M., and VAUGHAN, P. R., (1967), "Stress and Strain Measurements in the Clay Core at Balderhead Dam", Transactions, Ninth International Congress on Large Dams, Istanbul, Vol. 3, 129—151.

KJELLMAN, W., KALLSTENUIS, T., and LILJEDAHL, Y., (1955), "Accurate Measurement of Settlements", Royal Swedish Geotechnical Institute, Proceedings No. 10.

KOBOLD, F., (1961), "Measurement of Displacement and Deformation by Geodetic Means", Proceedings, American Society of Civil Engineers, Vol. 87, SU2, 37—66.

LAMBE, T. W., (1968), "Behaviour of Foundations During Construction", Proceedings, American Society of Civil Engineers, Vol. 94, SM1, 93—130.

LAUFFER, H., and SCHOBER, W., (1964), "The Gepatsch Rockfill Dam in the Kauner Valley", Transactions, Eighth International Congress on Large Dams, Edinburgh, Vol. 3, 635—660.

LISTER, N. W., and MAYO, A. P., (1970), "A Gauge for the Measurement of Transient and Long Term Displacements in Road Pavements". Road Research Laboratory, Report LR. 353.

LITTLE, A. L., and VAIL, A. J., (1960), "Some Developments in the Measurement of Pore Pressure", Proceedings, Conference on Pore Pressure and Suction in Soils, Institution of Civil Engineers, London, 75—80.

MARGASON, G., (1970), "Settlement Behind Bridge Abutments. The Performance of a Stony-clay Fill in an Approach Embankment to an Overbridge on the M4 Motorway", Road Research Laboratory, Report LR. 311.

MARGASON, G., and CROSS, J. E., (1966), "Settlement Behind Bridge Abutments. The Use of Pulverised Fuel Ash in Constructing the Approach Embankments to Bridges on the Staines By-pass". Road Research Laboratory, Report No. 48.

MARSAL, R. J., and RAMIREZ DE ARELLANO, L., (1967), "Performance of El Infiernillo Dam", Proceedings, American Society of Civil Engineers, Vol. 93, SM4, 265—298.

McROSTIE, G. C., BURN, K. N., and MITCHELL, R. J., (1972), "The Performance of Tied Back Sheet Piling in Clay", Canadian Geotechnical Journal, Vol. 9, No. 2, 206—218.

MENDES, L. P., BROWN, E. L., MOREAU, R., and BOYER, B., (1970), "Supervision of the Behaviour of Daniel Johnson Dam (Manicouagan 5)", Transactions, Tenth International Congress on Large Dams, Montreal, Vol. 3, 1183—1205.

MEZHNEV, D. I., (1967), "Coefficient of Elastic Yielding of Sand Back Fill of Dock-Type Lock Chambers", Hydrotechnical Construction No. 10, October, 1062—1066.

MILNER, R. M., (1969), "Accuracy of Measurement with Steel Tapes", Building, September 19, pp. 38/139—140, 142.

MOFFITT, F. H., (1970), "Field Evaluation of the Hewlett-Packard Model 3800 Distance Meter", ASP-ASCM Fall Technical Conference, Denver, Colorado (reprint).

MÜLLER, G., and MÜLLER, L., (1970), "Monitoring of Dams with Measuring Instruments", Transactions, Tenth International Congress on Large Dams, Montreal, Vol. 3, 1033—1046.

MURRAY, R. T., and IRWIN, M. J., (1970), "The Performance of an Inclinometer for Measuring Lateral Movements in Soil", Road Research Laboratory, Report LR. 332.

OBERTI, G., (1964), "Dam Measurements in Italy", Report of Italian Sub-committee, Transactions, Eighth International Congress on Large Dams, Edinburgh, Vol. 4, 395—433.

PARSONS, J. D., and WILSON, S. D., (1956), "Safe Loads on Dog-Leg Piles", Transactions, American Society of Civil Engineers, Vol. 121, 695—721.

PENMAN, A. D. M., (1969), "Instrumentation for Earth and Rockfill Dams", Building Research Station, England, Current Paper No. 35/69.

PENMAN, A. D. M., and MITCHELL, P. B., (1970), "Initial Behaviour of Scammonden Dam", Building Research Station, England, Current Paper No. 20/70.

PENMAN, A. D. M., and CHARLES, J. A., (1971), "Measuring Movements of Engineering Structures", Building Research Station, England, Current Paper No. 32/71.

PENMAN, A. D. M., BURLAND, J. B., and CHARLES, J. A., (1971), "Observed and Predicted Deformation in a Large Embankment Dam During Construction", Proceedings, Institution of Civil Engineers, London, Vol. 49, 1—21.

PLANICKA, A., and NOSEK, L., (1970), "Terrestial Photogrammetry in Measurement of Deformations of Rockfill Dams", Transactions, Tenth International Congress on Large Dams, Montreal, Vol. 3, 207—215.

POTTER, J. F., (1969), "Gauge for Measuring Dynamic and Long Term Strains in Soil", Road Research Laboratory, Report LR 251.

PRANGE, B., (1971), "The State of Telemetry in Soil Mechanics", Proceedings, Roscoe Memorial Symposium, Cambridge University, 476—488.

REYNOLDS, J. D., and DEARINGER, J. A., (1970), "Measuring Building Movement by Precise Survey", Proceedings, American Society of Civil Engineers, Vol. 96, SU1, 87—96.

RICO, A., MORENO, G., and GARCIA, G., (1969), "Test Embankments on Texcoco Lake", Proceedings, Seventh International Conference on Soil Mechanics and Foundation Engineering, Mexico City, Vol. 2, 669—676.

ROMANIELLO, C. G., (1970), "Advancing Technology in Electronic Surveying", Proceedings, American Society of Civil Engineers, Vol. 96, SU2, 287—297.

RUSSELL, T., (1960), "A Hydrostatic Settlement Gauge", Proceedings, Third Australia — New Zealand Conference on Soil Mechanics and Foundation Engineering, 108—110.

SHANNON, W. L., and STRAZER, R. J., (1968), "Shoring for the Seattle First National Bank Building, Seattle, Washington", American Society of Civil Engineers Annual Meeting and National Meeting on Structural Engineering, Pittsburgh.

SIMONS, I., EMSTIE, A. G., STRONG, P. F., and McCONNELL, R. K., (1968), "Sensitive Tiltmeter Utilizing a Diamagnetic Suspension", Review of Scientific Instruments, Vol. 39, No. 11, 1666—1671.

TAYLOR, D. K., (1967), "Notes on Observation of Building Settlements", Proceedings, Fifth Australia — New Zealand Conference on Soil Mechanics and Foundation Engineering, 246—252.

TELEMAC Ltd., (1972), "Vibrating Wire Measuring Instruments".

TERZAGHI, K., (1938), "Settlement of Structures in Europe and Methods of Measurement", Transactions, American Society of Civil Engineers, Vol. 103, 1432

TERZAGHI, K., and PECK, R. B., (1967), "Soil Mechanics in Engineering Practice", John Wiley and Sons, New York, Second Edition.

THOMPSON, P. J., and MAITICH, M. A. J., (1961), "The Performance of Some Steel Sheet Pile Bulkheads", Proceedings, 15th Canadian Soil Mechanics Conference, 80—114.

TOMLINSON, R. W., (1970), "New Distance Measuring Instruments", Proceedings, American Society of Civil Engineers, Vol. 96, SU2, 149—156.

TOMS, A. H., and BARTLETT, D. L., (1962), "Application of Soil Mechanics in the Design of Stabilizing Works for Embankments, Cuttings and Track Formations", Proceedings, Institution of Civil Engineers, London, Vol. 21, 705—732.

TSCHEBOTARIOFF, G. P., and WARD, E. R., (1957), "Measurements with Wiegmann Inclinometer on Five Sheet Pile Bulkheads", Proceedings, Fourth International Conference on Soil Mechanics and Foundation Engineering, London, Vol. 2, 248

VASILENKO, R. M., (1968), "Stereophotogrammetric Measurements of Deformation in Rockfill Dams", Hydrotechnical Construction, No. 2, February, 131—133.

VENES, E. C., (1967), Discussion on Fitzherbert and Barnett (1967), Proceedings, Institution of Civil Engineers, London, Vol. 37, 851—853.

WARD, W. H., BURLAND, J. B., and GALLOIS, R. W., (1968), "Geotechnical Assessment of Site at Mundford, Norfolk, for a Large Proton Accelerator", Geotechnique, Vol. 18, No. 4, 399—431.

WARD, W. H., and THOMAS, H. S. H., (1965), "The Development of Earth Loading and Deformation in Tunnel Linings in London Clay", Proceedings, Sixth International Conference on Soil Mechanics and Foundation Engineering, Montreal, Vol, 2, 432 — 436.

WILSON, S. D., (1962), "The Use of Slope Measuring Devices to Determine Movements in Earth Masses", Symposium on Field Testing of Soils, STP. 322, American Society for Testing and Materials, 187—198.

WILSON, S. D., (1970), "Observational data on Ground Movements related to Slope Instability", Proceedings, American Society of Civil Engineers, Vol. 96, SM5, 1521—1544.

WILSON, S. D., and HANCOCK, C. W., (1965), "Instrumentation for Movements Within Rockfill Dams", Instruments and Apparatus for Soil and Rock Mechanics, STP. 392, American Society for Testing and Materials, 115—130.

	Data from Instrumented
6	Foundations
	and
	Foundation Structures

6.1. Introduction

In chapters 2 to 5 the need to obtain quantitative ground data and the use of general measurement principles and techniques were discussed. The basic philosophy of measurement and field evaluation programmes in foundation engineering is to obtain quantitative information concerning the interrelationships between the foundation structure and the ground or of the ground mass due to load change. Because of the great complexity of an ever-increasing number of large and expensive civil engineering structures such as dams, excavations and the foundations of heavy buildings it is not always possible to predict ground stress change and deformation prior to construction with a high degree of confidence. For this reason it has become part of the design and construction process in recent years to carry out pilot studies or test programmes in which the basic design concepts or parameters are evaluated under field conditions (e. g. pile tests, plate loading tests, embankment trials). In some circumstances such work, while adding to the general knowledge of foundation performance at a particular site, does not enable the behaviour of the foundation to be determined and an instrumentation programme is drawn up for part or all of the foundation. In the literature there are numerous reports on the successful application of instrumentation programmes for obtaining general data to be used on other sites in the local area, or of data which can be used in the design of additional parts of a structure on a site (e. g. tunnels, large foundations, slopes).

The primary purpose of this Chapter is to review work which has been carried out for a number of specific cases and to show how the instruments were deployed and to give typical results. It will be appreciated that cost and site restraints have had a severe limiting influence on most if not all of these sites, yet very useful data were obtained which have added to general knowledge and, in some cases, have led to the revision of existing theories and design methods. For convenience of presentation seven interrelated topics are considered.

6.2. Foundations

Foundations are either shallow or deep (Chapter 1). In this section a number of categories are considered. Generally the civil engineer is interested in load on the foundation and its movement (usually settlement) under this load. In some cases movements induced in the ground mass by the loading of a foundation are also required as well as movements and pressure changes in the ground in the vicinity of the foundation.

6.2.1. Shallow Foundations

With shallow foundations the most common instrumentation programme is that of settlement measurement of individual footing bases. A typical layout of settlement points for a multi-storey building in Edmonton is given in Figure 145 (De Jong and Morgenstern [1971]). Special settlement plugs were installed in the reinforced concrete columns of the lowest floor of the 26-storey block. The foundations comprise spread footings located at depths between 7.9 m and 6.7 m. Three benchmarks were located in the vicinity of the building. Surveying was carried out by precise level using a millimetre graduated rod Figure 146 shows the calculated footing contact pressure with measured settlement while Figure 147 gives a time-settlement relationship for two typical footings. De Jong and Harris (1971) discuss the uses of these data in the derivation of moduli of deformation for the glacial tills of this region while De Jong and Morgenstern (1971) present a complete frame analysis of the structure which allows for the settlement of the foundations as they occur. The solution was performed by use of Structural Design Language II (STRUDL). (Roesset and Efimba [1968] and the idealization necessary for this analysis is described. These authors conclude that . . . "the distortion of a real structural frame due to small differential settlements can generate reactions of appreciable magnitude". This conclusion demonstrates the necessity for the instrumentation of all footings of a building for settlement measurement if a reliable stress analysis of the structure is to be performed.

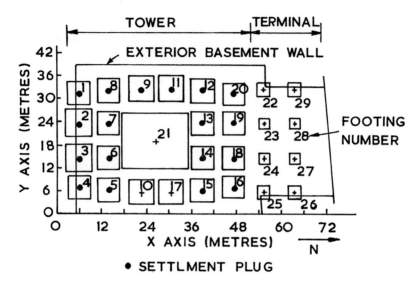

Fig. 145: Layout of settlement points for a multi-storey building
(De Jong and Morgenstern [1971]).

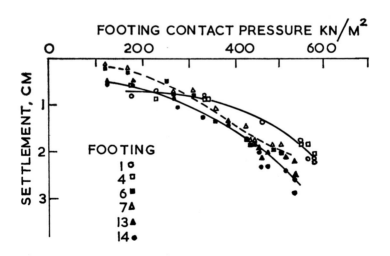

Fig. 146: Calculated footing contact pressure with measured settlement
(De Jong and Morgenstern [1971]).

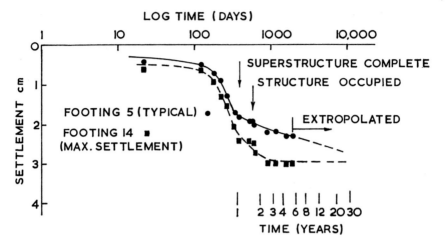

Fig. 147: Time-settlement relationship for a typical footing
(De Jong and Morgenstern [1971]).

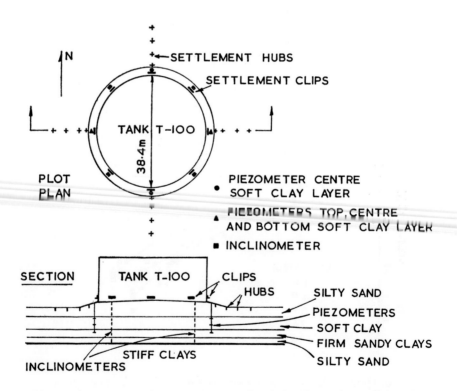

Fig. 148: Arrangement of instruments around tank foundation (Darragh [1964]).

Taylor (1967) describes some methods, difficulties and results of observing building settlements in New Zealand and he compares the measurements with estimated values. Generally it is an expensive and difficult exercise to instrument all of the footings of a large building. The approach has been to instrument a few only, Taylor (1967) for example. In most cases, where settlement magnitude is of interest, this is adequate.

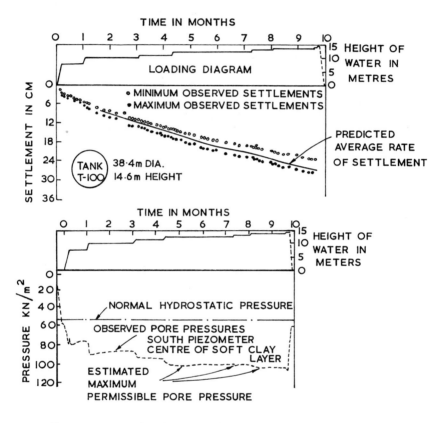

Fig. 149: Measured settlements and pore water pressure in clay layer
(Darragh [1964]).

Oil tanks are a special form of shallow foundation ideally suited to tolerate large settlement and differential settlement. Most tanks are test-loaded and in several cases a limited instrumentation programme of the foundations may be carried out. Darragh (1964) describes the use of water test programmes in which surveys of the vertical settlements of the tank shell and bottom, and of vertical and lateral movements of settlement points on the ground surface outside the tanks as well as of pore water pressure and lateral movements in the soil beneath the edges of the tank, were carried out. A typical arrangement of instruments for a tank test is shown in Figure 148. The piezometers were of a

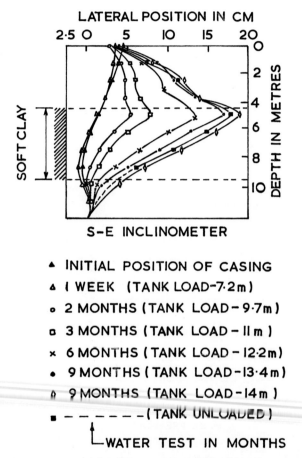

Fig. 150: Lateral displacement of soil at edge of tank as a function of depth, time and load (Darragh [1964]).

special type (Roberts and Darragh [1962]). Figure 149 shows the measured settlements of the tank and the pore water pressures observed in a soft layer of clay, while Figure 150 gives the observed lateral displacements of the soil away from the edge of the tank as a function of depth, time and tank load. The testing of one tank and the observing of its performance permitted the confident water testing of the remaining tanks at this site in Mississippi. Other examples of tank load testing are given by Gibson and Marsland (1960), Penman and Watson (1965, 1967)) and Meigh and Corbett (1969). Penman and Watson (1967) give details of the remote settlement gauges used for settlement measurement beneath the tank floor.

An example of dwelling house settlement measurements is given by Wallace and Otto (1964) for the Selfridge Air Force Base, Michigan, U.S.A. while Horne and Lambe (1964) describe the settlement measurement programme on the M.I.T. campus.

Much more sophisticated instrumentation may be required for machine foundation studies owing to the small movements which occur. For reinforced turbo-blocks Fitzherbert and Barnett (1967) used a micro-alignment telescope and a Watts micrometer water level to determine the elevations of the turbine shaft bearings and levels on the machine

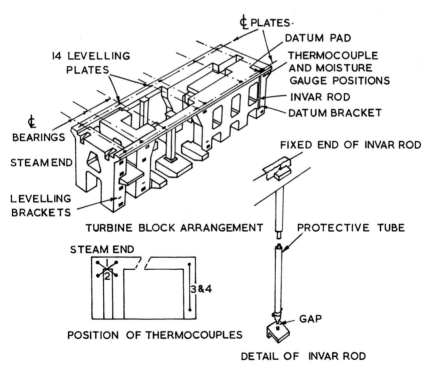

Fig. 151: Layout of instruments in a turbo-foundation
(Fitzherbert and Barnett [1967]).

block. A geodetic level was used to transfer the level to a fixed bench-mark. Special invar rods were used to measure the distortion of the foundation block. Thermocouples embedded in the concrete block gave a measure of concrete temperature. Humidity cells were also embedded at the same locations as the thermocouples. Figure 151 shows the arrangement of the levelling plates and brackets, the thermocouples and invar rods. A levelling accuracy of $\pm$ 0.125 mm was achieved. It should be noted that the instruments were installed after construction of the turbo-block. Fitzherbert and Barnett also describe the instruments which are installed in the turbine blocks of new stations during the construction stages. Details of the data logging, interpretation and frequency of reading are also given. For vibration instrumentation of such foundations the reader is referred to Pretlove (1965) and Grant (1966) for further specialist information.

Perhaps one of the most sophisticated foundation instrumentation pro-grammes was that used around a large scale field bearing test at the proposed Proton Accelerator test site at Mundford, Norfolk. Details are given by Ward et al. (1968) and Burland and Lord (1969). The test tank of 18.3 m diameter by 18.5 m high was used to load a large volume of the underlying chalk. The vertical deflections under and adjacent to the tank at various depths were measured by transducers registering on suspended invar wires which were anchored to the walls of 0.9 m diameter shafts terminated a short distance above the ground water table. Movements at greater depth were measured relative to the bottom of the shafts by transducers mounted on top of vertical steel tubes grouted in the chalk bedrock and protected by a guide sleeve. The vertical deflection of the ground beneath the base of the tank relative to the first measuring level was measured by a special transducer installed before tank construction. Figure 152 shows a section through the lines of the shafts used for vertical movement measurement. A number of precise water level gauges (see Figure 123) were installed at the top of each shaft and at a number of other locations.

All transducers, 62 in all, were connected to a data logger (Peekel) via fourcore screened cables. The transducers were calibrated in-situ to ensure reliability under site conditions. An accuracy of 0.005 mm for the shaft deflection gauges and 0.1 mm for the water level gauges is stated. Each set of reading of the installation was derived from ten com-plete scans of all channels and the mean reading for each channel com-puted.

The vertical deflections at various depths in shafts S1 to S4 after the first filling of the tank are shown in Figure 153 while Figure 154 gives the relationship between bearing pressure and the vertical deflection at the various measuring levels in shafts S1 and S4. Ward et al. (1968) discuss

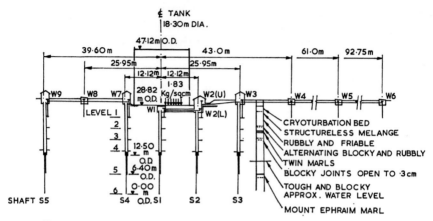

Fig. 152: Layout of instruments for a large scale tank load test on chalk
(Ward et al. [1968]).

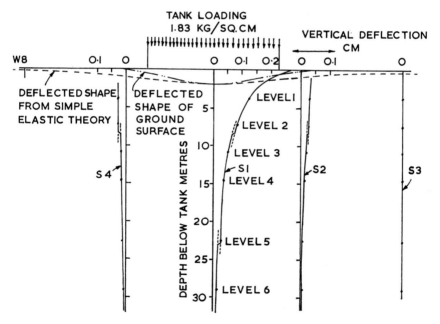

Fig. 153: Vertical ground displacements during first filling of the tank
(Ward et al. [1968]).

the significance of these results and by interpretation using classical methods of analysis, the modulus of deformation of the ground was related to the grade of the chalk. The grade was determined by visual inspection. Creep of the chalk was observed by keeping the load on the tank for a long time. Based on these very extensive and extremely accurate measurements, a detailed appreciation of the ground properties at this site was obtained which showed that it was feasible to construct the proposed accelerator facility.

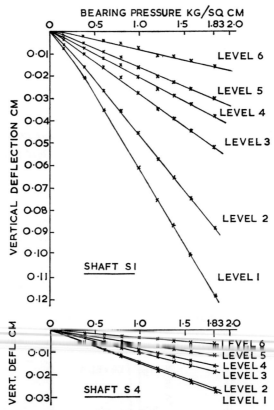

Fig. 154: Bearing pressure and vertical displacement at various depths
(Ward et al. [1968]).

It is unlikely that this degree of sophistication will be required on more traditional civil engineering foundations. However, the principles of instrument layout and use may be applied to measure deformations of the ground in the vicinity of a raft, or other large foundations.

6.2.2. Deep Foundations

With deep foundations such as piles and caissons, the civil engineer is interested in load, settlement and load distribution along the length of the pile or caisson. In special cases the performance of the pile and the piling equipment may also require evaluation during pile driving operations. First, the behaviour of piles under static loads is considered.

The distribution of load along piles may be obtained by the use of deformation gauges (tell tales) and they normally consist of a steel

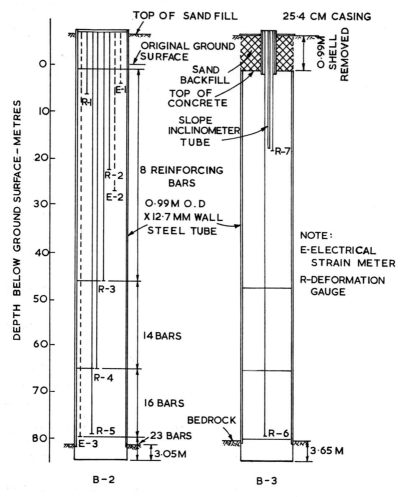

Fig. 155: Layout of deformation gauges in pile (Bozozuk and Labrecque [1968]).

sounding rod protected inside a steel tube embedded in a concrete pile or welded to the outer face of a steel H-pile. Details are given by Hanna (1966). Bozozuk and Labreque (1968) describe the instrumentation programme used to measure the downdrag on 82 m long composite piles driven through clays to bedrock. They used five deformation mechanical gauges and three electrical strain meters. Details of the arrangement of these gauges are given in Figure 155. In addition ten settlement gauges were installed in the ground at various depths in the vicinity of the pile as well as a number of Geonor piezometer tips. Figure 156 shows the recorded axial deformations of the pile with time due to the drag-down forces produced by the surface fill. Simple methods of data interpretation enable the axial load in the pile at various depths to be estimated. Such data are of great value in the interpretation of pile load tests (Hanna [1966]). It is also possible to embed a multiple position rod or wire extensometer down the length of the pile to measure axial shortenings, but the additional costs relative to the tell tale rod system favour the use of the rods for routine work at least.

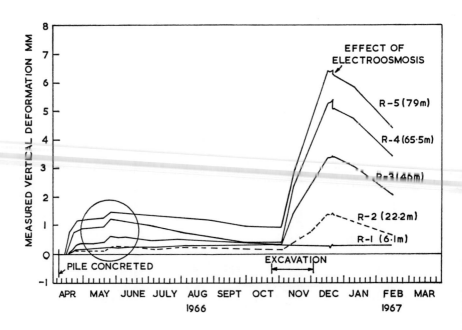

Fig. 156: Recorded axial deformation of pile with time due to drag down loading (Bozozuk and Labrecque [1968]).

Both Fellenuis (1972) and Hanna (1968) describe the use of the inclinometer for measurement of the driven shape of piles. Figure 157 shows
the measured shapes of three H-section piles driven through a firm to
stiff clay to shale bedrock. The inclinometer was a Wilson Series 200
Slope indicator and details of the method of inclinometer use are given
by Hanna (1968). Inclinometer measurements on piles are seldom required unless the pile lengths are very great ($>$ 30 m) and there is some
doubt about the tolerances to which such piles can be driven. Details of
extreme pile misalignment are given by the Swedish Pile Commission
(1964).

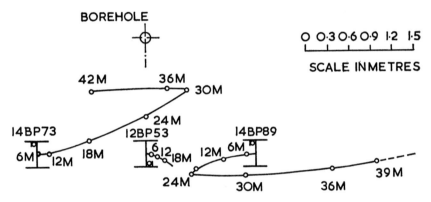

Fig. 157: Measured shapes of three H-section driven piles (Hanna [1968]).

The instrumentation of large clusters of piles is a more difficult task than
the instrumentation of a single pile. Adams and Hanna (1970) describe
their instrumentation techniques for the recording of ground displacements due to the driving of a large cluster of displacement piles. The
pile clusters were of 750 H-section piles and, as the piles were progressively driven from the centre of the group outwards, ground surface
movements in three directions at five locations, Figure 158, were measured as well as pore water pressures outside of and in the centre of the
pile cluster (see Figure 72). Ideally, use of one or more inclinometer
installations would have given the distribution of ground movements
with depth.

Measurement of load distribution within a cluster of piles may be
measured by inserting a load cell in the top of each pile. The photoelastic load cell of the design by Hooper (1972) is suitable for this work,

provided that a viewing system can be incorporated in the pile cap or basement of the structure. Contact pressure between the ground surface and the pile cap can be recorded by earth pressure cells placed in contact with the soil prior to the pouring of the pile cap. The Glötzl cell is attractive due to its mode of operation (mechanical), cost and simplicity of the operation. Thermocouples should be buried beside the cells to enable temperature corrections to be applied. Settlement and distribution of settlement with depth below the pile cap may be measured by one or more sets of multiple position borehole extensometers (rod or wire type) or by use of the B.R.S. magnet-type extensometer. Cost considerations and accessibility will control the choice of instruments used.

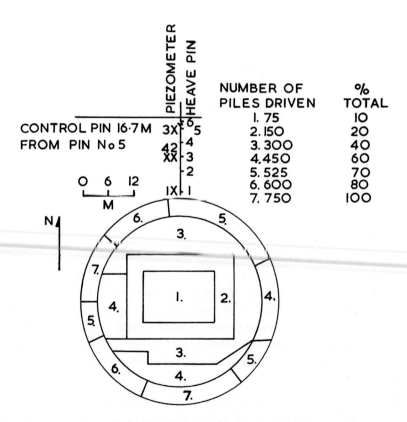

	NUMBER OF PILES DRIVEN	% TOTAL
	1. 75	10
	2. 150	20
	3. 300	40
	4. 450	60
	5. 525	70
	6. 600	80
	7. 750	100

Fig. 158: Layout of movement pins to record ground surface movements due to pile driving (Adams and Hanna [1970]).

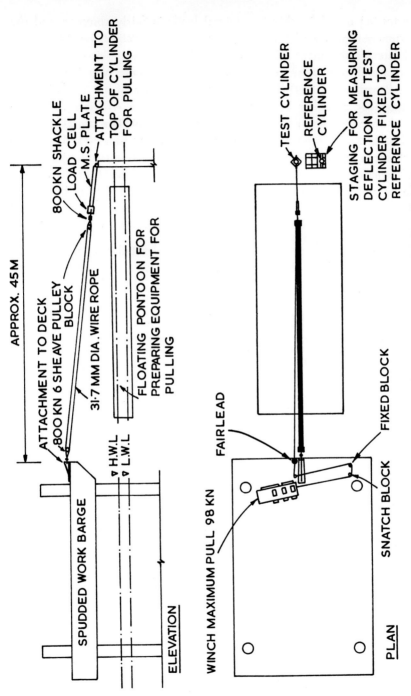

Fig. 159: Arrangement for testing of a mooring dolphin cylinder (Broadhead [1969]).

The testing of piles subject to lateral loads is fairly common and the instrumentation may be used to record pile deflection, bending stress and lateral movement of the pile top. In marine environments very large lateral loads arise and the load testing of these piles is a difficult task. Broadhead (1969) describes the load testing of a 1.2 m diameter cylinder for a tanker berth at Das Island in the Arabian Gulf. The layout of the test equipment is shown in Figure 159. The lateral load was applied 23.2 m above sea bed level and was of magnitude 80 t. A spudded work barge in the lifted position provided the reaction for pulling, while a reference cylinder was used to measure the deflection of the test cylinder. The lateral deflections of the cylinder at 0.4 m and 2.76 m below the line of pull are plotted in Figure 160 against applied load. Theoretical predictions based on two assumptions are superimposed on this plot.

Where a lower degree of accuracy can be tolerated, two piles can be pulled together by a chain operated pulling device; the load measured

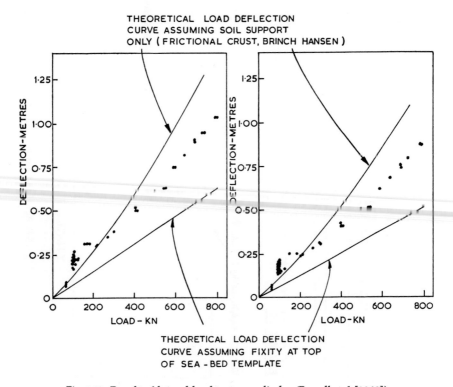

Fig. 160: Result of lateral load test on cylinder (Broadhead [1969]).

by a dynamometer; and the closure of the pile heads measured by steel tape (Tomlinson [1969]).

Whitaker (1970) and Chellis (1961) review most the standard methods of pile test instrumentation while Whitaker and Cooke (1966) describe the use of instruments in the testing of underreamed piles in clay.

Excellent examples of settlement measurements on large groups of piles are given by Parker and Bayliss (1970), Greenfield (1970) and Bartholomew and Simons (1970).

Ground anchors are a form of tension pile, but to date very little instrumentation work has been carried out apart from load cell installations to give top loads. It is possible to instrument the anchor shaft to give a measure of load distribution (Adams and Glyn [1972]), to

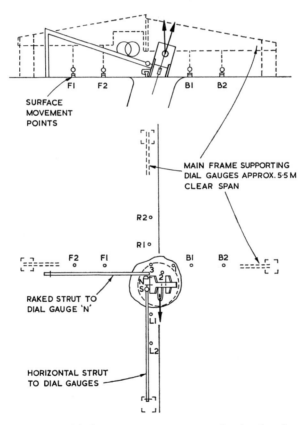

Fig. 161: Layout of dial gauges for measuring anchor head and ground surface movements (Ashbee [1972]).

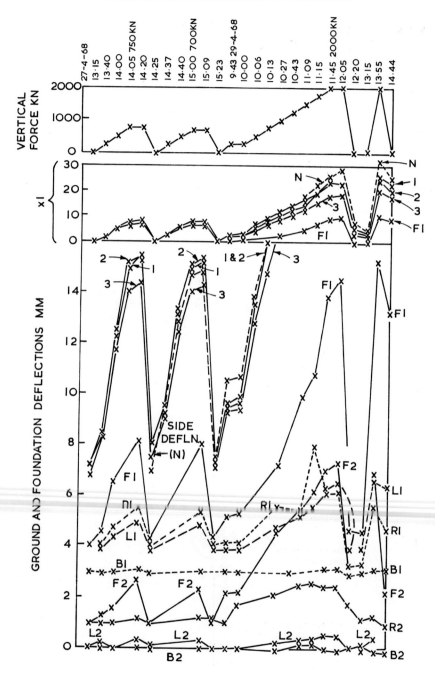

Fig. 162: Ground and anchor head displacements during vertical uplift test
(Ashbee [1972]).

measure displacement distribution along the anchor shaft (Shannon and Strazer [1968]) by extensometer wires and to measure the ground movement distribution above an anchor by the installation of a multiple position borehole extensometer above and very near to the anchor. For such an installation to be of quantitative value, the relative positions of the anchor borehole and the extensometer borehole must be surveyed by an inclinometer. The photographic technique, Section 5.9.1., has merit.

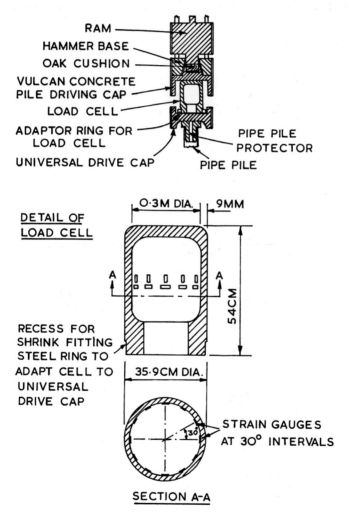

Fig. 163: Pile instrumentation layout including detail of load cell used in Michigan study of pile driving hammers (Housel [1965]).

Very often the loading of anchors is not parallel to the axis of the anchor shaft but inclined. Ashbee (1972) describes the arrangement of instruments used to record ground and anchor top movements for an inclined anchor tested under combined horizontal and vertical loading. The layout of the dial gauges is shown in Figure 161 and typical test data for a 7.32 m long anchor of 0.9 m nominal diameter inclined at 30° to the vertical and pulled in a vertical direction are given in Figure 162. The Michigan study of pile driving hammers is one of a very few studies on pile driving where extensive site instrumentation was employed. It

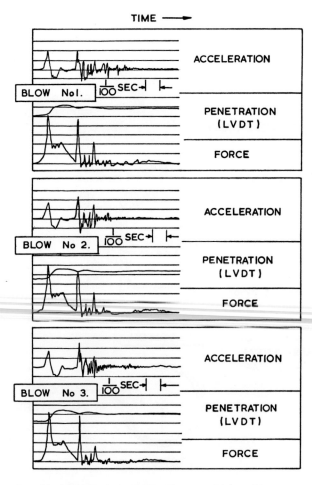

Fig. 164: Record of the three consecutive hammer blows showing records of acceleration, penetration and force (Housel [1965]).

comprised a load cell for measuring force output from the hammer; an accelerometer for measuring acceleration of the pile; and an assembly to record pile head displacements. The pile instrumentation layout is shown in Figure 163. The load cell comprised 24 SR-4 type strain gauges located around the inside of the cell. Details of this cell are given by Michigan State Highway Commission (1965). Details of typical data from three consecutive hammer blows are given in Figure 164. From data of this nature a very comprehensive evaluation of pile hammer performance was achieved. The principles of instrumentation used on this study may be applied to other dynamic measurement work, e. g. drop forge hammer foundation studies. Davisson and McDonald (1968) discuss the instrumentation of a diesel pile driving hammer.

6.3. Excavations

The formation of an excavation, either temporary or permanent, causes a load change in the ground resulting in a three dimensional displacement of the ground. To control such movements to acceptable levels, various types of earth retaining structure may be used, see Chapter 1. There are numerous examples of field evaluation studies of excavation performance and the following contains a brief account of a few of these examples.

The Oslo subway system is perhaps the best known example of an extensive field instrumentation programme being used for design and construction control purposes. Details of this structure are contained in a number of technical reports (NGI Reports 1 to 9 [1962]) and a review is given by Bjerrum et al. (1965), while Palmer and Kenney (1972) discuss an analytical interpretation of some of these field data. The instrumented section at Vaterland I is taken as an example. Five levels of strutting were used, and the strut loads in all struts at three adjacent strut sections were measured by use of vibrating wire strain gauge cells (Figure 36). Earth pressure cells and piezometers were mounted on both sides of one sheet pile wall, Figure 165, and multiple piezometers were installed in the clay. Surface settlement gauges of the Borros type (Figure 109) were spaced away from both edges of the excavation and inclinometer tubes were attached to several of the sheet piles. Some of the field observations made are given in Figure 166. These include the sequence of excavation, temperature, strut loads, settlements and ground movements and earth pressure distributions against the wall. Bjerrum et al. (1965) conclude ". . . It will be many years before rational design procedures are developed to handle such questions. In the meantime excavations will be necessary and will be built. For the purpose of constructing them safety and economically, one approach that can be taken is to install observation instruments that can be used for control during construction in order to obtain data that can be used at some later time for design purposes. This approach is currently popular in the field of earth-dam construction, but it is equally applicable to other soil engineering works such as strutted excavations". The principles of instrumentation use demonstrated in Figure 165 can be applied to other types of excavation problem with a greater or lesser degree of sophistication depending on the data required.

Lambe et al. (1970) present measurements made on a test section of braced excavation on the extension of the Massachusetts Bay Transportation Authority (MBTA) subway system. This study is of particular importance, because four foundation engineers gave their solution to

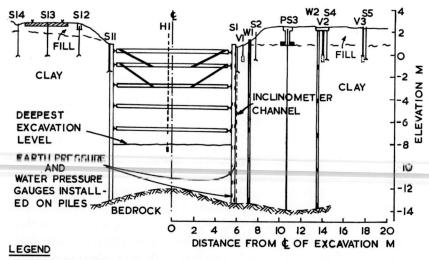

LEGEND

H – HEAVE GAUGE
PS – PRECISION SETTLEMENT GAUGE
S – SETTLEMENT GAUGE
V – SINGLE PIEZOMETER
W – MULTIPLE PIEZOMETER

Fig. 165: Arrangement of measuring instruments at Vaterland I test section on Oslo subway (Bjerrum et al. [1965]).

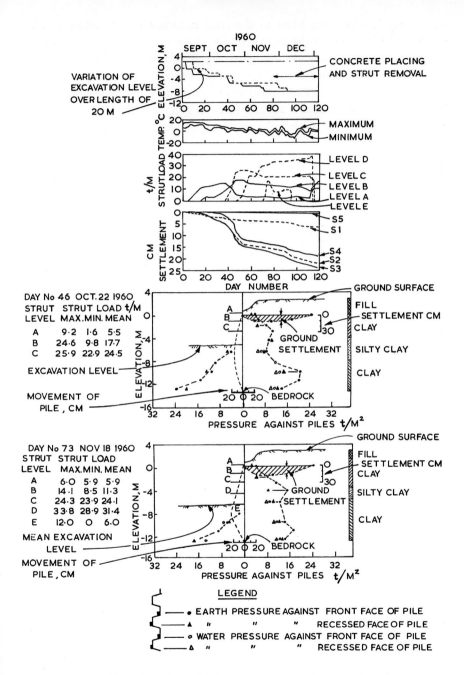

Fig. 166: Typical results of field measurements at Vaterland I test section
(Bjerrum et al. [1965]).

the excavation problem prior to the field evaluation (see Golder et al. [1970]). A plan view of the test section is given in Figure 167 and details of the measurements made are given by Lambe et al. They conclude that the results obtained more than justified the very great effort required to obtain them. Figure 168 draws attention to the differences between the measured strut loads at the test section and the initial design assumption, as well as the predictions made by the four authorities.

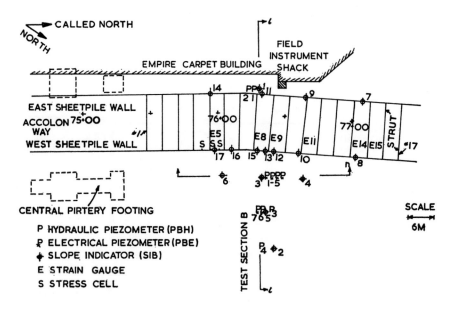

Fig. 167: Layout of test section of MBTA subway system (Lambe et al. [1970]).

A state-of-the-art report is given by Lambe (1970) and he cites several examples of strutted excavations where instrumentation of part of the site played a major role in the successful completion of the project, as well as adding to the knowledge of the general subject.

The movements associated with the Britannic House excavation (Cole and Burland [1972]) are of interest owing to the very limited instrumentation provided. Figures 114 and 115 showed the arrangement of the movement measuring points on this very restricted site. Excavation

progress at the north end of the site (AA section, Figure 114) is given in
Figure 169, while the measured outward movements of the diaphragm
wall as a function of time (excavation progress) are given in Figure 170.
These movement measurements were time dependent, demonstrating
the importance of the provision of struts, props or tie-backs if the
movements are to be kept to small values. The data provided at this
site were analysed using a finite element technique, and the stiffness of

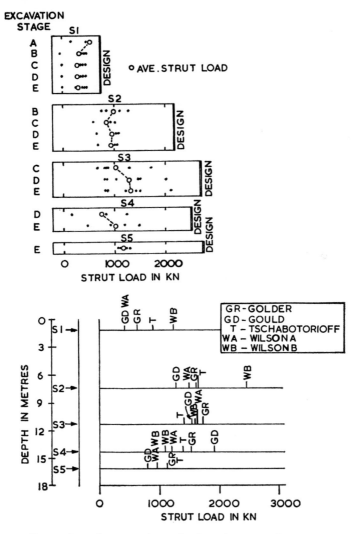

Fig. 168: Comparison of measured strut loads with various design assumptions
(Lambe et al. [1970]).

the London clay as a function of depth was deduced. Thus it was possible to make use of the field observations at this site for the design of other structures in the same soil formation. These techniques of measurement and analysis can be applied to other sites in very different ground conditions.

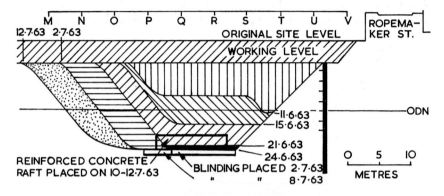

Fig. 169: Excavation progress at Britannic House excavation (Cole and Burland [1972]).

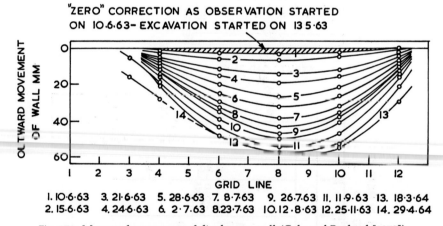

Fig. 170: Measured movement of diaphragm wall (Cole and Burland [1972]).

Peck (1969) has collected pertinent movement data recorded for a number of excavations in clays and sands and has summarized these data in dimensionless plots. While he does not refer specifically to the instrumentation programmes employed, his extensive bibliography does give reference to many examples of excavation instrumentation. An interesting study was carried out by Rodriguez and Flamand (1969) of a deep excavation associated with the Mexico City subway. The excavation, 11.3 m deep, was in a sensitive and soft clay. Steel sheet piling strutted at four levels was used. It was necessary to lower the ground water table inside the sheeting and an electro-osmotic pumping system was employed. Because base failure of the excavation was considered critical 13 deep heave points were installed at a depth of 19.5 m inside the excavation and at 13.5 m on the outside of the excavation. Four slope indicator tubes, length 28 m, were used to measure the horizontal soil deformations throughout the depth affected by a probable bottom failure. Readings were taken every 8 hours. The ground water lowering was monitored by 31 pneumatic piezometers and 4 Casagrande type piezometers. The strut loads were measured by Freyssinet pressure cells installed in a closed circuit arrangement, load readings being taken every 6 hours.

There are many other examples of excavation instrumentation and details of a very elaborate programme are given by Underwood et al. (1964) for the Oahe dam stilling basin excavation.

6.4. Tunnels

During the construction of a tunnel, the ground tends to "flow" towards the face of the tunnel causing movements in the adjacent ground. Where there are nearby buildings or adjacent underground structures, these movements can cause structural distress. This general subject has been reviewed in detail by Peck (1969). After the tunnel lining has been installed, small changes in tunnel shape occur due to a re-adjustment of the ground stress system in the vicinity of the tunnel. The subject of tunnel instrumentation therefore is an important one. Most measurements have taken place in the tunnels of London and several examples are now referred to.

During the construction of the Victoria Underground line, observations were made of the convergence of the clay towards the tunnel. The tunnel is 25 m deep and was driven with a hand shield of 4.1 m diameter. The convergence measurements were taken with sleeved rods anchored in the clay at one end and extending into nearby underground structures at the reference end. A set of convergence measurements was taken at the axis level of the tunnel at distances of 0.46 m, 1.98 m and 3.5 m from the face of the approaching tunnel, Figure 171. The reference ends of the movement pins were located in an adjacent tunnel 7.6 m away. The lateral displacement of the existing tunnel was checked by means of another rod 6 m long extending into the clay on the other side of the tunnel. Figure 171 shows the recorded movements as the shield approached and passed the movement gauges. Ward (1969) also refers to a set of axial convergence measurements along the axis of the tunnel.

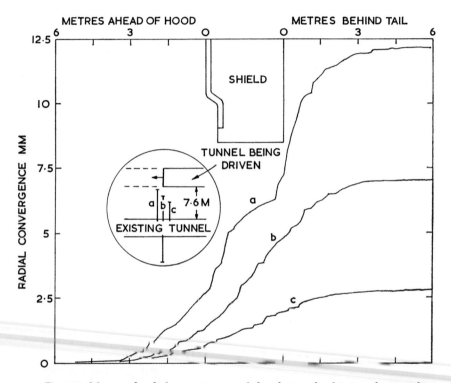

Fig. 171: Measured radial convergrence of clay during the driving of a tunnel in London clay (Ward [1969]).

The reference ends of the movement rods were located in a chamber. Reference rod A is on the central axis of the tunnel, rod B is on the periphery of the excavation and rod C, 0.3 m outside the periphery of the excavation. The build up of lateral movement towards the shield as it approached the reference rods is shown in Figure 172.

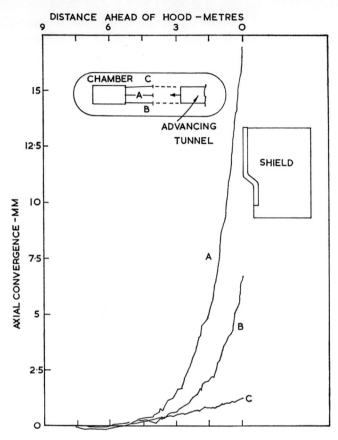

Fig. 172: Axial displacement of clay in front of tunnelling shield (Ward [1969]).

Muir Wood (1969, 1971) measured the movements of an airfield runway due to the construction of a cargo tunnel at Heathrow airport. The instrumentation programme comprised the following:

(a) surface movement points transverse to the tunnel line gave the horizontal and vertical movements,

(b) three movement rods similar to those used by Ward (1969) gave vertical movements 0.5 m below tunnel invert level, 0.9 m above the crown and 0.75 m below the top of the clay stratum,

(c) deformation of the tunnel lining was recorded by means of an invar tape,

(d) loads in the lining were measured by pairs of photoelastic load cells mounted at the crown, invert and at axis level on both sides.

The recorded ground movements as the tunnel shield approached and passed the level of the recording gauges are shown in Figure 173. The records of tunnel deformation showed that there was a small increase in tunnel diameter of about 1.5 mm in the first year. This is in disagree-

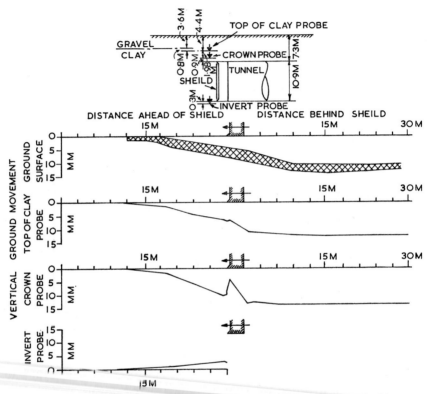

Fig. 173: Measured ground movement with passage of tunnelling shield (Muir Wood [1969]).

ment with the measurements of Ward and Thomas (1965) on the much deeper Victoria Line Tunnel, where the horizontal diameter increased and the vertical diameter decreased. Figure 174 gives the change in diameter of three tunnel linings as a function of time.

The measuring rods used by Ward and Thomas (1965) were of 50 mm diameter aluminium alloy tube. A screw micrometer was mounted at one end. A correction was made for temperature. The rod and a reference bar for checking against accidental damage to the rod were stored in a box in each tunnel adjacent to the ring under observation. A measurement accuracy of ± 0.025 mm was attained.

In addition to the measurements referred to above, it is possible to install earth and pore water pressure cells at the lining/soil interface to record total and effective stresses; to install a number of convergence

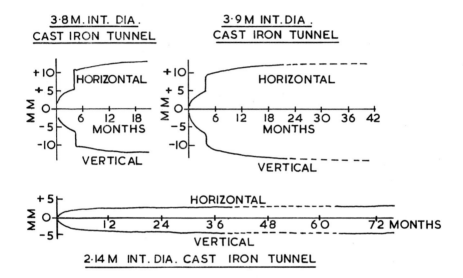

Fig. 174: Measured change in diameters of three tunnel linings in London clay
(Ward and Thomas [1965]).

bolts in the tunnel lining to give the change in shape of the tunnel; and to install rod or wire extensometers to measure the movements of points well away from the tunnel lining. During the driving of single or multiple tunnels, ground movements in the vertical direction can be recorded by one or more multiple extensometer installations while the horizontal movements can be recorded by borehole inclinometer or by the methods referred to by Ward and Muir Wood. Ward and Chaplin (1957) describe methods of measuring stresses in tunnel linings. Some details of tunnel instrumentation are given by Interfels (1970).

Proctor and Atkinson (1972) describe the use of close range photo-grammetry as a practical method of measuring the shape of tunnels. The work was carried out in the new Mersey Tunnel and this study was essentially an attempt to show that this technique could be used for routine survey work on future tunnel linings. Details of instruments required, targets and computations necessary are given.

Pipelines and culverts are a special form of tunnel in which the soil is placed around the structure, an excavation having been formed. Thus an excavation problem followed by a backfilling problem results. The civil engineer has interests in the movements associated with trench construction and backfilling; the earth and pore water pressures and their distribution which develop at the soil/structure interface and also in the backfill; and the change in shape of the pipe or culvert under the soil load. This also includes stretching of pipes and culverts due to the spreading of an embankment fill. There are a number of reports dealing with the instrumentation of such structures. Schear and Willett (1965) describe the use of strain gauges to measure stresses in a culvert wall; Carlson pressure cells to measure contact pressures; pressure cells in the backfill; and settlement gauges in the backfill. A similar type of instru-mentation programme is described by Davis and Bacher (1968). The convergence of pipelines and culverts can be determined by similar techniques to those employed in tunnels (Ward and Thomas [1965]) if access inside the pipe is practicable. Where this is not so, usually in pipes of 1 m diameter and smaller, dial gauges or displacement transducers mounted on a "spider" and bearing on reference studs on the walls can be used. With dial gauges illumination is necessary and readings may be taken by telescope from the end of the pipe. Longitudinal stretching can be measured by tape measurements to the end of the pipe or culvert from reference pins located along the length of the pipe or culvert. The position of the end of the pipe or culvert reference is defined by survey methods for each set of readings.

6.5. Slopes

Because most if not all natural soils comprise different materials or the presence of thin zones of weaker material due to geological details, the zone of ground movement associated with slope instability is usually not well defined. There are, however, exceptions, but it is now recognised that few slopes fail along the classical circular arc rupture surface. The measurement of ground movements related to slope instability has been practised for many years and with the advent of the slope indicator, this trend has accelerated. Below, several examples of slope movement measurement are mentioned.

6.5.1. Soil Creep

With natural slopes the near surface materials undergo a slow downhill movement referred to as "creep". Creep depends on slope inclination, soil type and rainfall. While there are many reports on soil creep, few give quantitative details on its distribution with depth. Wilson (1970) reports on a 10 year observation period of a 30° slope where a glacial till overlies bedrock. An inclinometer was used for movement measurement and Figure 175 shows movement profiles separated by 8 years. The creep rate is approximately 8 mm per year. One third of the movement occurred in the top 1.5 m.

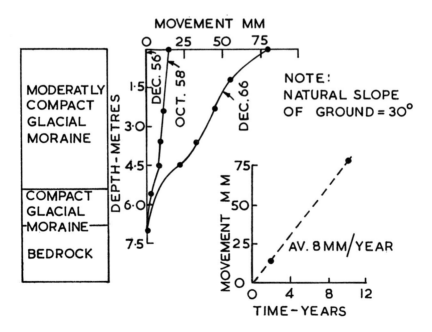

Fig. 175: Measured soil movement (creep) with depth (Wilson [1970]).

It will be appreciated that creep is not necessarily synonymous with slope instability and the case of ice flow is used as an example. Wilson (1970) reports movements of the Tuto ice ramp in Greenland. In nature there is a balance between snow accumulation and melt, but at the Thule Air Force Base this balance was modified by the construction of a gravel road which acted as an insulating layer and prevented summer thaw. This caused a ridge to grow out of the adjacent ice and the U.S. Corps of Engineers installed inclinometers to measure the ice movements

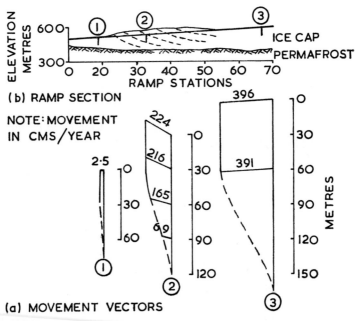

Fig. 176. Movement distribution in an ice ramp (Wilson [1970]).

associated with this growth. Figure 176 gives some of the movement measurements taken. At 1.5 km upslope from the start of the ramp the top 60 m of ice moved as a rigid block at a velocity of about 12 mm per day and this velocity decreased almost linearly with depth to zero at the underlying till interface. Near to the end of the ramp the movement vectors were in an upwards direction with the inclination being 32° to the horizontal at the ground surface. At the toe of the ramp the movements were almost zero. Wilson (1970) points out the similarity between these movements and those which occur geologically with clays subjected to the process of erosion.

6.5.2. Progressive Movements (Failure)

Bjerrum (1966) has described the mechanics of progressive failure in over-consolidated clays and clay-shales. Several examples of monitoring the movement of such slopes are given by Wilson (1970). An interesting case occurred during the construction of a motorway in Seattle, U.S.A. A heavily overconsolidated clay forms a slope which was cut into. Even shallows cuts caused serious ground movements and Figure 177 demonstrates the magnitude of these movements.

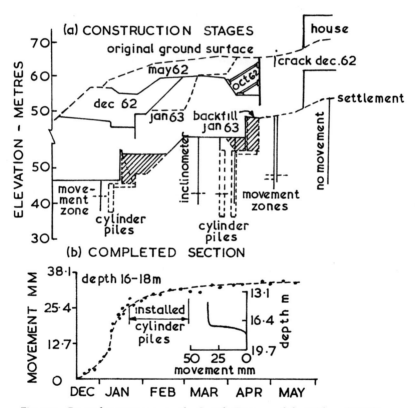

Fig. 177: Ground movements on the Seattle Freeway slide (Wilson [1970]).

Inclinometer measurements gave the ground displacements. Figure 177 shows the general problems and also gives details of the method of stabilization employed.

Ground movements are sometimes caused by placing fill on existing slopes. In the case of old landslides, ground movements may be reactivated by relatively small fills. The Portuguese Bend Landslide in California is taken as an example. During the early 1950's, a road was constructed over an old slide area requiring the placement of several hundred thousand cubic meters of fill. Movement started almost immediately, and the zone of ground movement grew until a new landslide developed as shown in Figure 178. It will be noted that a very small volume of fill in relation to the total volume of material involved in the landslide was necessary to cause the movements. There was a correlation between rainfall intensity and movement which is also shown in Figure 178.

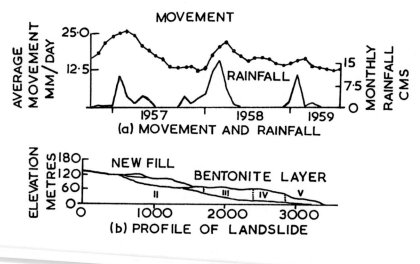

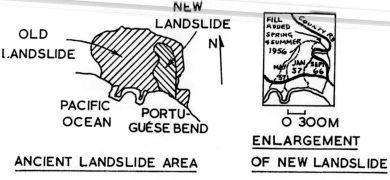

Fig. 178: Movement at Portuguese Bend landslide, California (Wilson [1970]).

Gray (1969) discusses the instrumentation of natural forested slopes while there are many examples of slope movements in the literature, a review of which is given by Skempton and Hutchinson (1969).

Details of the measurement of movements on a regional scale were presented at a meeting of The Royal Society of London on The Measurement and Interpretation of Changes of Strain in the Earth (1972). While many of the techniques described do not have direct application in civil engineering, it has been demonstrated that there are instruments available which can record very small movements in the earth's crust. Perhaps some of these instruments will be adapted for use by Civil Engineers in the future.

6.6. Earth and Rock Fill Dams

The need to instrument earth and rock fill dams has been recognised for several decades and such programmes of field study are now common. The main purposes of dam instrumentation are (a) to assure the performance of the structure during reservoir filling, (b) to understand the distribution of stresses, strains and movements within the dam and its foundations and (c) to monitor performance during dam use. For field measurements to be of use, they must be started during the initial stages of construction and be continued at intervals for an indefinite period of time. Following an earthquake or a severe flood the stability of the dam can be evaluated by taking a new set of readings.

There are many reports in the technical journals and conference proceedings and the following cases are given to illustrate the practice of dam instrumentation.

The Muddy pumped storage dam (Wilson and Marano [1968]) is built on a very unfavourable foundation and consequently a conservative design was used. In addition extensive instrumentation was incorporated in the design and construction to observe performance during construction; to control the rate of first filling of the reservoir; and to monitor the long-term performance of the dam, which is subjected to alternating cycles of fast filling and rapid drawdown. The instruments provided measures of horizontal and vertical movement and pore water pressures at three sections. Surface monuments enabled the post-construction settlements and movements of the downstream face to be determined. Seepage through the dam was recorded by various measuring weirs. A plan and elevation view of the instrument locations is given in Figure 179. Because of the large movements anticipated, the riser pipes from the piezometers were encased in a 50 mm diameter spiral corrugated plastic hose. The inclinometer was of the Wilson Slope Indicator type.

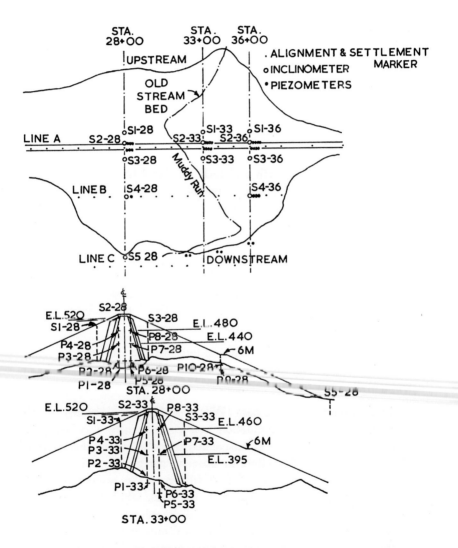

Fig. 179: Plan and elevation view of instrument layout in Muddy Run dam
(Wilson and Marano [1969]).

Figure 180 shows the vertical movements during construction and first filling of the reservoir. Generally the magnitude of the movement depended on the compressibility of the material, the thickness of the underlying soil layers and the height of the embankment above. It will be noted that there are considerable differential movements between the

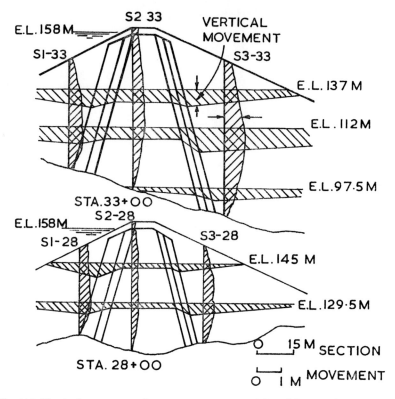

Fig. 180: Vertical movements during construction and first filling of the reservoir (Wilson and Marano [1969]).

core and the rockfill shoulders. Figure 181 gives the internal horizontal movements at each of the three instrumented sections. It will be noted that the embankment spread during construction. The cross valley movements measured parallel to the axis of the dam are given in Figure 182. Wilson and Marano (1968) conclude that the instruments provided the data which they were installed to measure. However on future sites they recommended that both stresses and strains along the contact between the compressible rockfill shells and the core should be measured. Infernillo Dam is an extensively instrumented dam of 120 m in height

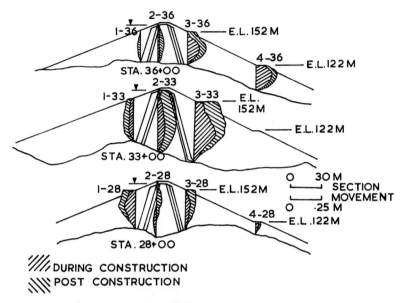

Fig. 181: Measured internal horizontal movements at three sections
(Wilson and Marano [1969]).

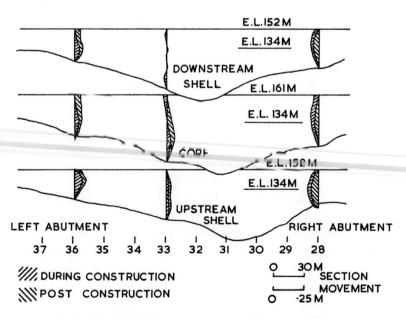

Fig. 182: Cross valley movements parallel to axis of dam
(Wilson and Marano [1969]).

(Marsal and Ramirez [1967]). A plan location of the instruments in this dam is given in Figure 183. Typical lateral movement data recorded by an inclinometer installation are given in Figure 184. Vertical movements, determined by the use of a settlement probe down the inclinometer casing, are also given in this figure.

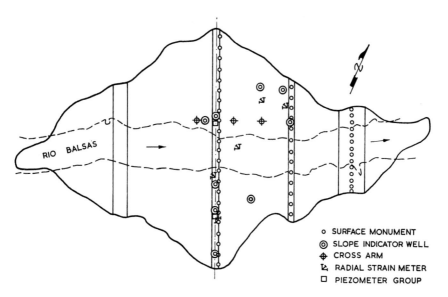

Fig. 183: Plan of Instrumentation at Infernillo Dam (Wilson and Hancock [1964]).

A more recent dam in which many special instruments were installed is the Scammonden dam. This is a 80 m high earth — rockfill dam, which carries a motorway at its crest. Figure 185 gives a detail of the main instrumentation section. Settlements of the clay core were greater than those of the adjoining rockfill. The resulting shearing strains occurred in the filter and rockfill materials rather than in the clay core material. The vertical support given to the core by the rockfill reduced the vertical stress measured at the base of the core to 84 per cent of the overburden pressure. Details are given by Penman and Mitchell (1970).

Good examples of pore water pressure measurements in earth dams and their foundations are given by Bishop, Kennard and Vaughan (1964), Bishop and Vaughan (1962), Al-Dhahir et al. (1969), Wilkinson et al. (1969), Ruffle (1970), Rowe (1970) and many others.

When analysing embankments for earthquake loading conditions, it is essential that records of acceleration be obtained at various locations on the embankment and also nearby. Recorders must be three-component, self-contained units which actuate themselves when a certain level of acceleration occurs. Wilson (1967) mentions that five accelerometers are installed at Infernillo dam: three on the dam, one on the right bank and one in the underground power-house on the left bank (Marsal and Ramirez [1967]). Wilson (1967) also refers to a new type of recorder installed at Oroville dam. It has a frequency of response from 0.1 to 20 cps and can be set to trigger and record over an energy level range 0.001 g to 1.0 g. The instrument is placed in the fill.

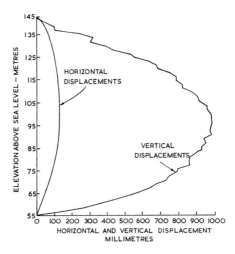

Fig. 184: Lateral and Vertical movements taken in an inclinometer casing
(Wilson and Hancock [1964]).

Generally the instrumentation of earth and rockfill dams is an expensive operation requiring considerable resources. Today it is possible to measure the overall performance of such structures as well as details such as strains at boundaries and arching effects. Reference to the examples quoted and to many other papers on earth dam design and performance will show how the subject has developed over the years and the range of quantities which can be recorded. Penman et al. (1971) and Clough and Wooward (1967) have shown how use can be made of such data to calibrate a finite element analysis technique. Much work of this nature is to be expected in the future, not only for earth dams, but for all foundation structures.

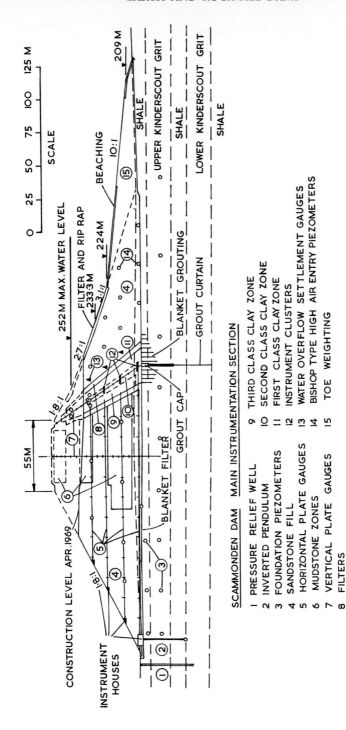

SCAMMONDEN DAM MAIN INSTRUMENTATION SECTION

1 PRESSURE RELIEF WELL
2 INVERTED PENDULUM
3 FOUNDATION PIEZOMETERS
4 SANDSTONE FILL
5 HORIZONTAL PLATE GAUGES
6 MUDSTONE ZONES
7 VERTICAL PLATE GAUGES
8 FILTERS

9   THIRD CLASS CLAY ZONE
10 SECOND CLASS CLAY ZONE
11 FIRST CLASS CLAY ZONE
12 INSTRUMENT CLUSTERS
13 WATER OVERFLOW SETTLEMENT GAUGES
14 BISHOP TYPE HIGH AIR ENTRY PIEZOMETERS
15 TOE WEIGHTING

Fig. 185: Details of Scammonden Dam instrumentation layout.
(Penman and Mitchell [1970]).

6.7. Rigid Permanent Structures

There are several general categories of rigid retaining foundation structure and this section refers to those of the retaining wall type. Because of the permanent nature of these structures and the complexity of analysis involved, it is only during the last decade or so that a serious attempt has been made to understand the real behaviour of such structures. This understanding is still far from complete.

6.7.1. Cantilever Retaining Walls

These structures have a fairly narrow base and support fill or backfill on one side. While such structures are rigid in flexure, they can translate by fairly large amounts depending on soil and ground water conditions. To control such movements anchoring techniques are common. They also

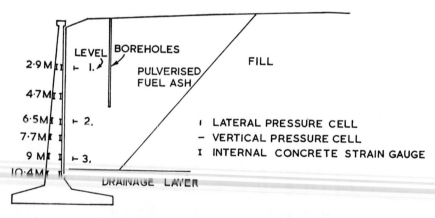

Fig. 186: Arrangement of test section of rigid retaining wall (Sims at al. [1970]).

enable much higher walls to be built. Sims et al. (1970) describe the instrumentation of a 12 m high test wall behind which backfill was placed as shown in the section of Figure 186. Lateral and vertical total earth pressures in the backfill were measured by the B.R.S. total earth pressure cells (Figure 94). Internal concrete strains in the wall near to both faces were measured by vibrating wire strain gauges of the Road

Research Laboratory type. The arrangement of the gauges is shown in Figure 186. In addition to the loading from the backfill, a series of loading tests was carried out using the Ministry of Transport HB 45 t vehicle positioned behind the wall. Figure 187 gives the measured vertical and lateral total earth pressures at level 1 (2.9 m below top of wall) as a function of time. It will be noted that both pressures are greater than the theoretical values of overburden pressure and active pressure. The causes of this are not known for certain, but the shape of the zone of backfill may have given rise to the development of arching in the fill.

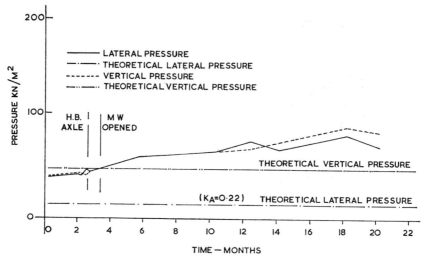

Fig. 187: Average lateral and vertical earth pressure at level 1. (Sims et al. [1970]).

The significance of the lateral earth pressure build up is shown in the earth pressure profiles, Figure 188, where the measured pressures are several times the theoretical active value. Sims et al. (1970) did not install inclinometers in the fill behind the wall. This would have been a valuable addition to the instruments already described and would also have added to the value of the Finite Element Analysis which they used.

Adams and Hanna (1970) describe the use of the Glötzl earth pressure cell for earth pressure determination on the back face of a very stiff wall supporting a granular backfill. Earth pressure changes due to nearby pile driving operations were also investigated.

In the case of bridge abutments supported on piles driven through compressible soils, it may also be necessary to monitor pore water pressures and movements (horizontal and vertical) in the compressible layer; downdrag on the piles; lateral or extension strains in the backfill behind the wall; bending and rotation of the wall; and earth pressures in the fill. The provision of instruments to measure all of these quantities, although expensive, is now possible and, until several such programmes of field evaluation are carried out, the subject of bridge retaining wall design must still remain speculative.

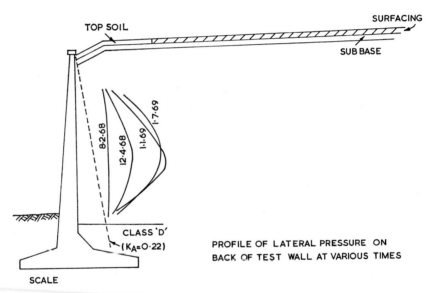

Fig. 188. Lateral earth pressure distribution against the wall (Sims et al. [1970]).

6.7.2. Foundation Walls of Structures

These walls are braced by the structures floor system. Huder (1969) discusses movements of a slurry trench wall subjected to a large water head differential. The excavation was 17 m deep in glacial soils with the water table 1.2 m below ground surface. The movements of the wall at four locations were obtained by inclinometer tubes and data typical of this site are given in Figure 189. Examples of the instrumentation of a rigid tied wall are given by Kapp (1969) for the World Trade Centre excavation in New York, while Kuesel (1969) discusses some of the field studies performed during construction of the BART subway system in San Francisco.

The Pleasant Valley pumping plant in California presented some unusual foundation problems due to the very large and deep excavation works

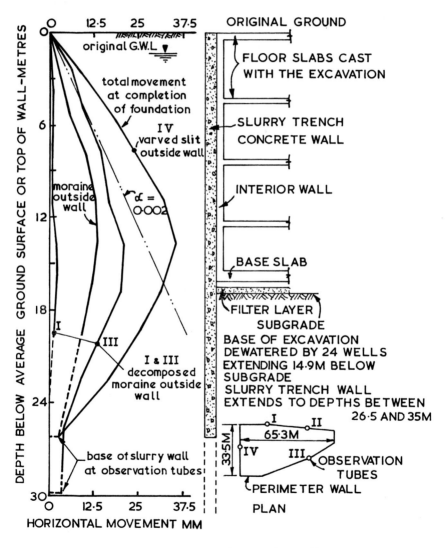

Fig. 189: Movements of a foundation wall (Gould [1970]).

involved (28 m). Stress meters and piezometers were used to record pressures beneath and along the back of a rigid wall, and also as a check on the efficiency of a pressure relief drain. The test structure was 10 m high and a layout of the piezometers and stress meters is given in Figure 190. Details of instrument installation are given in Figures 16 to 18 of the instrumentation report, Roth (1970). The observed total and pore water pressure distributions are shown for two sections, one near to the relief well and the other through backfill. The fill was a silty clay placed at 98 per cent proctor density.

Bara and Hill (1967) describe the instrumentation provided for the Dos Amigos Pumping plant.

6.7.3. Dock and Lock Structures

These structures differ from those of sections 6.7.1. and 6.7.2. in that a very rigid floor slab is connected to the retaining wall. Consequently

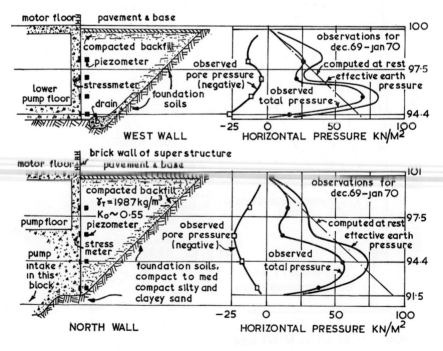

Fig. 190: Layout of stressmeters and piezometers for retaining wall at Pleasant Valley Pumping Plant (Roth [1970]).

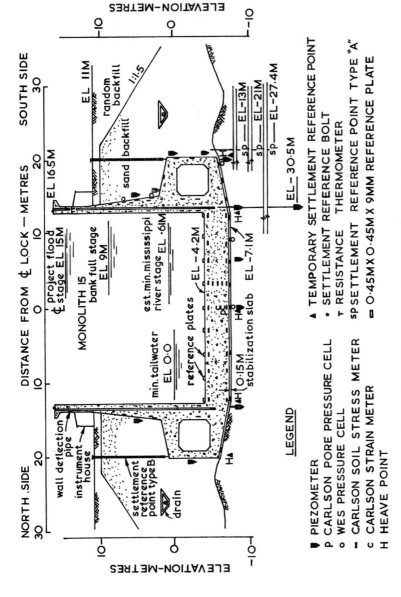

Fig. 191: Section through instrumented monolith, Port Allen Lock structure (Kaufman and Sherman [1964]).

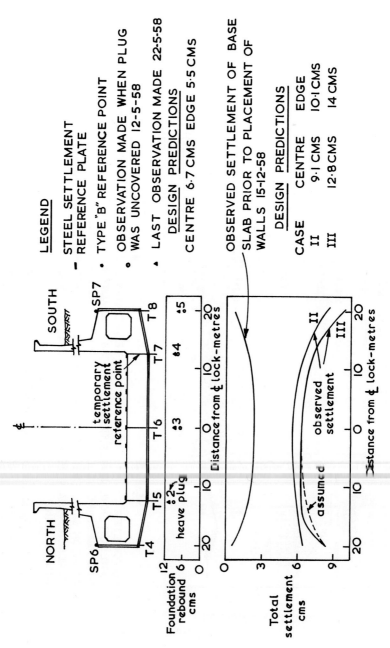

Fig. 192: Measured rebound and settlement of monolith (Kaufman and Sherman [1964]).

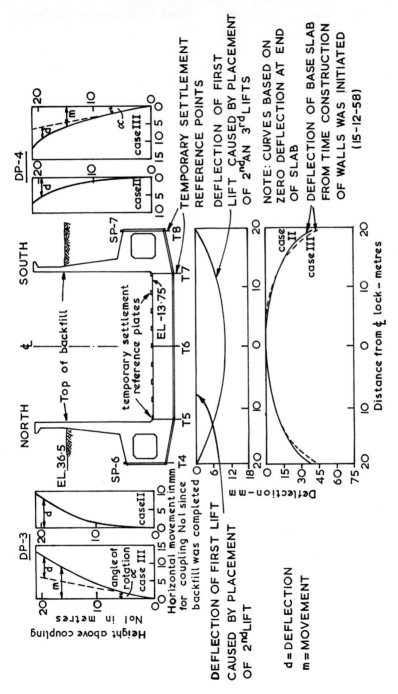

Fig. 193: Measured deflection of walls and base slab of monolith (Kaufman and Sherman [1964]).

movement of the retaining walls is controlled by loading and deflection of the floor slab. One of the best examples of a lock structure is the Port Allen Lock on the Mississippi River. The navigation chamber is 25.6 m wide by 360 m long with 20.5 m high walls and a 3.4 m thick floor slab. Backfill behind the walls comprised a clean sand. The instrumentation programme consisted of (a) earth pressure cells on the outside of the lock walls and under the floor slab, (b) strain meters, concrete pressure cells and resistance thermometers installed in the walls and floor, (c) heave gauges and settlement points to measure lock and soil movements, (d) piezometers to record water pressures in the vicinity of the structure and in the underlying sand and silt strata and (e) wall deflection pipes to measure tilting of the lock walls. The instruments were located in the central section of the lock. Figure 191 shows a section through the monolith. Valuable descriptions of the various instruments used at this site and methods of installation are given by Kaufman and Sherman (1964).

The rebound of the foundation due to excavation works is given in Figure 192, while Figure 193 shows the recorded deflections of the walls

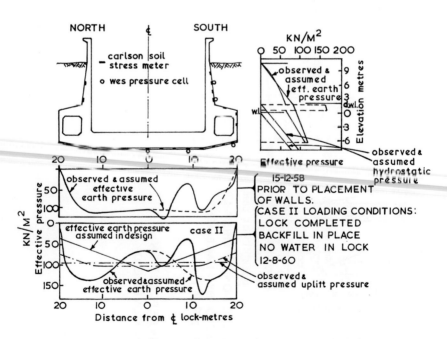

Fig. 194: Measured effective earth pressure distribution on the lock structure
(Kaufman and Sherman [1964]).

and base slab. The layout of the instruments is also indicated in this figure. The effective earth pressure distribution around the lock is given in Figure 194.

The authors conclude that the instruments used performed in a satisfactory manner and, provided they are carefully checked and tested prior to installation, provide an accurate and reliable means of obtaining field measurements. The devices installed were working after 5 years.

This project is of interest because a sophisticated finite element analysis was used to complement the instrumentation studies. The data from the instrumentation programme were used to assess the accuracy of the finite element analysis. Details are given by Duncan and Clough (1971) and further comment is made in Chapter 7.

Uff (1969) describes the instrumentation of a trial section of diaphragm wall for the Seaforth dock structure, Liverpool. The wall was of a wine

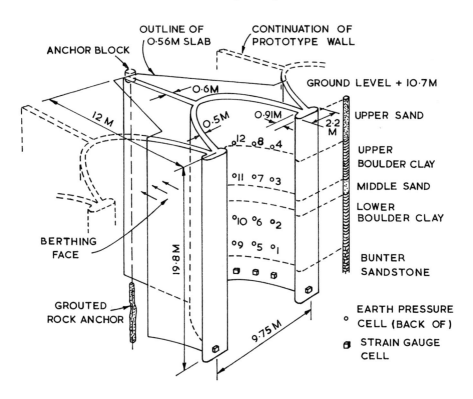

Fig. 195: Layout and instrumentation of test wall (Uff [1969]).

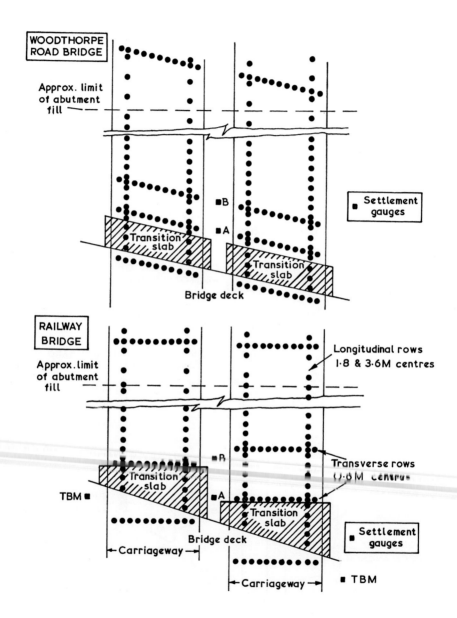

Fig. 196: Layout of instrumented section of Staines By-Pass
(Margason and Cross [1966]).

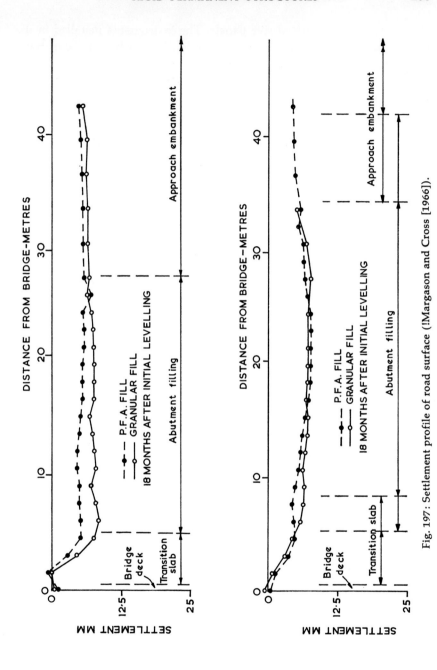

Fig. 197: Settlement profile of road surface (|Margason and Cross [1966]).

glass shape and comprised five panels. The instruments installed in the wall included 12 total earth pressure cells of the vibrating wire type; 5 acoustic strain gauge cells to record bearing pressures; and 9 hydraulic piezometers. A layout of the instruments is shown in Figure 195. Details of pressure cell installation are given by Uff (1969). At this site yield of the wall was determined by levelling to markers on the top of the wall and measuring offsets against an optical line. A total yield of 9 mm was recorded.

6.8. Roads

Measurement of the performance of roads and their foundations has usually been restricted to settlement of the road surface and movement of the foundations of the road. The layout of an instrumented section of Motorway at the Staines By-Pass is shown in Figure 196. In this example the settlement of the subsoil was recorded by rod-type gauges founded in blocks of concrete at original ground level. Levelling was by an automatic precise level to an accuracy of $\pm$ 1.2 mm. For settlement of the road surface metal studs were driven into the bituminous wearing course and their elevations with respect to a benchmark determined by levelling. The settlement profile of the road surface is shown in Figure 197, while the settlement of the subsoil as a function of time at two positions is shown in Figure 198. Details of this instrumented section are given by Margason and Cross (1966).

Heath et al. (1972) describe the results of extensive measurements made on rail track foundations by British Rail. They measured the earth pressure distribution beneath a test track using earth pressure cells of the Sparrow and Tory (1966) type. Details of earth pressure cell installation are given by ORE (1966, 1968). A layout of the earth pressure cells is shown in Figure 199. In addition to earth pressure measurements Heath et al. (1972) instrumented a number of sites with the instruments shown in Figure 200. Measuring plates were installed under each end of ten adjacent sleepers and the elevations of these plates with respect to a fixed datum determined. Figure 201 gives measurements taken at a stable and an unstable site.

By the use of other instruments such as piezometers, inclinometers and profile settlement gauges it is possible to determine pore water pressure

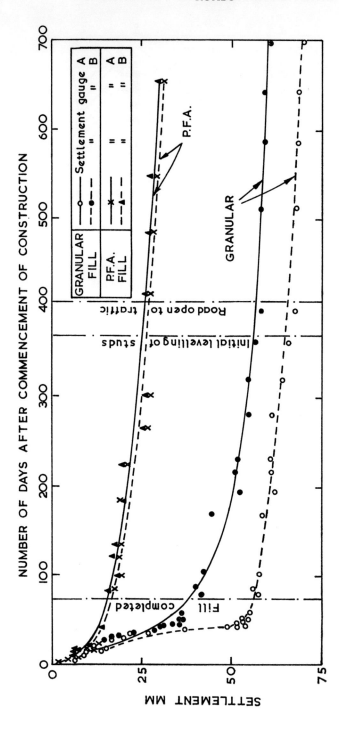

Fig. 198: Settlement of road subsoil as a function of time (Margason and Cross [1966]).

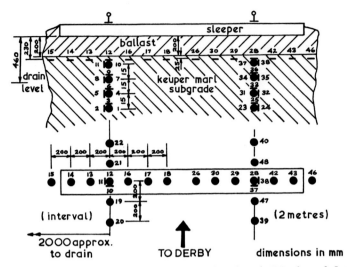

Fig. 199: Layout of earth pressure cells beneath rail track (Heath et al. [1972]).

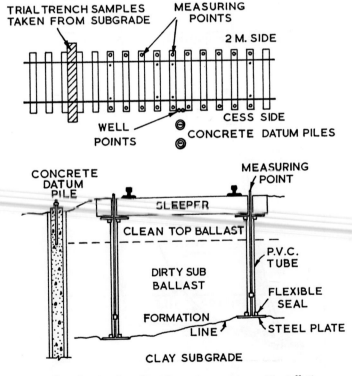

Fig. 200: Example of rail track settlement measurement installation
(Heath et al. [1972]).

distributions and lateral and vertical movements of the subsoil at any location.

Where very large movements are expected to occur the leads to the various instruments must be capable of accommodating these movements without malfunctioning.

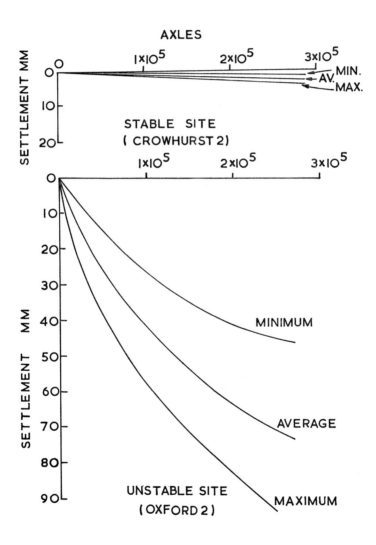

Fig. 201: Settlement of rail track as a function of axle passes for stable and unstable foundation conditions (Heath et al. [1972]).

Table 3. Instruments for tied-back retaining wall instrumentation

Quantity to be measured	Instrument Available	General comment on advantages, limitations
Ground surface movements near to the retaining wall	Settlement: Optical levelling on the reference points	Simple and inexpensive; excellent reliability; benchmark; accuracy ± 0.5 mm; care required to prevent pin disturbance.
	Lateral movement: offsets from line defined by theodolite: tape measurements between survey pins	Simple and inexpensive; requires fixed reference stations.
	Crack opening by use of Demec gauges or calipers	Simple, inexpensive, direct; necessary to protect the measurement studs.
Sub-surface movement of adjacent soil mass	Vertical: heave gauges; multiple position extensometers; settlement gauges (single and multiple)	Usually few are used due to the costs involved; require datum for absolute movements; protection of top end of instruments from construction activity required.
	Inclined: multiple position extensometers	— do —
	Lateral: extensometers; inclinometers	Extensometers are expensive and are susceptible to damage at wall face; got to refer to fixed reference. Inclinometers give full depth profile of lateral movement.
Movement of wall	Vertical: optical levelling on to reference points	Simple and inexpensive; necessary to have a fixed benchmark.
	Lateral: Line of sight and offsets to reference pins; suspended plumb line to give lateral displacement with depth; inclinometer installed in the wall	Require datum for absolute movements; plumbline is expensive to install; inclinometer most satisfactory and can be used with all types of wall construction; expensive to use.

Table 3 Cont'd. . . .

Quantity to be measured	Instrument Available	General comment on advantages, limitations
Movement of anchor	Extensometer attached to anchor zone and conducted in tube parallel to axis of anchor	Simple and direct; measures movements relative to wall only; susceptible to damage if not protected.
Anchor load	Strain gauges on anchor rod; load cells; vibrating wire type; resistance strain gauge type; photoelastic type; mechanical type; indirect type	Strain gauged rods have a low level of reliability due to bonding and water-proofing difficulties; inexpensive. Electrical load cells are accurate but leads must be protected; may be sensitive to temperature change. Photoelastic cell is simple but visual access required. Load cells require centring device if reliable load measurements are to be taken; expensive. Mechanical cell: Simple but expensive; require access to the cell for visual reading.
Load at base of wall	Load cells	Difficult to install; expensive.
	Tell tale rods	Not very accurate; inexpensive.
Earth pressure on wall	Earth pressure cells of the NGI type for soft clays or of the B.R.S. type for a diaphragm wall	Expensive; risk of electrical malfunction; require a gauge house; installation difficulties.
	Piezometer to record pore water pressure; may be hydraulic, electrical etc.	Simple to install and read; possible to take readings during excavation construction; piezometer selected dependent on soil conditions.
Earth and Pore Water pressures in retained soil	Very difficult to install earth pressure cells	
	Piezometers of hydraulic, electrical etc. types	No difficulty; got to protect leads to gauge house.

6.9. Rocks

Instruments used in rock engineering differ in many respects from those used in soils. The most important point to remember is that great accuracy over short distances is of a very limited use owing to the extreme importance of local features such as joints and discontinuities which control the behaviour of the rock mass. The selection of instruments for rock study must be based on the principles of rock mechanics. Hartmann (1967) discusses, in considerable detail, the selection and use of instruments for tunnel construction, Roberts (1968) reviews methods of stress and strain measurement in rock masses, while there are numerous reports in the various rock mechanics and engineering geology journals and conference proceedings and Large Dams Congresses on the selection and use of instruments for field measurement purposes.

Generally it is possible to measure surface and rock mass deformations using monuments and rod or wire extensometers respectively; stress and pore water pressure measurements at structure/rock interface using Glötzl type and other cells; convergence measurements of openings by use of a range of deformeters and convergence measuring devices; and load and stress cells for insertion in the rock mass.

An extensive range of equipment is available from Interfels GmbH and Terrametric Inc. and they quote several examples of rock instrumentation. Müller and Müller (1970) discuss the selection of instruments for monitoring dam behaviour, Dunnicliff (1968) discusses tunnel instrumentation of the Tarbela dam project, while Ward et al. (1968) have drawn attention to the very high degree of accuracy required in the measurement of rock deformations.

The subject of rock instrumentation is outside the scope of this text and is covered in detail by Natau (1973) and partly also by Dreyer (1972).

6.10. Summary

In earlier chapters and also in this chapter a number of instruments have been described or referred to. On reading the references cited it will be observed that many factors other than accuracy must be considered when selecting an instrument. As a general rule each part of an instrumentation scheme or programme should be conceived in such a manner as to make a specific measurement for a specific purpose. The range of the measurement, the accuracy and the time period must also be considered at this stage.

To illustrate this approach the case of tied-back retaining wall instrumentation is considered and Table 3 refers to instruments which are available and which can be used in this environment. A similar approach may be followed for other instrumentation problems and Gould and Dunnicliff (1971) present a very useful summary of instruments available for movement measurement.

It will be appreciated that all instruments have some drawback in use. However, by the careful selection of the instruments and their installation in the ground and subsequent recording, the possibility of the complete malfunctioning of an instrumentation scheme is very remote.

References

ADAMS, J. I., and HANNA, T. H., (1970), "Ground movements due to pile driving", Proceedings, Conference on the behaviour of piles, Institution of Civil Engineers, London, 127—134.

ADAMS, J. I., and GLYN, T. W., (1972), "A study of anchorages for transmission tower foundations", Canadian Geotechnical Journal, Vol. 9, No. 1, 89—104.

AL-DHAHIR, Z. A., KENNARD, M. F., and MORGENSTERN, N. R., (1969), "Observations of pore pressures beneath the ash lagoon embankments at Fiddler's Ferry power station", Proceedings, Conference on In Situ Investigations in Soils and Rocks, British Geotechnical Society, 265—276.

ASHBEE, R. A., (1972), "Uplift and side loading tests on two augered concrete footings in chalk (Lovedean 400 kV sub-station)", Central Electricity Research Laboratories, Laboratory Note No. RD/L/N. 70/72.

BARA, J. P., and HILL, R. R., (1967), "Foundation rebound at Dos Amigos pumping plant", Proceedings, American Society of Civil Engineers, Vol. 93, No. SM5, 153 — 168.

BARTHOLOMEW, R. F., and SIMONS, N. E., (1970), "Settlement observations on a piled foundation", Proceedings, Conference on Behaviour of Piles, Institution of Civil Engineers, London, 79—82.

BISHOP, A. W., and VAUGHAN, P. R., (1962), "Selset Reservoir: design and performance of the embankment", Proceedings, Institution of Civil Engineers, London, Vol. 21, 305—346.

BISHOP, A. W., KENNARD, M. F., and VAUGHAN, P. R., (1964), "Developments in the measurement and interpretation of pore pressures in earth dams", Transactions, 8th International Congress on Large Dams, Edinburgh, Vol. 2, 47—72.

BJERRUM, L., (1966), "Progressive failure in slopes of overconsolidated plastic clay and clay shales", Proceedings, American Society of Civil Engineers, Vol. 93, No. SM5, 1—49.

BJERRUM, L., KENNEY, T. C., and KJAERNSLI, B., (1965), "Measuring instruments for strutted excavations", Proceedings, American Society of Civil Engineers, Vol. 91, SM1, 111—141.

BOZOZUK, M., and LABRECEQUE, A., (1968), "Downdrag measurements on 270-ft. composite piles", A.S.T.M. Special Technical Publication 444, — Performance of Deep Foundations, 15—40.

BROADHEAD, A., (1969), Contribution to Discussion on Session D, Proceedings, Conference on In Situ Investigations in Soils and Rocks, British Geotechnical Society, 240—243.

BURLAND, J. B., and LORD, J. A., (1969), "The load-deformation behaviour of Middle chalk at Mundford. Norfolk: a comparison between full scale performance and in-situ and laboratory measurements", Proceedings, Conference on In Situ Investigations in Soils and Rocks, British Geotechnical Society, 3—16.

CHELLIS, R. D., (1961), "Pile Foundations" (2nd edition) McGraw-Hill, New York.

CLOUGH, R. W., and WOODWARD, R. J., (1967), "Analysis of embankment stresses and deformations", Proceedings, American Society of Civil Engineers, Vol. 93, SM1, 529—550.

COLE, K. W., and BURLAND, J. B., (1972), "Observations of retaining wall movements associated with a large excavation", Proceedings, Fifth European Conference on Soil Mechanics and Foundation Engineering, Madrid, Vol. 1, 445—453.

DARRAGH, R. D., (1964), "Controlled water tests to preload tank foundations", Proceedings, American Society of Civil Engineers, Vol. 90, SM5, 303—330.

DAVIS, R. E., and BACHER, A. E., (1968), "California's Culvert research programme — description, current status and observed peripheral pressures", Highway Research Record No. 249 — Retaining Walls and Culverts, 14—23.

DAVISSON, M. T., and McDONALD, V. J., (1968), "Energy Measurements for a diesel hammer", A.S.T.M Special Technical Publication 444, Performance of Deep Foundations, 295—313.

DUNCAN, J. M., and CLOUGH, G. W., (1971), "Finite element analysis of Port Allen Lock", Proceedings, American Society of Civil Engineers, Vol. 97, SM8, 1053—1068.

DE JONG, J., and HARRIS, M. C., (1971), "Settlements of two multistorey buildings in Edmonton", Canadian Geotechnical Journal, Vol. 8, No. 2, 217—235.

DE JONG, J., and MORGENSTERN, N. R., (1971), "The influence of structural rigidity on the foundation loads of the C. N. Tower Edmonton", Canadian Geotechnical Journal, Vol. 8, No. 4, 527—537.

DREYER, W., (1972), "The Science of Rock Mechanics. Part I. The Strength Properties of Rocks". Series on Rock and Soil Mechanics, Vol. 1, No. 2, Trans Tech Publications, Cleveland.

FELLENIUS, B. H., (1972), "Bending of piles determined by inclinometer measurements", Canadian Geotechnical Journal, Vol. 9, No. 1, 25—32.

FITZHERBERT, W. A., and BARNETT, J. H., (1967), "Causes of movement in reinforced concrete turbo-block and developments in turbo-block design and construction", Proceedings, Institution of Civil Engineers, London, Vol. 36, 351—394.

GOLDER, H. Q., GOULD, J. P., LAMBE, T. W., TSCHEBOTARIOFF, G. P., and WILSON, S. D., (1970), "Predicted performance of braced excavation", Proceedings, American Society of Civil Engineers, Vol. 96, SM3, 801—816.

GOULD, J. P., (1970), "Lateral pressures on rigid permanent structures", Lateral stresses in the ground and the design of earth retaining structures, American Society of Civil Engineers, 219—270.

GOULD, J. P., and DUNNICLIFF, F. C. J., (1971), "Accuracy of field deformation measurements", Proceedings, Fourth Pan American Conference on Soil Mechanics and Foundation Engineering, Puerto Rico, 313—366.

GIBSON, R. E., and MARSLAND, A., (1960), "Pore water pressure observation in a saturated alluvial deposit beneath a loaded oil tank", Proceedings, Conference on Pore Pressure and Suction in Soils, Institution of Civil Engineers, London, 112—118.

GRAY, H., (1969), "Effects of forest clear cutting on the stability of natural slopes" Reprint, Slope Indicator Company, Seattle.

GREENFIELD, F. C., (1970), "Early settlement of tall buildings founded on piles in London clay", Proceedings, Conference on Behaviour of Piles, Institution of Civil Engineers, London, 71—78.

GRANT, G. L., (1966), "A method of measuring of a turbine bearing support structure", Proceedings, Conference on Vibration in Civil Engineering, British National Section of International Association of Earthquake Engineering, London, 111—120.

HANNA, T. H., (1966), "Distribution of load in long piles", Ontario Hydro Research Quarterly, Vol. 18, No. 4, 1—7.

HANNA, T. H., and ADAMS, J. I., (1968), "Comparison of field and laboratory measurements of Modulus of deformation of a clay", Highway Research Record No. 243, 12—22.

HANNA, T. H., (1968), "The bending of long H-section piles", Canadian Geotechnical Journal, Vol. 5, No. 3, 150—172.

HARTMANN, B. E., (1967), "Rock Mechanics Instrumentation for tunnel construction", Terrametrics, Inc. Golden, Colorado, U.S.A.

HEATH, D. L., SHENTON, M. J., SPARROW, R. W., and WATERS, J. M., (1972), "Design of conventional rail track foundations", Proceedings, Institution of Civil Engineers, London, Vol. 51, 251—268.

HOOPER, J. A., (1972), „The theory and design of photoelastic load gauges incorporating glass element transducers", International Journal of Rock Mechanics and Mining Sciences, Vol. 9, No. 3, 363—401.

HORNE, H. M., and LAMBE, T. W., (1964), "Settlement of buildings on the M.I.T. Campus", Proceedings, American Society of Civil Engineers, Vol. 90, SM5, 181—196.

HOUSEL, W. S., (1965), "Michigan study of driving hammers", Proceedings, American Society of Civil Engineers, Vol. 91, SM5, 37—64.

HUDER, J., (1969), "Deep braced excavation with high ground water table", Proceedings, Seventh International Conference on Soil Mechanics and Foundation Engineering, Mexico City, Vol. 2, 443—448.

INTERFELS Ltd., (1970), Measuring Instruments Catalogue.

KAPP, M. S., (1969), "Slurry trench construction for basement wall of World Trade Center", Civil Engineering, (New York), April, 36—40.

KAUFMAN, R. I., and SHERMAN, W. C., (1964), "Engineering measurements for Port Allen Lock", Proceedings, American Society of Civil Engineers, Vol. 90, SM5, 221—247.

KUESEL, T. R., (1969), Discussions to Session 4, Proceedings, Seventh International Conference on Soil Mechanics and Foundation Engineering, Mexico City, Vol. 3.

LAMBE, T. W., (1970), "Braced excavations", American Society of Civil Engineers, Specialty Conference on Lateral Stresses in the Ground and Design of Earth Retaining Structures, 149—218.

LAMBE, T. W., WOLFSKILL, L. A., and WONG, I. H., (1970), "Measured performance of braced excavation", Proceedings, American Society of Civil Engineers, Vol. 96, SM3, 817—836.

MARGASON, G., and CROSS, J. E., (1966), "Settlement behind bridge abutments: the use of pulverised fuel ash in constructing the approach embankments to bridges on the Staines By-Pass", Road Research Laboratory, Report No. 48.

MARSAL, R. J., and RAMIREZ DE ARELLANO, L., (1967), "Performance of El Infernillo Dam", Proceedings, American Society of Civil Engineers, Vol. 93, SM4, 265—298.

MEIGH, A. C., and CORBETT, B. O., (1966), "A comparison of in-situ measurements in a soft clay with laboratory tests and the settlement of oil tanks", Proceedings, Conference on In-Situ Investigations in Soils and Rocks, British Geotechnical Society, 173—180.

Michigan State Highway Commission, (1965), "A performance investigation of pile driving hammers and piles". A study in co-operation with The Bureau of Public Roads, U.S. Department of Commerce, The Michigan Road Builders Association, Wayne State University and Representative Hammer Manufacturers, March.

MUIR WOOD, A. M., (1969), Contribution to discussion on Session 4, Proceedings, Seventh International Conference on Soil Mechanics and Foundation Engineering, Mexico City, Vol. 3.

MUIR WOOD, A. M., and GIBB, F. R., (1971), "Design and construction of the cargo tunnel at Heathrow Airport, London", Proceedings, Institution of Civil Engineers, London, Vol. 48, 11—34.

MÜLLER, G, and MÜLLER, L., (1970), "Monitoring of Dams with Measuring Instruments", Transactions, Tenth International Congress on Large Dams, Montreal, Vol. 3, 1033—1046.

NATAU, O. P., (1973), "State of Stress Measurements in Rock Masses". Series on Rock and Soil Mechanics, Vol. 1, No. 4, Trans Tech Publications Cleveland.

N. G. I., (1962), "Measurements at a strutted excavation", Oslo Subway, Grönland 1, km 1.559, Report 1.

N. G. I., (1962), "Measurements at a strutted excavation", Oslo. Tech.Sch.Report 2.

N. G. I., (1962), "Measurements at a strutted excavation, Oslo Subway, Enerhaugen South, km 1.982", Report 3.

N. G. I., (1962), "Measurements at a strutted excavation", The New Headquarters Building of the Norwegian Telecommuncation Administration, Oslo, Report 4.

N. G. I., (1962), "Measurements at a strutted excavation", Oslo Subway, Grönland 2, km 1.692, Report 5.

N. G. I., (1962), "Measurements at a strutted excavation", Oslo Subway, Vaterland 1, km 1.373, Report 6.

N. G. I., (1962), "Measurements at a strutted excavation", Oslo Subway, Vaterland 2, km 1.408, Report 7.

N. G. I., (1962), "Measurements at a strutted excavation", Oslo Subway, Vaterland 3, km 1.450, Report 8.

N. G. I., (1962), "Vibrating Wire measuring devices used at strutted excavations", Report 9.

Office of Research and Experiments, (1966). Interim Report No. 4, ORE, Utrecht.

Office of Research and Experiments, (1968). Interim Report No. 8, ORE, Utrecht.

PALMER, J. H. L., and KENNEY, T. C., (1972), "Analytical study of a braced excavation in weak clay", Canadian Geotechnical Journal, Vol. 9, No. 2, 145—164.

PARKER, A. S., and BAYLISS, F. S. U., (1970), "The settlement behaviour of a group of large silos on piled foundations", Proceedings, Conference on Pile Behaviour, Institution of Civil Engineers, London, 59—70.

PECK., R. B., (1969), "Deep excavations and tunnelling in soft ground", State-of-the-art Report, Proceedings, Seventh International Conference on Soil Mechanics and Foundation Engineering, Mexico City, 225—290.

PENMAN, A. D. M., and WATSON, G. H., (1965), "The improvement of a tank foundation by the weight of its own test load", Proceedings, Sixth International Conference on Soil Mechanics and Foundation Engineering, Montreal, Vol. 1, 169—173.

PENMAN, A. D. M., and WATSON, G. H., (1967), "Foundations for storage tanks on reclaimed land at Teesmouth", Proceedings Institution of Civil Engineers, London, Vol. 37, 19—42.

PENMAN, A. D. M., and MITCHELL, P. B., (1970), "Initial behaviour of Scammonden Dam", Building Research Station, England, Current paper No. 20/70.

PENMAN, A. D. M., BURLAND, J. B., and CHARLES, J. A., (1971), "Observed and predicted deformation in a large embankment dam during construction", Proceedings, Institution of Civil Engineers, London, Vol. 49, 1—21.

PRETLOVE, A. J., (1966), "Some current methods in vibration measurement", Vibration in Civil Engineering, Proceedings, Symposium organised by British National Section of the International Association of Earthquake Engineering, London, 95—118.

PROCTOR, D. W., and ATKINSON, K. B., (1972), "Experimental photographic wriggle survey in the Second Mersey Tunnel", Tunnels and Tunnelling, March, 115—118.

ROBERTS, A., (1968), "Measurement of Strain and Stress in rock masses", Chapter 6 in Rock Mechanics in Engineering Practice edited by K. G. Stagg and O. C. Zienkiewicz, Wiley, 157—202.

ROBERTS, D. V., and DARRAGH, R. D., (1962), "Aerial fill settlements and building foundation behaviour at the San Francisco Airport", A.S.T.M. Special Technical Publication No. 332, 211.

RODRIQUEZ, J. M., and FLAMAND, C. L., (1969), "Strut loads recorded in a deep excavation in clay", Proceedings, Seventh International Conference on Soil Mechanics and Foundation Engineering, Mexico City, Vol. 2, 459—468.

ROSSETT, I. M., and EFIMBA, R. E., (1968), „ICES — STRUDL II, Student Manual, Massachussetts Institute of Technology, Research Report, R 68—71.

ROTH, W. H., (1970), "Foundation Instrumentation at Pleasant Valley pumping plant", U. S. Department of the Interior, Bureau of Reclamation, Report REC-OCE-70-23.

ROWE, P. W., (1970), "Derwent dam — embankment stability and displacements", Proceedings, Institution of Civil Engineerings, London, Vol. 45, 423—452.

RUFFLE, N. J., (1970), "Derwent Dam — design considerations", Proceedings, Institution of Civil Engineers, London, Vol. 45, 381—400.

Royal Society of London, (1972), A meeting for discussion on "The measurement and interpretation of changes of strain in the earth", May 10 — May 12.

SCHEAR, A. C., and WILLETT, G. A., (1969), "Rebuilt Wolf Creek Culvert Behaviour", Highway Research Record No. 262, Pipes and Culverts, 1—13.

SHANNON, W. L., and STRAZER, R. J., (1968), "Shoring for the Seattle First National Bank building, Seattle, Washington", American Society of Civil Engineers, Annual Meeting and National Meeting on Structural Engineering, Pittsburgh.

SIMS, F. A., FORRESTER, G. R., and JONES, C. J. F., (1970), "Lateral pressures on retaining walls", The Journal of the Institution of Highway Engineers, June, 19—30.

SKEMPTON, A. W., and HUTCHINSON, J. N., (1969), "Stability of natural slopes and embankment foundations", State-of-the-art report, Proceedings, Seventh International Conference on Soil Mechanics and Foundation Engineering, Mexico City, 291—340.

SPARROW, R. W., and TORY, A. C., (1966), "Behaviour of soil mass under dynamic loading", Proceedings, American Society of Civil Engineers, Vol. 92, SM 3, 59—86.

Swedish Pile Commission, (1964), "Driving and test loading of long concrete piles, Tests at Gubbero, Gothenburg", IVA Subcommittee on Piles, Report 99 (National Swedish Council for Building Research).

TAYLOR, D. K., (1967), "Notes on observation of building settlements", Proceedings, Fifth Australia-New Zealand Conference on Soil Mechanics and Foundation Engineering, 246—252.

TOMLINSON, M. J., (1969), Contribution to Discussion on Session D, Proceedings, Conference on In-Situ Measurements in Soils and Rocks, British Geotechnical Society, 243.

UFF, J. F., (1969), "In-Situ measurements of earth pressure for a quay wall at Seaforth, Liverpool", Proceedings, Conference on In-Situ Measurements in Soils and Rocks, British Geotechnical Society, 229—239.

UNDERWOOD, L. B., THORFINNSON, S. T., and BLACK, W. T., (1964), "Rebound in redesign of Oahe Dam hydraulic structures", Proceedings, American Society of Civil Engineers, Vol. 90, SM 2, 65—86.

WALLACE, G. B., and OTTO, W. C., (1964), "Differential settlement at Selfridge Air Force Base", Proceedings, American Society of Civil Engineers, Vol. 90, SM 5, 197—220.

WARD, W. H., (1969), "Contribution to discussion on Session 4, Proceedings, Seventh International Conference on Soil Mechanics and Foundation Engineering, Mexico City, Vol. 3, 320—325.

WARD, W. H., and CHAPLIN, T. K., (1957), "Existing stresses in several old London underground tunnels", Proceedings, Fourth International Conference on Soil Mechanics and Foundation Engineering, London, Vol. 2, 256—259.

WARD, W. H., and THOMAS, H. S. H., (1965), "The development of earth loading and deformation in tunnel linings in London clay", Proceedings, Sixth International Conference on Soil Mechanics and Foundation Engineering, Montreal, Vol. 2, 432—436.

WARD, W. H., BURLAND, J. B., and GALLOIS, R. W., (1968), "Geotechnical assesment of site at Mundford, Norfolk, for a large proton accelerator", Geotechnique Vol. 18, No. 4, 399—431.

WHITAKER, T., (1970), "The design of piled foundations", Pergamom Press, London.

WHITAKER, T., and COOKE, R. W., (1966), "An investigation of the shaft and base resistances of large bored piles in London clay", Symposium on Large bored piles, the Institution of Civil Engineers, London, 7—49.

WILKINSON, W. B., BARDEN, L., and ROCKE, G., (1969), "An assessment of in-situ and laboratory tests in predicting the pore pressure in an earth dam", Proceedings, Conference on In-Situ Investigations in Soils and Rocks, British Geotechnical Society, 277—284.

WILSON, S. D., (1970), "Observational data on ground movements related to slope instability", Proceedings, American Society of Civil Engineers, Vol. 96, SM 5, 1521—1544.

WILSON, S. D., and HANCOCK, C. W., (1964), "Instrumentation for movements within rock-fill dams", American Society for Testing and Materials, Special Technical Publication No. 392 — Instruments and Apparatus for Soil and Rock Mechanics, 115—130.

WILSON, S. D., and MARANO, D., (1968), "Performance of Muddy Run Embankment", Proceedings, American Society of Civil Engineers, Vol. 94, SM 4, 859—882.

The Recording and Processing of Field Data

7.1. Introduction

In Chapters 2 to 6 illustrations were given of the manner in which instruments can be used to obtain meaningful data on the performance and behaviour of foundations. The choice of instrument and the analysis of the data which it provides are all part of the process of instrumentation. This includes the manner of collecting data and the subsequent processing of these data to produce the best result.

Data may be acquired by one or more observers reading a number of instruments and recording the observations on a data sheet or by electronic means whereby the results are processed and displayed in printed form, on magnetic or punched tape or photographically. The processing of data secured by instrumentation programmes can be carried out in a number of ways depending on the nature of the problem. These include comparison with predicted results by simple plotting (graphical) procedures, through simple slide rule or desk top calculator analyses to very sophisticated analyses using digital computing techniques.

The purpose of this Chapter is to present a very brief and qualitative description of data acquisition and processing and to illustrate this with several case histories. The foundation engineer will seldom, if ever, design complicated recorders for instrumentation purposes, although he will use such recorders. The principles of most of the recorders used by the foundation engineer are described in the relevant trade literature and also in the technical publications referred to. Further details will be found in a number of textbooks which include Jones (1965), Neubert (1963) Hendry (1964), Considine (1964) and others.

Because many of the instruments described in earlier chapters make use of transducers which enable the quantity being measured to be recorded by an indirect means, the subject of transducers is now mentioned.

7.2. Transducers

A transducer is an energy converter i. e. it translates a signal from one form to another. Transducers are used for the measurement of forces, pressures and displacements, and Figure 202 illustrates the measurement and recording approach which is usually followed. The principles of transducer design and use are given by Neubert (1963) and this section draws the reader's attention to several of the more common transducers which the foundation engineer may use.

The wire resistance strain gauge is used in many transducers and operates on the principle that the electrical resistance of a wire changes with strain according to the relationship

$$R = \varrho \cdot \frac{L}{A} \tag{7.1}$$

where R = electrical resistance, ϱ = resistivity of the wire, L – length of the wire and A = the cross-sectional area of the wire. It can be shown that if the conductor wire behaves elastically its strain sensitivity, known as gauge factor, is

$$G = \frac{d\varrho}{dL} \frac{\varrho}{L} + (1 + 2\nu) \tag{7.2}$$

where ν = Poisson's ratio of the wire. The value of the gauge factor G is in the range 1.9 to 2.4 and is defined as the unit change in resistance per unit change in strain. The resistivity of the wire ϱ is temperature dependent and consequently the transducer must be designed so that temperature effects during use are eliminated or allowed for.

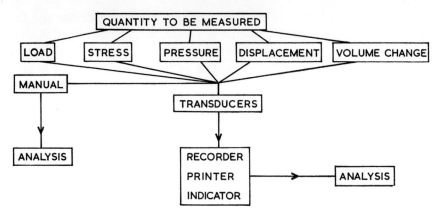

Fig. 202: The data recording problem.

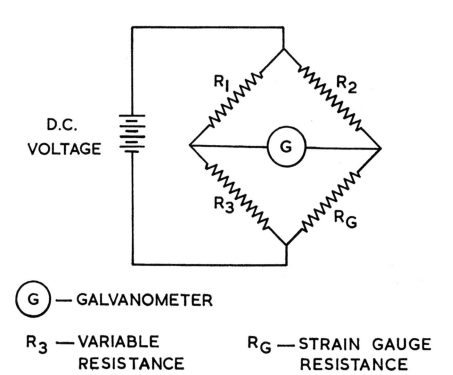

G — GALVANOMETER

R_3 — VARIABLE RESISTANCE R_G — STRAIN GAUGE RESISTANCE

Fig. 203: The Wheatstone Bridge circuit.

The Wheatstone bridge is the most common measuring device and the principle of measurement is shown in Figure 203. In this circuit R_3 is a variable resistance and R_G is the strain gauge resistance. The change in strain gauge resistance ΔR_G is obtained by balancing the circuit to give

$$\Delta R_G = \Delta R_3 \left(\frac{R_2}{R_1} \right) \tag{7.3}$$

This null method of strain measurement is not satisfactory for dynamic conditions. For such cases it is usual to measure the voltage imbalance of the Wheatstone bridge using, for example, a Cathode ray Oscilloscope. Some details are given by Hendry (1964).

Strain gauges are normally bonded to the sensing element and details of this operation as well as the uses of strain gauges are given by Perry and Lissner (1955).

There are a number of pressure transducers which make use of the wire resistance strain gauge, vibrating wire gauge, semiconductor strain gauges, piezoelectric crystals. An excellent review is given by Morgan and Moore (1968).

The displacement transducer is used extensively in foundation instrumentation. Two types are available. In the differential transformer type an iron core moves inside three coils as shown schematically in Figure 204. An alternating current is applied to the central coil and this induces

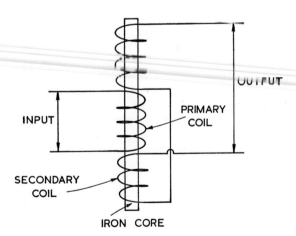

Fig. 204: The principle of the displacement transducer.

a voltage in the secondary coils. When the iron core moves, a greater voltage is induced in the secondary coil towards which the core moves. The relationship between voltage output and core displacement is linear and for this reason the instrument is referred to as a linear variable differential transformer (l. v. d. t.). Sensitivity is expressed in mV/mm displacement/V input. Further details are given by Morgan and Moore (1968). In the potentiometric displacement transducer a metal wiper traverses a precision wire wound resistance element, the voltage between the wiper and one end of the element being proportional to the displacement of the wiper.

The mechanical dial gauge is a transducer. With this instrument the displacement of the plunger placed in contact with the element which moves is transmitted via a rack and pinion to a gear train and pointer. The plunger is spring-loaded to keep it against the test piece. The gear train gives a magnification of up to 0.002 mm divisions on the graduated dial scale. Dial gauges may be connected in parallel with a l. v. d. t. to facilitate automatic recording.

The photoelastic transducer is described by Hawkes et al. (1965) and appears to have many potential field uses. Hooper (1972) considers the theory and design of photoelastic force transducers and further details are given in Chapter 2.

7.3. Data Acquisition

As mentioned in Section 7.2. the transducer is the essential link which generates the electrical signal and hence provides a record of the physical quantity being measured. The signal from the transducer may be a voltage, a current, a resistance, a frequency or an electric pulse. For example a strain gauge gives a resistance representation of deformation over a finite length. The case of a thermocouple is considered. A recording potentiometer can be used to record voltages which are measures of temperature given by the thermocouples. However, if the voltage signal from the thermocouple is required as a digital signal, a much more complicated system results. The digital signal could be used to operate a printer and thus the numerical value can be printed onto a sheet of paper.

More generally a data acquisition system consists of three components:

(a) Input — the transducers and signal conditioners such as amplifiers and filters,

(b) Signal Conversion — Here the input signal is converted to a voltage which is expressed in digital form. This is achieved by converting the voltage to frequency which in turn may be used to drive counting circuits,

(c) Output — In this stage the digital signal is expressed in a form suitable for (i) printing on a sheet of graph paper, (ii) plotting on graph paper, (iii) punching on cards or tape, (iv) storing on magnetic tape.

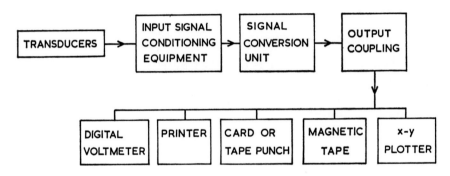

Fig. 205: Arrangement of a data acquisition system.

A general arrangement of a data acquisiton system is shown in Figure 205. It is usual to have more than one transducer in the data acquisltion system. To use equipment efficiently a scanner, which is a device for sampling the transducer outputs in rapid sequence, is used. The standard scanning unit usually has 1 to 100 channels available and it can be programmed to collect at predetermined time intervals. This is achieved by incorporating a digital clock and time standard in the scanner unit. In more sophisticated data acquisition systems it is advantageous to apply signal conditioning to the output from the scanner/programmer unit. Conditioning may be in the form of amplification, filtering, voltage to frequency conversion etc. A schematic of a multi-channel data acquisition system is shown in Figure 206.

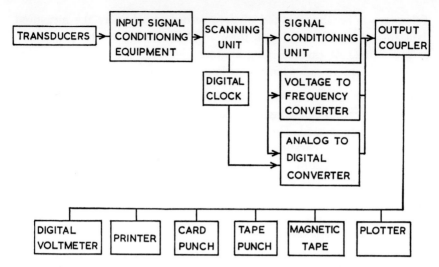

Fig. 206: Arrangement of multi-channel data acquisition system.

7.4. Display Instruments

Where automatic recording of the output from transducers is used, the output is displayed and numerous instruments are available for this purpose. Graphic recorders in their simplest form use a. d. c. meter movement with a pen attached to the pointer. It is usual to move the paper past the pen at a constant speed. Such instruments are referred to as strip-chart recorders.

The x—y recorder provides a graphic representation of data in two dimensions. With some instruments the abscissa can be controlled as a function of time. Consequently the x—y recorder can double as a strip chart recorder of limited chart length. Of the recorders available the potentiometric recorder is most suitable. The chart width is about 250 mm and single or multipoint plotting is possible. An internal scanning system ensures that each channel is separately identified. A wide range of chart speeds is possible.

In order to display data which have been processed with a digital instrument, several digital displays are available. These include typewriters, line printers and digital x—y recorders. Several instruments present data as illuminated decimal digits (e. g. frequency recorders, digital voltmeter).

Telemetry is another method of data recording whereby the measured data are converted into digital form and transmitted via telephone line or radio link. At the receiving stations the data are displayed or fed direct to recorders such as printers, data loggers etc.

The trend in foundation instrumentation is towards illuminated digital readout so that no balancing of circuits is necessary. In many cases solid state circuiting is used. The digital voltmeter in the control box usually is a 5-digit unit. Operation of the control box is via a d. c. rechargable battery housed within the control box. The read-out equipment for vibrating wire gauges is now in the form of a digital display. Several inclinometers also use such a display. Where a number of gauges are to be monitored by a single read out-unit, a switching unit is required. These may be manual or remote controlled.

It will be appreciated that the control box should be robust yet light, should be insensitive to the climatic conditions which occur on site, should be very simple to operate and should be reliable. The trends during the past five years in field recorder design have been in this direction.

7.5. Data Processing

Where large quantities of data have to be dealt with, the digital computer is an obvious choice. Data Processing is the calculation of results from field data, e. g. the interpretation of inclinometer readings. The A.G.S. Omnidirectional inclinometer is used as an example. As the inclinometer probe is lowered down the guide casing, the electrical output is punched on a paper tape. With high speed recording the probe can be lowered without stopping to record data — hence the time required to take readings is reduced to a minimum. The tape is then processed for numerical print out for manual analysis and plotting or to a time-shared computer for automatic analysis and plotting. The question of computer programmes therefore arises in the interpretation and use of data from instrumented foundations. This topic is considered in Section 7.6.

For the majority of sites data processing will remain a manual operation for some time to come owing to the limited information to be processed and the cost involved. However for long term studies the storage and retrieval of data gathered over a period of time is essential. The computer programme known as FIDAS (Field Instrument Data Acquisition System) can accommodate data from piezometers, surface movement monuments, settlement gauges and earth pressure cells. In use this system describes the soils, stores the data and outputs on demand any selected data over a selected period of time in graphical or printed form. (A.G.S. [1968]). The use of programmes similar to FIDAS will grow as the power of the computer for storage and data processing becomes known.

7.6. Methods of Analysis of Foundation Data

Traditionally in the analysis of foundations idealizations of the soil and structure properties have been required to enable a method of solution to be formulated. In the case of deformations linear elastic theory has been used, whereas in the case of earth pressures, theories based on the state of limiting equilibrium have been developed to provide means of computing these forces. With such methods little allowance is made for the actual deformations which occur. In most practical problems movements have to be limited to tolerable values. While this may appear to be a relatively easy problem from an analysis point of view, it must be appreciated that very little information exists on the earth pressure state in a soil mass and the equations which describe it. Also little is known about the influence of construction practice and soil-structure interaction. Consequently the boundary conditions which apply to most foundation problems can only be described as crude idealizations of the real problem.

The case of the analysis of an excavation in clay is used as an example of the application of linear elastic methods. The factor of safety of the base of an excavation in clay with respect to heave is given by

$$F = N_c \cdot C_u/(\gamma \cdot H) \qquad (7.4)$$

where N_c is a factor depending on the shape of the excavation, C_u is the undrained shear strength of the clay, γ is the bulk density of the clay and H is the depth of the excavation. When the factor of safety of the excavation is high the displacements in the soil are small and elasticity theory has been used for their prediction. This requires a knowledge of the modulus of deformation of the soil mass and its variation with depth. Dibiagio (1966) considered the general problem illustrated in Figure 207. He studied the effects of Ko variation and excavation depth

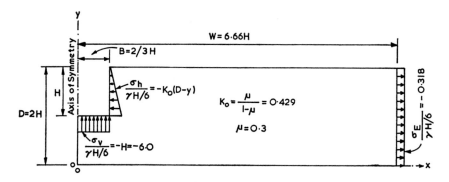

Fig. 207: Geometry and loading conditions of unbraced excavation studied by Di Biagio (1966).

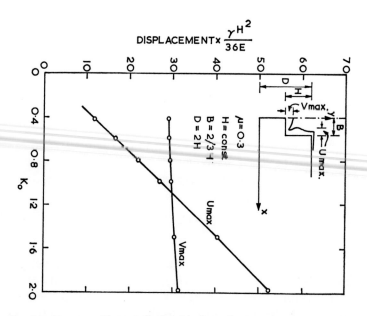

Fig. 208: Heave and lateral displacements in the vicinity of an excavation (Di Biagio [1966]).

to a rigid base on heave and lateral displacements and he found that heave was insensitive to Ko and lateral displacement was directly proportional to it (Figure 208) while the displacements due to change in position of a rigid boundary vary as shown in Figure 209.

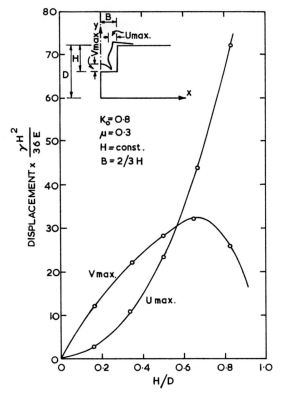

Fig. 209: Heave and lateral displacements in the vicinity of an excavation (Di Biagio [1966]).

During the past decade and in particular during the last five years considerable advances in the analysis of complex engineering problems have been made possible by the introduction of the finite element method of analysis (Zienkiewicz [1971]). The basic principle of this method of analysis is the idealization of the actual continuum (soil and structure) as an assemblage of discrete elements interconnected at their nodal points. In the analysis of two-dimensional stress fields triangular or rectangular plate elements are usually used. Compatability between the edges of adjacent elements is achieved by assuming that the deformations within each element vary linearly in the x- and y- directions. Thus the stiffness characteristics of the elements can be calculated. The stiffness of the complete assemblage of elements is obtained by superposing the stiffness coefficients of the individual elements connecting to each nodal point. Denoting the vector of all nodal point displacements by {r} and the vector of the corresponding nodal forces by {R}, these vectors are connected by the structure stiffness matrix {K} in the manner

$$\{R\} = \{K\}\,\{r\} \tag{7.5}$$

The order of the matrix is 2N where N is the number of nodal points in the idealization. Displacement boundary conditions for any of the nodal points can be allowed for. Solution of these equations of equilibrium gives the nodal displacements. The stresses in all of the elements, {σ}, are obtained from the nodal displacements by the matrix transformation

$$\{\sigma\} = \{S\}\,\{r\} \tag{7.6}$$

The transformation matrix {S} allows for the assumed linear displacement patterns in the elements as well as for their material parametric constants.

It will be recognised that real soils seldom obey the simplifying assumptions of elasticity theory. Techniques have been developed to represent soil element behaviour in a more realistic manner and some details are given by Palmer and Kenney (1972), Zienkiewicz and Naylor (1970), Smith (1970), Desai and Abel (1972) and Reese (1969).

To illustrate the use and power of the finite element method several examples are considered in the following sections.

7.6.1. Excavations

Three sources are referred to. First, the case of the Britannic House excavation, Cole and Burland (1972), is considered. For details of the site and excavation refer to Figures 114, 115, 169 and 170. It was assumed that the initial vertical and horizontal stresses in the ground were given by

$$\sigma_v = \gamma \cdot Z \qquad (7.7)$$

and

$$\sigma_H = Ko\,(\sigma_v - u) + u \qquad (7.8)$$

where u is the pore water pressure, Z is the depth, Ko is the coefficient of earth pressure at rest and γ the bulk density of the soil. The appropriate values of u were obtained from piezometers while the value of Ko at various depths was obtained from data due to Skempton (1961) and Bishop et al. (1965). The variation assumed is shown in Figure 210.

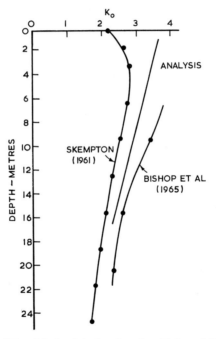

Fig. 210: Variation of Ko with depth in London clay (Cole and Burland [1972]).

In the finite element idealization the mesh was extended to the base of the Woolwich and Reading beds and a fixed boundary imposed. A zero horizontal displacement condition was imposed 100 m away from the top of the excavation. Poisson's ratio for the clay was 0.49.

From the knowledge of the stresses removed due to excavation formation and the measured inward deflection of the wall, the stiffness of the soil with depth was deduced by a trial and error procedure. Figure 211 shows the deduced variation of modulus of deformation E with depth based on the wall displacement profiles which are shown on the left side of the figure. The value of the modulus of deformation of the ground decreased with time and it will be noted that for the data pertaining to July 21, the modulus value was zero above 6 m depth. In fact a tension crack was observed on site at this time and just back from the face of the excavation.

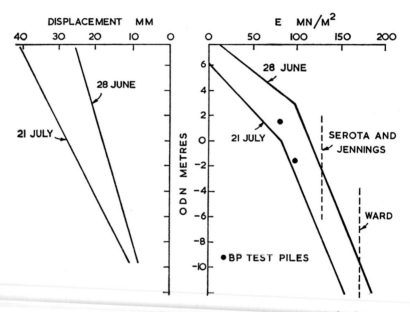

Fig. 211: Computed value of modulus of deformation with depth
(Cole and Burland [1972]).

The predicted displacements based on the finite element idealization, and calibrated by the above procedure, are shown in Figure 212. Generally the horizontal displacements outside the excavation are 2 to 3 times the vertical displacements.Perhaps the most significant feature of this study is that in the past designs have been based on a vertical movement criterion. This work shows the need to revise this philosophy especially for structures founded near to excavations in very stiff and overconsolidated clays.

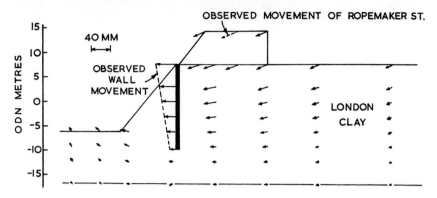

Fig. 212: Predicted displacements associated with the excavation for the
Britannic House (Cole and Burland [1972]).

The second example is a parametric study carried out by Morgenstern
and Eisenstein (1970) to examine the earth pressures on the back of a
rigid retaining wall. A homogeneous, isotropic, linearly elastic soil was
assumed and the back face of the wall was considered to be smooth.
The finite element idealization is shown in Figure 213. They examined
the cases of rough and smooth boundaries, lateral yield conditions, and
the presence of a boundary below the excavation. Figure 214 presents
computed earth pressure diagrams for the various boundary conditions
studied. These are given on the figure. The trends shown in this figure
are significant and when refined further by the use of more realistic
soil parameters may be incorporated in design rules. The power of finite
element analysis is illustrated by these examples. However the authors
conclude that questions of soil description, particularly anisotropy and
time dependence, may control behaviour and in cases where these
conditions prevail, the use of advanced techniques of analysis is super-
fluous.

The third case is the study of the braced excavation problem of Palmer
and Kenney (1972). They modelled their study on the Vaterland I site
on the Oslo subway for which extensive field data were available. A
pictorial representation of the excavation is shown in the top part of
Figure 215 while the bottom part of the figure shows the finite element
idealization used. Because it was known that shear stress reversals
could lead to a reduction in soil strength (Kenney [1967]) an allowance
of 20 % was made for this phenomenon on the excavation side of the

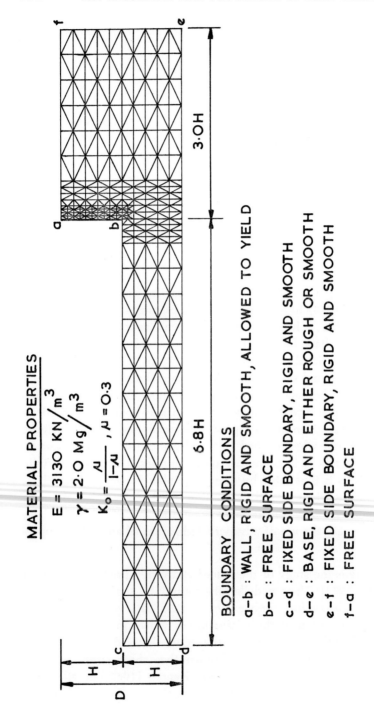

MATERIAL PROPERTIES

$E = 3130 \; KN/m^3$

$\gamma = 2.0 \; Mg/m^3$

$K_o = \dfrac{\mu}{1-\mu} \;,\; \mu = 0.3$

BOUNDARY CONDITIONS

a–b : WALL, RIGID AND SMOOTH, ALLOWED TO YIELD

b–c : FREE SURFACE

c–d : FIXED SIDE BOUNDARY, RIGID AND SMOOTH

d–e : BASE, RIGID AND EITHER ROUGH OR SMOOTH

e–f : FIXED SIDE BOUNDARY, RIGID AND SMOOTH

f–a : FREE SURFACE

Fig. 213: Finite element idealization of the retaining wall study carried out by Morgenstern and Eisenstein (1970).

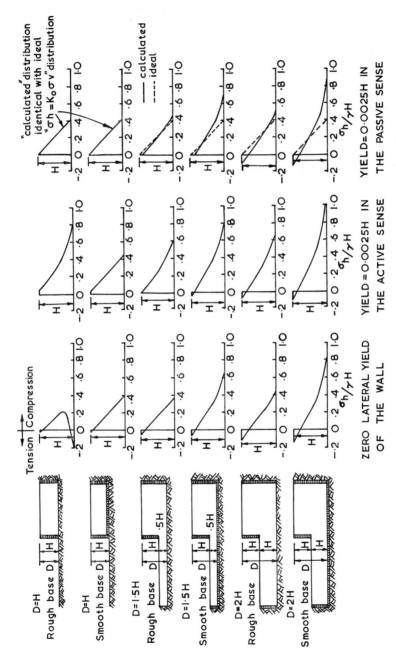

Fig. 214: Computed earth pressure distributions for a range of wall yields and boundary conditions (Morgenstern and Eisenstein [1970]).

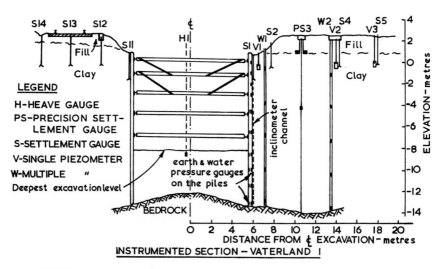

INSTRUMENTED SECTION — VATERLAND I

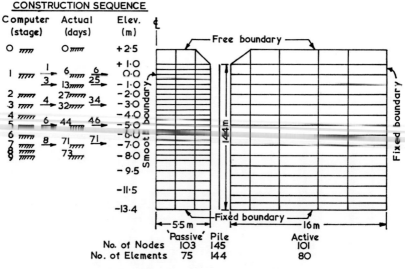

FINITE   ELEMENT   CONFIGURATION

Fig. 215: The Vaterland I excavation (a) the instrumented section,
(b) the finite element idealization (N. G. I. 1962).

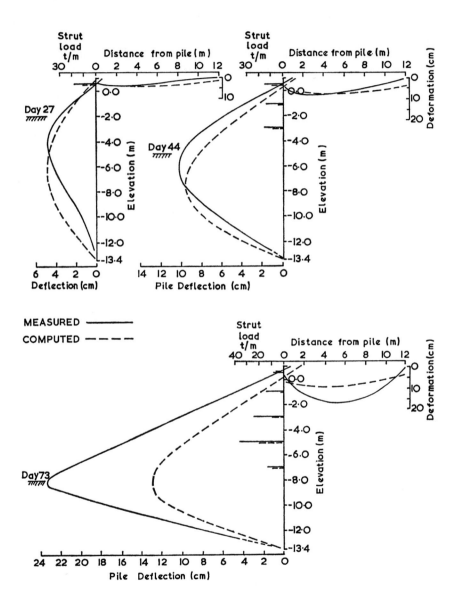

Fig. 216: Comparison of field measurements with computer simulation —
Vaterland I (Palmer and Kenney [1972]).

wall. By assigning soil constants as detailed by Palmer and Kenney, the excavation behaviour was simulated and Figure 216 compares predicted behaviour with measured performance. It will be noted that the simulation is not completely satisfactory but it was considered sufficient by these authors to enable them to proceed with an elaborate parametric study of a range of excavation and soil variables which included initial stress state, modulus of deformation, stress reversal effects, soil adhesion, pile and strut stiffness, strut prestress level and strut spacings. A summary of the relative influence of the various parameters is given in Table 4.

Parameter	Relative Influence*	
	Deformations	Maximum Strut Loads
Soil Conditions:		
Initial stress ratio ⎫ Shear strength ⎬ strength reserve	−1	−1
Shear strength reduction	+1	+1
E soil	−3	−2
Soil − pile adhesion	−1	−1
Support Conditions:		
Effective strut stiffness	−3	+3
EI pile	−3	+2
Prestress	−2	+3
Vertical strut spacing	+2	+3

* (i) Graded from minor influence = 1 to major influence = 3.

  (ii) The sign indicates the change in deformations or maximum strut loads for an increase in the value of the parameter (+ for increases, − for descreases).

Table 4. Relative Influence of Various Parameters (Palmer and Kenney [1972]).

7.6.2. Piles

Ellison et al. (1971) describe the use of a finite element model for bored piles in which triangular and quadrilateral ring elements were used in the mesh shown in Figure 217. In this idealization slippage between the soil and the pile shaft, when maximum skin friction resistance was reached, was achieved by a system of spring elements. The formation

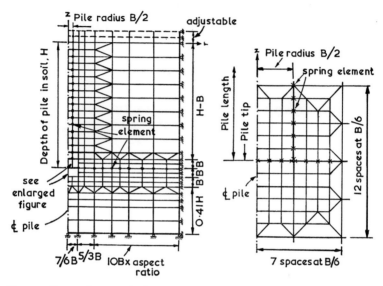

Fig. 217: Finite element idealization of a bored pile in clay (Ellison et al. [1971]).

of a tension crack at pile tip level and slippage between the pile tip and soil were also allowed for in this manner. Ellison (1969) used the field test data of Whitaker and Cooke (1966) and, taking constants for the London clay derived from extensive publications on that soil stratum and suitably idealized for computation purposes, they predicted load/deformation diagrams. Figure 218 gives a comparison between field and theoretical load/deformation curves for two piles, while figure 219 shows the computed displacements in the vicinity of the pile tip. These authors conclude that the finite element model is reliable and can be used to predict the behaviour of bored piles in clay. It should be possible to extend this method of analysis to groups of piles and underreamed piles. The biggest problem facing the foundation engineer is in the description of the soil behaviour in parametric form.

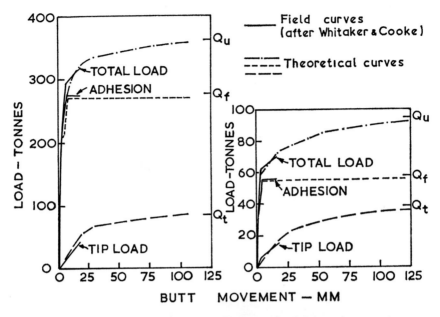

Fig. 218: Comparison of field and theoretical load deformation curves
(Ellison et al. [1971]).

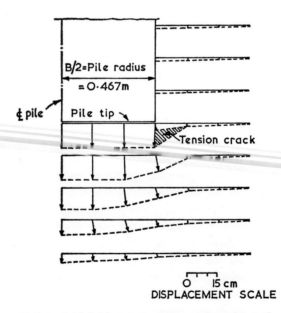

Fig. 219: Computed displacement of clay in the vicinity of a pile tip
(Ellison et al. [1971]).

7.6.3. Slopes

Duncan and Dunlop (1969) discuss the stress analysis of excavation slopes which they simulated using the finite element method. The primary purpose of the study was to determine differences in behaviour of slopes excavated in soils with low and high initial horizontal stresses. These conditions were considered to be representative of normally and heavily overconsolidated clays. Excavation of the slope was simulated analytically by application of stress changes $\Delta\sigma$ to the excavated slope. The ground

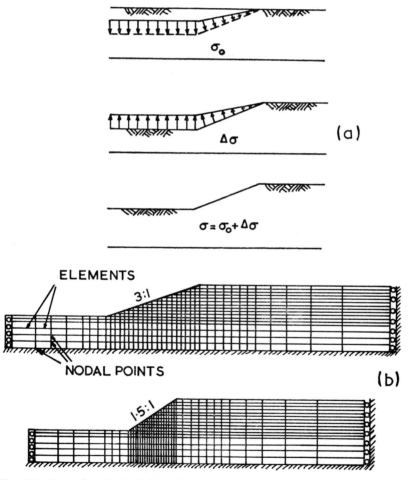

Fig. 220: (a) Analytical simulation of an excavation, (b) finite element representation (Duncan and Dunlop [1969]).

responds to these stress changes which can be computed using the finite element method. The idealization of excavation simulation is shown in Figure 220 (a) while Figure 220 (b) shows the subdivision of the slope into a large number of elements connected at their nodal points. A combination of both rectangular and triangular elements was used. Duncan and Dunlop have calculated the stress distributions in several slopes for Ko values of 0.81 and 1.60. They have also calculated displacement fields and Figure 221 shows a comparison of the surface displacements for two initial stress state conditions and three slopes.

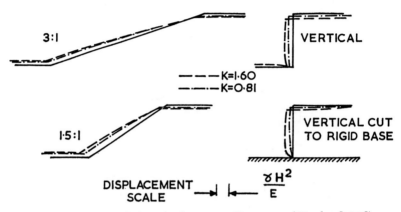

Fig. 221: Computed slope displacements (Duncan and Dunlop [1969]).

This paper and the techniques described therein has shown that it is possible to carry out a complete stress and deformation analysis of an excavated slope. The accuracy of the analysis will depend primarily on the parametric constants used to describe soil behaviour. For this reason alone it is necessary to monitor displacements in the field, preferably at depth in the soil mass and use these measurements to "calibrate" the finite element idealization. Such an approach has been followed by Cole and Burland (1972).

7.6.4. Embankments

Following the extensive instrumentation of the Scammonden dam, a finite element method of analysis was used to compute movements within the dam. The primary purpose of the study was to ascertain the

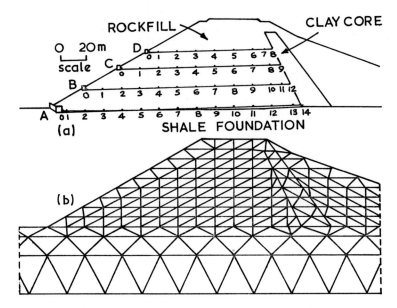

Fig. 222: Scammonden Dam cross section: (a) position of the field movement gauges, (b) the finite element mesh (Penman et al. [1971]).

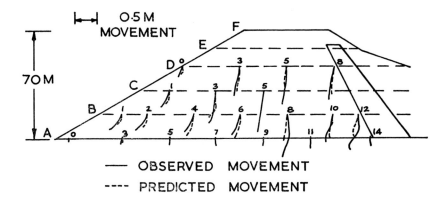

Fig. 223: Comparison of observed and predicted movement vectors, Scammonden Dam (Penman et al. [1971]).

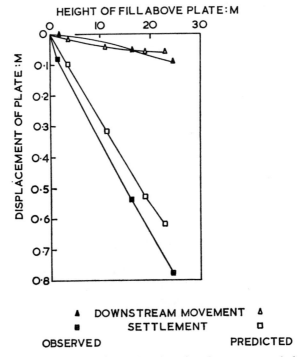

Fig. 224: Comparison of observed and predicted movements of plate D5,
Scammonden Dam (Penman et al. [1971]).

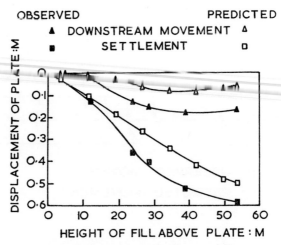

Fig. 225: Comparison of observed and predicted movements of plate B10,
Scammonden Dam (Penman et al. [1971]).

value of a standard elastic analysis method in embankment design because the elastic method has much merit from the practising engineer's point of view. The idealization used is shown in Figure 222. Penman et al. (1971) in their analysis used moduli of deformation, E, and Poisson's ratio, v, for the clay core, rock fill shoulders and foundations based on simplifying assumptions, details of which are given in their paper.

Vectors showing the observed and predicted movements of a number of the instrumentation points are given in Figure 223. All points are not shown in order to achieve clarity. It will be noted that the overall agreement is good. The central region of the dam displayed a predominantly vertical movement with a small downstream movement. Data typical of this movement pattern are given by Figure 224 for station D5.

It was possible to simulate the influence of construction procedure on deformations and the data for instrument point B10 are typical, Figure 225.

Penman et al. (1971) point out the limitations of their study, in particular the assumed properties of the rockfill which were based on laboratory tests. They also believe that the agreement between observation and prediction could be improved by the use of a more sophisticated method of analysis, e. g. Duncan and Chang (1970).

Other analyses of earth dams are reported by Clough and Woodward (1967), Dong et al. (1968) and Broughton (1970).

7.6.5. Lock Structure

As mentioned in Chapter 6 the U-shaped lock structure behaves in a complex manner owing to interaction between the floor slab and the walls. For the Port Allen Lock in Louisiana, a comprehensive instrumentation programme was undertaken and an analysis of these data has been carried out by Duncan and Clough (1971) using an incremental finite element method to simulate lock construction in a series of steps. A schematic representation of these steps is shown in Figure 226 (a), the finite element mesh used being reproduced in Figure 226 (b). To illustrate the power of this method of analysis two sets of measurements are considered. First, the structural deflections of the floor slab and wall

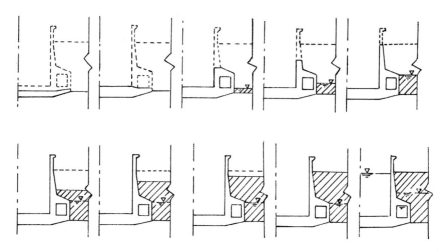

Fig. 226: (a) Finite element representation of concrete and fill placement,
Port Allen Lock (Duncan and Clough [1971]).

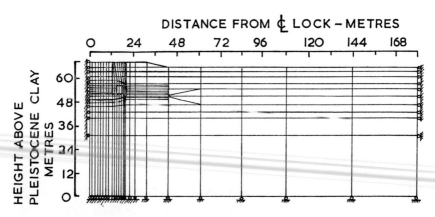

Fig. 226: (b) Finite element mesh employed for analysis of Port Allen Lock
(Duncan and Clough [1971]).

are given in Figure 227. It will be noted that very good agreement exists
with prediction. The second case, Figure 228, gives a comparison between
measured and calculated effective pressures on the structure. Again the
agreement is very good.

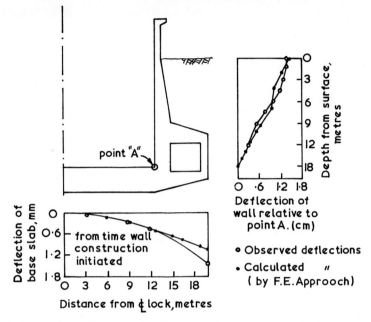

Fig. 227: Comparison of measured and computed movements of the lock structure (Duncan and Clough [1971]).

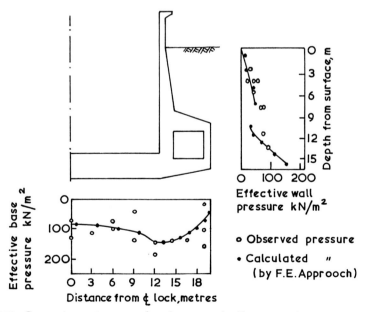

Fig. 228: Comparison of measured and computed effective earth pressure around lock structure (Duncan and Clough [1971]).

Duncan and Clough also simulated the filling of the lock with water and calculated the movements created in the adjacent ground. Because of the complex interaction phenomena there were many apparent anomalies in the observed data. They conclude "... If this behaviour was measured and not calculated, or calculated but not measured, it would probably be attributed to some type of inaccuracy. Because it was measured and calculated, however, this behaviour must be considered normal under the conditions involved".

7.6.6. Structures

The subject of soil-structure interaction is a complex one owing to the lack of quantitative data on the interaction between the structure and the ground (see section 7.6.5. for example). One of the best examples of field data interpretation is that by De Jong and Morgenstern (1971) for the C N Tower in Edmonton, Canada. They analysed the 26-storey tower by use of a general computer programme known as STRUDL, a subsystem of ICES (Integrated Civil Engineering System). These authors found that variation of structural rigidity with height must be considered especially when the displacements occurring during the construction period dominate the settlement history of the building.

Much research relying on detailed field instrumentation supported by interpretation techniques such as that used by De Jong and Morgenstern is expected in the future.

7.6.7. Foundations

There are many cases where use may be made of elasticity theory to aid in the interpretation of field measurements. The case of the CERN test site at Mundford is taken as an example. By measurement of the vertical deformations at various depths beneath a large test tank (Figures 152 to 154), Ward et al. (1968) noted that the test tank foundation was behaving reasonably elastically over the range of applied loads. As a first approximation they assumed that the stress distribution beneath the tank is given by isotropic elastic theory and hence values of the modulus of deformation, E, were estimated at various depths. Based on this assumption the modulus values, E, computed are shown in Table 5 as well as the grades of chalk (established by visual inspection).

Large scale plate loading tests were also carried out as this site in cased shafts but in this case the stiffness of the chalk was defined by an "equivalent modulus of deformation" based on the standard expression

$$E = q \frac{\pi}{4 \, \Delta} \cdot D \, (1 - \nu^2) \qquad (7.9)$$

where q = average applied pressure, Δ = settlement, D = plate diameter and ν = Poisson's ratio.

Hanna and Adams (1968) interpreted plate load test, tank test, excavation test and fill test data in a somewhat similar manner in an attempt to arrive at an equivalent modulus of deformation which could be used for design purposes.

It is becoming increasingly clear however, that natural soils are far from isotropic and the modulus of deformation will vary with depth. As shown by Ward et al. (1968) a practical answer to this problem is possible if extensive field measurements of deformation are made at various levels in the ground.

Level	Average depth below tank (m)	Chalk Grade	Immediate vertical strain (%)		Young's modulus E (kg/cm²)	
			1st loading	2nd loading	1st loading	2nd loading
0—1	1.91	V	0.04500	0.03650	3 700	4 600
1—2	5.57	IV—III	0.00877	0.00929	16 900	15 900
2—3	9.13	III	0.00715*	0.00745*	16 600	16 500
3—4	12.76	III—II	0.00381	0.00402	22 200	21 100
4—5	18.59	II	0.00117	0.00127	43 700	40 200
5—6	25.77	II	0.00065*	0.00070*	47 000	43 600

* Adjusted to eliminate influence of marl seam.

Table 5: Values of Young's modulus E estimated from the immediate vertical strains measured beneath the centre of the tank at maximum load for two loading cycles (Poisson's ratio assumed equal to 0.1). (Ward et al. [1968]).

7.6.8. Other Examples

Most correlations between field measurements and theoretical predictions have been with pore water pressure development in earth dams. The use of the field piezometer, and its development to enable measurements of water pressure in partly saturated soils to be made, has led to a rational basis for embankment design. Good examples of such correlations are to be found in many publications including those of Bishop and Al-Dhahir et al. (1967) and Wilkinson et al. (1969).

The powerful and versatile methods of stress analysis which are available can be used to estimate stress and strain changes in a foundation subject to load. The accuracy of any prediction depends on the parametric constants assumed for soil behaviour and how realistic they are. Because the engineer is usually dealing with a natural material (the soil) in a natural environment, the local geology of the site plays an important role in the subsequent behaviour of the foundation. The Rankine lecture by Rowe (1972) discusses the significance of soil fabric. Neglect of soil fabric, or inability to allow for it in a stress analysis will lead to error. Consequently the value of any theoretical analysis of a foundation will be controlled to some extent at least by the engineer's knowledge of the natural soil and how well he can describe this soil.

7.7. General

The examples referred to in the previous sections show the approach which can be followed by the foundation engineer in making use of field measurement data. It will be noted that the field instrumentation programme is essential and without the data which it provides any stress or deformation analysis will be limited.

By careful selection of the quantities to be measured along with a relatively simple method of stress analysis, it is possible to obtain a very useful quantitative assessment of the behaviour of the ground. The studies of Cole and Burland (1972) for the Britannic House excavation and Duncan and Clough (1971) for the Port Allen Lock illustrate this point.

References

A.G.S., (1969), Applied Geodata Systems Inc., Cambridge, Massachusetts, U.S.A. Trade Literature.

AL-DHAHIR, Z. A., KENNARD, M. F., and MORGENSTERN, N. R., (1969), "Observations on pore water pressures beneath the ash lagoon embankments at Fiddler's Ferry Power Station", Proceedings, Conference on In-Situ Measurements in Soils and Rocks, British Geotechnical Society, 265—276.

BISHOP, A. W., WEBB, D. L., and LEWIN, P. I., (1965), "Undisturbed samples of London clay from the Ashford Common shaft: strength-effective stress relationships", Geotechnique, Vol. 15, No. 1, 1—31.

BISHOP, A. W., and AL-DHAHIR, Z. A., (1969), "Some comparisons between laboratory tests, in-situ tests and full scale performance, with special reference to permeability and coefficient of consolidation", Proceedings, Conference on In-Situ Investigations in Soils and Rocks, British Geotechnical Society, 251—264.

BROUGHTON, N. O., (1970), "Elastic analysis for behaviour of rockfill", Proceedings, American Society of Civil Engineers, Vol. 96, No. SM 5, 1715—1733.

CLOUGH, R. W., and WOODWARD, R. J., (1967), "Analysis of embankment stresses and deformations", Proceedings, American Society of Civil Engineers, Vol. 93, No. SM 4, 529—549.

COLE, K. W., and BURLAND, J. B., (1972), "Observations of retaining wall movements associated with a large excavation", Proceedings, Fifth European Conference on Soil Mechanics and Foundation Engineering, Madrid, Vol. 1, 445—453.

CONSIDINE, D. M., (1964), Handbook of applied instrumentation. McGraw Hill Book Company, New York.

DE JONG, J., and MORGENSTERN, N. R., (1971), "The influence of structural rigidity on the foundation loads of the C. N. Tower, Edmonton", Canadian Geotechnical Journal, Vol. 8, No. 4, 527—537.

DESAI, C. S., and ABEL, J. F., (1972), "Introduction to the Finite Element Method. A numerical method for engineering analysis". Van Nostrand Reinhold Company, New York.

DI BIAGIO, E. L., (1966), "Stresses and displacements around an unbraced rectangular excavation in an elastic medium", Ph. D. Thesis, University of Illinois.

DONG, S. B., MASSON, H., and WESTMANN, R. A., (1968), "Embankment analysis and field correlation", Highway Research Record, No. 223, 9—17.

DUNCAN, J. M., and DUNLOP, P., (1969), "Slopes in stiff-fissured clays and shales", Proceedings, American Society of Civil Engineers, Vol. 95, No. SM 2, 467—492.

DUNCAN, J. M., and CHANG, C. Y., (1970), "Non-linear analysis of stress and strain in soils", Proceedings, American Society of Civil Engineers, Vol. 96, SM 5, 1629—1653.

DUNCAN, J. M., and CLOUGH, G. W., (1971), "Finite Element Analysis of Port Allen Lock", Proceedings, American Society of Civil Engineers, Vol. 97, No. SM 8, 1053—1068.

ELLISON, R. D., (1969), "An analytical study of the mechanics of single pile foundations", Ph. D. Thesis, Carnegie-Mellon University, U.S.A.

ELLISON, R. D., D'APPOLONIA, E., and THIERS, G. R., (1971), "Load-deformation mechanism for bored piles", Proceedings, American Society of Civil Engineers, Vol. 97, No. SM 4, 661—678.

HANNA, T. H., and ADAMS, J. I., (1968), "Comparison of field and laboratory measurements of modulus of deformation of a clay", Highway Research Record, No. 243, 12—22.

HAWKES, I., HOOPER, J. A., and ROSE, H., (1965), "Photoelastic instrumentation in Civil Engineering structures", Proceedings, Conference on Experimental Methods of Investigating Stress and Strain in Structures, Prague, Vol. 2, 642.

HOOPER, J. A., (1972), "The theory and design of photoelastic load gauges incorporating glass element transducers", International Journal of Rock Mechanics and Mining Sciences, Vol. 9, No. 3, 363—401.

HENDRY, A. W., (1964), "Elements of experimental stress analysis", Pergamon Press.

JONES, E. B., (1965), "Instrument Technology", Vol. 1, Butterworths, London.

KENNEY, T. C., (1967), "Shearing resistance of natural quick clays", Ph. D. Thesis, University of London.

MORGENSTERN, N. R., and EISENSTEIN, Z., (1970), "Methods of estimating lateral loads and deformations", Specialty Conference, Lateral Stresses in the ground and design of earth retaining structures, American Society of Civil Engineers, 51—102.

MORGAN, J. R., and MOORE, P. J., (1968), "Experimental Techniques, Chapter 5 in Soil Mechanics: selected topics edited by I. K. Lee, Butterworths, London.

NEUBERT, H. K. P., (1963), "Instrument Transducers", Clarendon Press.

Norwegian Geotechnical Institute, (1962), "Measurement at a strutted excavation, Oslo Subway, Vaterland I, km 1.373", Report 6.

PALMER, J. H. L., and KENNEY, T. C., (1972), "Analytical study of a braced excavation in weak clay", Canadian Geotechnical Journal, Vol. 9, No. 2, 145—164.

PENMAN, A. D. M., BURLAND, J. B., and CHARLES, J. A., (1971), "Observed and predicted deformation in a large embankment dam during construction", Proceedings, Institution of Civil Engineers, London, Vol. 49, 1—21.

PERRY, C. C., and LISSNER, H. R., (1955), "The strain gauge primer", McGraw-Hill, New York.

REESE, L. C., (1969), "Soil parameters in finite element analysis", Keynote paper, Session IV on Soil Mechanics and Foundations. Symposium on Application of Finite Element Methods in Civil Engineering, Vanderbilt University, Nashville, Tennessee, U.S.A.

ROWE, P. W., (1972), "The relevance of soil fabric to site investigation practice", Geotechnique, Vol. 22, No. 2, 193—300.

SKEMPTON, A. W., (1961), "Horizontal stresses in an overconsolidated Eocene clay", Proceedings, Fifth International Conference on Soil Mechanics and Foundation Engineering, Paris, Vol. 1, 351—357.

SMITH, I. M., (1979), "Plane plastic deformations of soil", Roscoe Memorial Symposium, Cambridge University, 548—563.

WARD, W. H., BURLAND, J. B., and GALLOIS, R. W., (1968), "Geotechnical assessment of a site at Mundford, Norfolk, for a large proton accelerator", Geotechnique, Vol. 18, No. 4, 399—431.

WHITAKER, T., and COOKE, R. W., (1966), "An investigation of the shaft and base resistance of large bored piles in London clay", Symposium on large bored piles, The Institution of Civil Engineers, London, 7—49.

WILKINSON, W. B., BARDEN, L., and ROCKE, G., (1969), "An assessment of in-situ and laboratory tests in predicting the pore pressures in an earth dam", Proceedings, Conference In-Situ investigations in Soils and Rocks, British Geotechnical Society, 277—284.

ZIENKIEWICZ, O. C., (1971), "The finite element method in Engineering Science", McGraw-Hill, London, 2nd Edition.

ZIENKIEWICZ, O. C., and NAYLOR, D. J., (1970), "Discussion on the adaption of critical state soil mechanics theory for use in finite elements", Roscoe Memorial Symposium, Cambridge University, 537—547.

8 | Instrumentation of Laboratory Scale Foundations

8.1. Introduction

In the testing of laboratory scale soil specimens or foundation structures very little effort has been devoted to the measurement of stress and deformation due to the technical difficulty and costs involved. The state of the subject is very well expressed by Roscoe (1970) in his Rankine Lecture. ". . . The first point is the need, especially in research, for a radical change of outlook. We should stop concentrating attention on the shear strength of soils and think in terms of their stress-strain behaviour, especially at stress levels corresponding to working loads which will probably be less than half the values required to produce failure. We must continue to develop laboratory and field test equipment to investigate the stress-strain behaviour of soils under as wide a range as possible of imposed stress and strain paths . . . At the same time boundary value problems should continue to be investigated in the same detail at model scale in the laboratory. The centrifuge will provide much reliable evidence but can never fully replace a properly instrumented full-scale field test".

The scale of testing and the resources available control the instrumentation techniques which can be employed in laboratory studies. In the following sections some of the methods which have been used in the past are mentioned. It will be appreciated that a very large range of custom made instruments is in use in laboratories throughout the world. It is impossible to carry out a detailed survey of these instruments. In fact it is considered dangerous to carry out such a survey because these "gadgets" have been developed over the years by a particular research group for a particular purpose. The inquisitive investigator will find details in the many Master and Doctor theses and reports from research establishments as well as in the technical journals and Conference Proceedings.

8.2. Displacement Measurements

At a laboratory scale displacements in the vicinity of foundation structures are usually of small magnitude. For this reason the equipment employed for their measurement must be highly accurate, yet simple in operation and its use in the soil mass must have a very small effect on the measurements being taken as well as on other measurements. Several methods of measurement have been used.

8.2.1. Mechanical Methods

The simplest displacement measurement is that of the surface of a soil mass. Small footings 15 to 20 mm diameter by 2 mm thick perspex with three protruding sharp nails about 10 mm in length can be gently pushed into the soil surface under finger pressure until the underside is in contact with the soil. A dial gauge or a l.v.d.t. attached to an independent and rigid datum is placed in contact with this disc. Vertical movements of the disc can be measured to 0.01 mm or better accuracy. Lateral surface displacements are much more difficult to measure with a high degree of accuracy. For low accuracy work a scale may be used to measure the separation of the discs. For more precise work a survey system using a catheometer or similar device is required. Due to the very limited space which is normally available in the vicinity of small scale test structures, such movement measurements are rarely made.

The measurement of movement at depth is a much more difficult task owing to the three-dimensional nature of the measurement problem. Carr and Hanna (1971) describe the use of a mechanical gauge which they developed to obtain movements in sand around a large scale plate anchor (diameter 0.15 m) in sand. The gauge comprises three parts: (1) a conductor tube; (2) a brass movement rod; and (3) a footing attached to the movement rod. The brass rod, attached to the movement footing, is conducted inside the conductor tube. Figure 229 illustrates the principle of the gauge. For horizontal movement measurement the gauges are installed during sand bed preparation. The conductor tube passes through an accurately located bushing in the wall of the sand container and the movement footing bears tightly against the end of the conductor tube. In this manner all of the horizontal movement gauges are positioned at predetermined locations while the sand bed is being prepared. The vertical movement gauges are carefully pushed through guide bushings, screwed into a rigid plate which is held above the sand surface, until a collar near the top end of the conductor tube reaches and bears on the top of the guide bushing. When the movement gauges are installed the guide bushes are screwed back about 5 mm as shown in Figure 229. Thus the end of the conductor tube is separated from the movement footing.

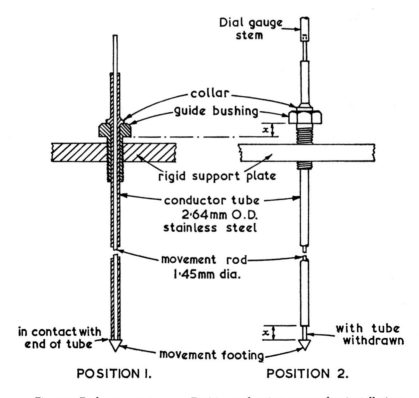

Fig. 229: Rod movement gauge: Position 1 showing gauge after installation; Position 2 showing gauge ready for use with conductor tube pulled about 5 mm from footing (Carr and Hanna [1971]).

The clearance between the conductor tube and the movement rod is sufficiently small to preclude fine sand sizes from entering and restricting the movement of the footing relative to the conductor tube.

Displacement of the top end of the movement rods is recorded by a mechanical dial gauge aligned to bear axially on the protruding end.

To date this technique has been used to record sand movements near to anchor plates, footing and retaining walls. Because the conductor tubes are of a finite area, they do cause a slight reinforcing of the soil mass. For this reason the scale of testing must be large, otherwise the movement gauges will modify the performance being measured. To date the accuracy of the measurements made has not been verified by other established methods of measurement such as the X-ray technique. Use of the technique in any laboratory instrumentation programme must bear this in mind as well as the scale limitation. Some further details of data provided by the rod movement gauges are given in Section 8.6.

8.2.2. Electrical Methods

Most electrical methods of deformation measurement in soil masses operate on the principle of measuring the change in separation of two discs embedded a short distance apart in the soil. Eggestad (1963) used the gauge shown in Figure 230. It consists of a coil and an iron core. The core moves inside the coil and thus changes the impedance of the coil, the coil being wound on a perspex spool attached to a perspex plate. The core is fixed to a thin brass rod and thus the gauges are connected together as shown in Figure 230. The variation of the impedance of the coil as the position of the iron core within the coil varied is determined by calibration. Accuracies of $\pm$ 0.01 to $\pm$ 0.03 mm are quoted for overall deformations of up to 8 mm.

Eggestad used these impedance gauges to record vertical and horizontal displacements beneath a circular surface footing in a dry sand. Owing to the presence of the gauges it was not possible to compact the sand and a pouring technique was employed. It is stated that the density "was fairly uniform". Because steel would affect the impedance of the coils a perspex loading plate was used, the test arrangement being as shown in Figure 231. Load was applied in increments and Figure 232 presents typical movement data for a medium-loose sand.

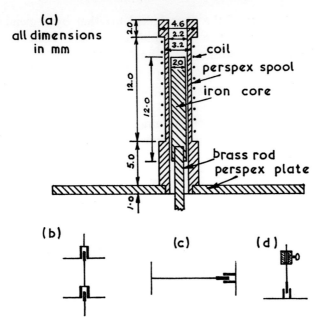

Fig. 230: (a) Cross section through movement gauge; (b) arrangement for vertical deformation measurements; (c) arrangement for lateral deformation measurements; (d) arrangement for surface deformation measurements (Eggestad [1963]).

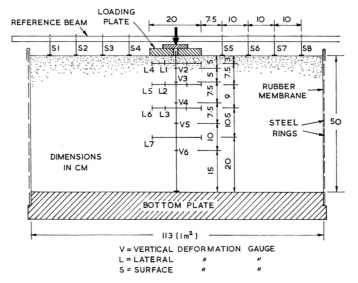

Fig. 231: Arrangement of movement gauges in the vicinity of a surface footing in sand (Eggestad [1963]).

To avoid the limitations of the discs linked together by a member as used by Eggestad (1963), two individual discs have been used by workers at the Illinois Institute of Technology (IIT). Morgan (1971) describes the system. It comprises one pair of coils — the reference set — to be mounted to allow the axial displacement to be varied and read on a micrometer. The other pair of coils (about 18 mm o. d. by 1.5 mm thick) is placed in the soil at about 12 mm spacing, as shown in Figure 233. One coil of each pair is driven from a 50 k. c. oscillator and the

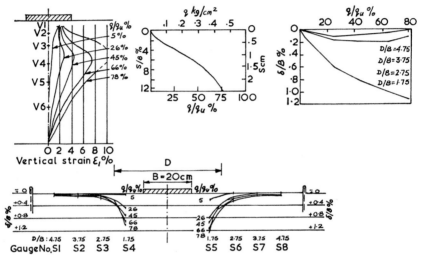

Fig. 232: Soil deformations for a surface loading test in medium loose sand (Eggestad [1963]).

output voltage induced in the other coil of each pair is connected, so that the output is the difference of the individual coil output voltages. Thus the change in spacing of the coils is obtained. Truesdale and Anderson (1964) give calibration and use details, especially the influence of rotation of the coils during placement or during a test. Other tests on the accuracy of this gauge are given by Morgan (1971).

Sparrow and Tory (1966) developed a strain cell which was electrically interchangeable with their earth pressure cell, Figure 90. The cell was designed to be soft and thus cause little reinforcing of the soil mass in which it was embedded. The cell is shown in Figure 234 and consists of a wrapped-round beam contained within a thin cylindrical box which forms one anchorage. A shaft connected to the beam and to a thin disc

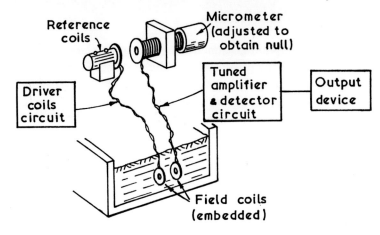

Fig. 233: Schematic diagram of soil strain coil gauge (Morgan [1971]).

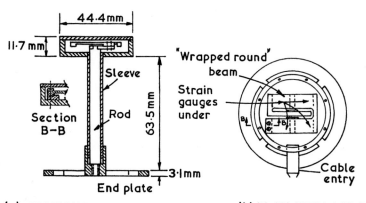

(a) SECTION THROUGH STRAIN CELL (b) PLAN WITH LID REMOVED

Fig. 234: Soil strain cell (Sparrow and Tory [1966]).

at the other end completes the unit. Relative movement between the two ends of the cell deflects the beam to give a voltage output proportional to the movement. The cells are calibrated using a bench micrometer. Other cells which operate on a similar principle are described by Selig (1964) and Morgan and Holden (1967).

It will be appreciated that with all of the "strain" gauges referred to in this sub-section, considerable interference to the soil mass results. These effects can be minimized by the use of a large scale of testing but they can never be eliminated.

8.2.3. Photographic Methods

In Section 5.2.7. the photogrammetric method of displacement measurement was mentioned, the principle being illustrated in Figure 117. Butterfield et al. (1970) describe the measurement of displacement fields around a cone-shaped wedge which is being pushed into a sand. Plane strain boundary conditions were imposed by the presence of a glass-sided flume, the wedge spanning the flume width. Photographs taken before and after each load increment give an apparent sand surface topography when viewed stereoscopically. This topography is then contoured to give displacement. Butterfield et al. point out the need for a stable photographic film, the need for a rigid camera support and the need for planer displacements.

When contouring from pairs of photographs, two overlapping images are produced on the plane of the tracing table. The scale is determined by the ratio H/D, Figure 117. Where the film plate has been set parallel to the plane of the displacement field and with no movement of the camera position between photographs, the projectors have to be set vertical and at the same height above the plotting table. Complete details of other adjustments necessary are also given by Butterfield et al. Further use of the technique is reported by Butterfield and Andrawes (1971).

A limitation of the photographic method is the need to use either a glass-sided flume with the foundation abutting against it or a two-dimensional model such as the pin analogy of Schnaebli (1957). An advantage of prime importance is that a permanent record of the whole field displacement is obtained and these records can be interpreted at any subsequent date.

A high degree of accuracy is possible and Butterfield and Andrawes (1971) suggest displacement measurement sensitivity of up to 5 microns.

8.2.4. X-Ray Methods

The principle of this method is simple. Lead shot is placed at the nodes of a co-planer regular network within the soil mass and the displacements of the lead shot are observed with X-rays. The technique was used in 1929 by Gerber and by Davis and Woodward (1949). The development of the X-ray technique to study strains in soil test specimens and in the vicinity of laboratory scale structures is primarily due to the efforts of Roscoe and co-workers at Cambridge since 1960, e. g. Roscoe et al. (1963).

During the test specimen preparation, lead shot is placed at regular and known intervals. This can be achieved by means of a special template which is placed on the level soil surface, the lead shot being placed in vertical holes in the template. The template is then removed and another layer of soil is placed. Alternate rows of lead shot are placed in such a manner that the vertical network is co-planar as shown in Figure 235.

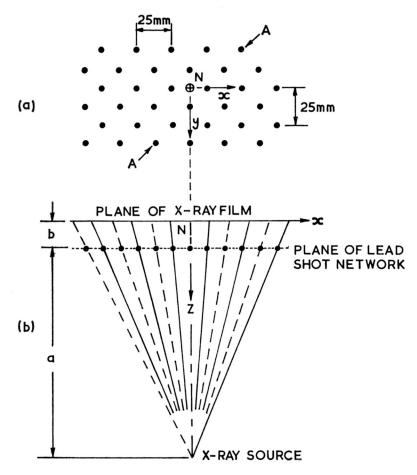

Fig. 235: Arrangement of lead shot and its projection on to the X-ray film
(Roscoe et al. [1963]).

The X-ray film is assumed to be co-planar with the lead shot network. By taking a series of radiographs at intervals during a test the displacements of the lead shot can be recorded on film. To determine displacements, successive radiographs taken during a test are superposed on an illuminator. A reference grid on each radiograph ensures correct alignment. The displacement of a lead shot particle is determined by measuring the distance between its images in successive radiographs.

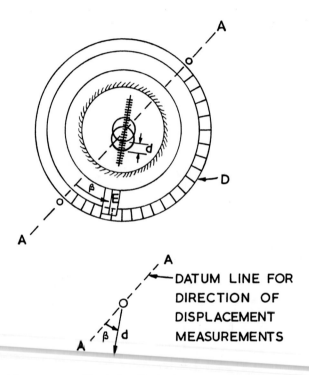

Fig. 236: Measurement of lead shot displacement using a microscope and protractor (Roscoe et al. [1963]).

Roscoe et al. describe a manual and a semi-automatic method of measurement. In the manual method a low power microscope containing a linear graduated scale in the eyepiece is superposed on two successive radiographs resting on an illuminator. The view through the microscope is shown in Figure 236. For each displacement the magnitude d and the direction β, relative to a fixed datum is measured.

For derivation of the strains within the soil, four lead shots at the corners of a mesh are considered. They have displacement components of u and w in the x and y directions as shown in Figure 237. The lengths of the mesh are l_x and l_y. The linear strains are

$$\delta \varepsilon_x = (u_1 - u_3)/l_x \text{ and } \delta \varepsilon_y = (w_2 - w_4)/l_y \tag{8.1}$$

and the volumetric strain is given by

$$\delta u = \delta \varepsilon_x + \delta \varepsilon_y \tag{8.2}$$

It follows from a Mohr circle of strain that the principal strains are

$$\begin{bmatrix} \delta \varepsilon_1 \\ \delta \varepsilon_3 \end{bmatrix} = \frac{1}{2} (\delta \varepsilon_x + \delta \varepsilon_y) \pm \frac{1}{2} \sqrt{[(\delta \varepsilon_x - \delta \varepsilon_y)^2 + \delta \varepsilon_{xy}{}^2]} \tag{8.3}$$

and

$$\alpha = \frac{1}{2} \operatorname{Tan}^{-1} [\delta \varepsilon_{xy}/(\delta \varepsilon_x - \delta \varepsilon_y)] \tag{8.4}$$

where the shear strain $\delta \varepsilon_{xy} = (w_1 - w_3)/l_x + (u_2 - u_4)/l_y$.

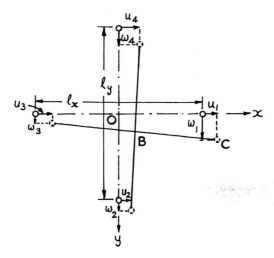

O   SHOT BEFORE DISPLACEMENT
⊙   SHOT AFTER DISPLACEMENT

Fig. 237: Incremental displacements of a lead shot mesh (Roscoe et al. [1963]).

and α is positive when measured clockwise from the x-axis. Roscoe et al. discuss in detail sources of error which may affect strain measurement. Since that paper the technique has been used extensively at Cambridge by a large number of research workers and it is now a standard method of test measurement in that laboratory.

The primary disadvantage of the technique is the thickness of the soil sample which can be penetrated by the X-rays. This depends on the power of the X-ray source and the time available for exposure of the film. All of the tests at Cambridge are of a relatively small scale due to this limitation.

X-ray techniques have been used by other workers and Kirkpatrick and Belshaw (1968) describe studies of strain measurements in large triaxial specimens.

Roscoe (1970) reviews the general problem of strain measurement in soils and shows how a number of measurement principles and techniques are used to solve laboratory scale problems.

8.2.5. Boundary displacements

In most large scale laboratory testing work dial gauges or l. v. d. t.'s are used to record displacements of footings, retaining walls etc. In order to obtain reliable movements it is essential (i) that the reference datum is rigid, (ii) there are sufficient movement points to give the displacements in the x, y and z directions or to enable them to be calculated. In very sensitive work the force from the spring of the dial gauge plunger may have to be allowed for.

8.3. Force Measurement

In most laboratory scale test work force is measured by a load transducer such as a proving ring, force block or a special force transducer, and a review was given in Chapter 2. The scale of testing usually requires the measurement of small forces and each topic presents different design problems. To illustrate the problems and how they may be approached three cases are considered.

Case I refers to the measurement of the prestress force applied between a prestress plate and an anchor. The load cell, prestressing jack and prestress plate form one unit as shown in Figure 238. The cell had a wall thickness of 0.2 mm for a design load of 2200 N and 0.71 mm for a design load of 10,000 N. Eight strain gauges were fixed in a temperature compensated arrangement on the inside of each load cell, the cell

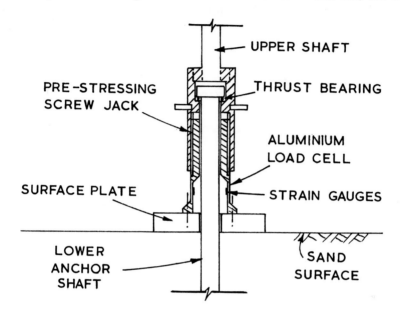

Fig. 238: Section through load cell used to record force in a prestressed anchor (Sparks [1972]).

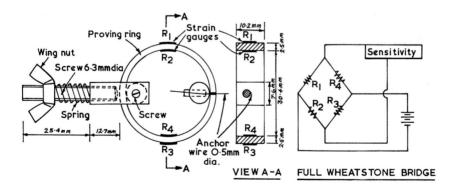

Fig. 239: Proving ring load cell for anchor wire load measurement.

unit being stress relieved before calibration. The prestressing jack consisted of a simple screw arrangement at the top of the load cell unit, a thrust bearing preventing rotation of the anchor shaft during the prestressing operation. The prestress plate was fixed to a flange on the lower end of the load cell. Further details are given by Sparks (1972).

Case 2. The measurement of anchor wire loads for a laboratory scale structure was obtained by small diameter proving ring transducers with two pairs of strain gauges connected to give a temperature compensated circuit. The rings had the facility to apply load by turning a screw at one end. Attachment of the rings to a special frame permitted the easy adjustment of the rings for different test set-ups. Figure 239 shows a detail of a typical ring. A range of sizes has been used for studies of anchored retaining walls. (Hanna and Matallana [1970]).

Case 3 refers to the measurement of axial load along long laboratory scale piles of 12 to 38 mm diameter. Load cells capable of measuring axial compressive or tensile forces were developed by Tan (1971). Two types of cell were used. In one, miniature proving rings were incorporated in the tubular pile by special screw joints which (a) permitted the sectional pile to be jointed together without twisting of the leads from the strain gauges, (b) enabled the pile to be assembled in a near perfectly straight condition. A detail of one of these load cell units is shown in Figure 240. The pile was 25.4 mm diameter. Figure 241 details the method of load cell arrangement in a typical pile. To prevent sand from entering between the pile sections a thin strip of tape was placed over the joints. The other cell unit consisted of a thin-wall tube in tension, and a detail of a typical load unit is shown in Figure 242. With this cell it was possible to instrument piles of 12 mm diameter and measure forces of a few grammes.

Both load cell units permitted bells to be placed along the length of the pile shaft by the use of special couplers. Special care was given to the methods of pile assembly to prevent fouling of the load cell leads and to ensure the pile was perfectly straight.

Other researchers have made use of different methods of load measurements and the work of Shenton (1965) is worthy of study. He made cells capable of measuring normal and shear forces on sections of the pile wall.

There are many other methods of force measurement which may be used in the laboratory, e. g. telemetry methods (Prange [1971]), photo-elastic methods (Hooper [1972]), but the simplest and cheapest is the strain gauge transducer. The above examples serve to illustrate the versatility of the strain gauge. Scott (1972) reviews the characteristics of the various types of strain gauge which are available.

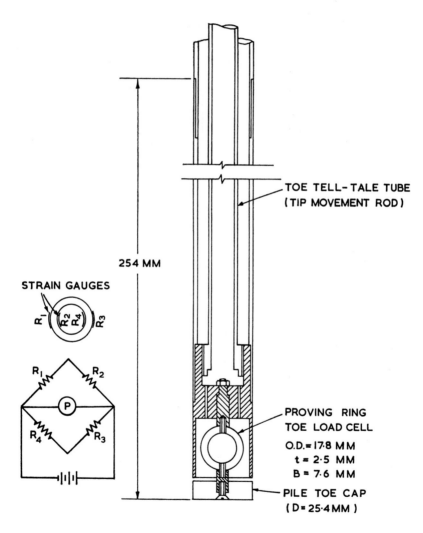

Fig. 240: Proving-ring type load cell for axial load measurement in a pile (Tan [1971]).

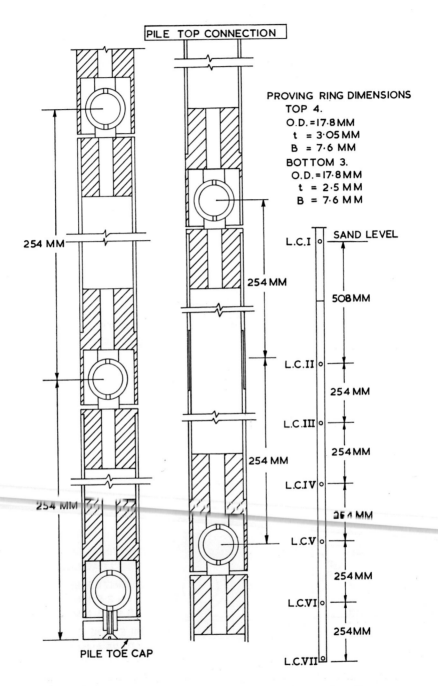

Fig. 241: Load cell arrangement in a typical pile (Tan [1971]).

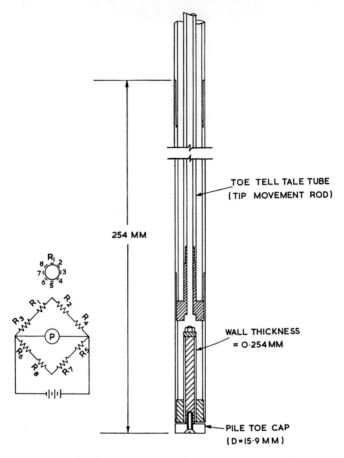

Fig. 242: Tube-type load cell for axial load measurement in a pile (Tan [1971]).

8.4. Contact Stress Measurement

The magnitude, direction and distribution of stresses on foundation boundaries control the behaviour of the foundation. In most laboratory research work normal stresses only have been considered but in some studies it is imperative that shear stresses are considered, e. g. retaining walls. The range of pressure values to be measured prevents a single transducer unit from being acceptable for all laboratory work. In this section several methods of contact stress measurement are considered.

8.4.1. Pneumatic Earth Pressure Cell

Rowe and Briggs (1961) and Peaker (1964) used a cell which operates on the principle that a change in pressure on a diaphragm produces a measurable displacement of fluid into a fine bore tube. Once calibrated the rise of fluid in a tube can be used to predict the average soil pressure acting on the diaphragm. In connection with studies of laboratory scale tied retaining walls in sand Hanna and Matallana (1970) modified the Rowe and Briggs cell. A detail of the cell used to measure maximum average normal earth pressures of up to 4 kN/m² is shown in Figure 243.

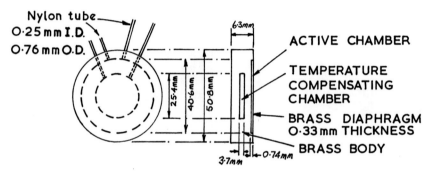

Fig. 243: Hydraulic normal earth pressure cell.

The cell was machined from a brass block and has an active and a dummy chamber. Both chambers are connected to 0.25 mm bore by 0.75 mm o. d. nylon tubes, the connections being made in Araldite glue. A paraffin treated with a small trace of "Waxoline Red" dye was introduced to the cell by a surgical syringe. Calibration in a temperature bath provided a simple means of temperature compensation, it being assumed that the dummy chamber is insensitive to external loading. In use the cell has given satisfactory results but suffers from (i) problems of maintenance (particularly leaks at the joints), (ii) arching across the diaphragm owing to the central deflection of the diaphragm (iii) the cell being of a relatively large diameter is incapable of measuring pressure gradients. Calibration and other details are given by Peaker (1965).

8.4.2. Beam Type Pressure Cell

To overcome some of the limitations of the hydraulic cell, Plant (1972) measured normal earth pressure distributions against a rigid retaining wall by means of beam cells. The principle of this cell is that a small central deflection of the rigidly clamped beam results in a signal from the temperature compensated strain gauge circuit. To control arching effects, the span to central deflection ratio was 2500 : 1 for the maximum design pressure of 6 kN/m². A detail of the cell and its use in the measurement of normal earth pressure on a rigid wall is given in Figure 244. Further details on the use of this cell are given by Plant (1972).

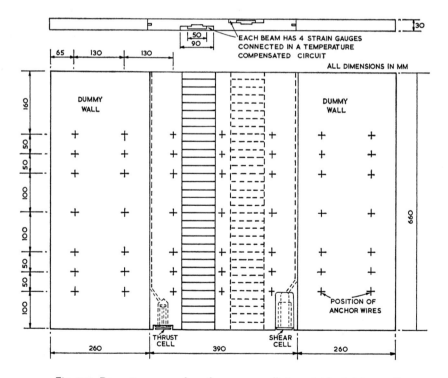

Fig. 244: Beam-type normal earth pressure cells in a rigid retaining wall (Plant [1972]).

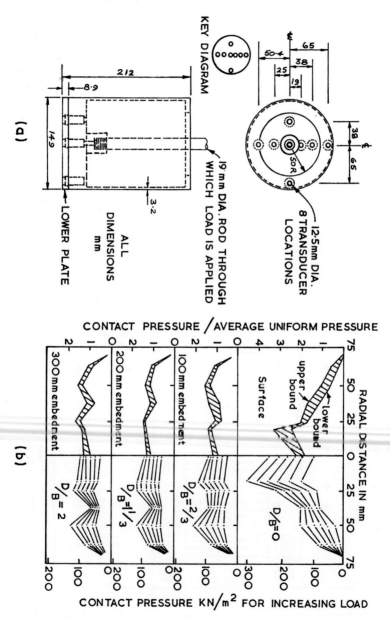

Fig. 245: (a) Details of a rigid footing and the layout of the earth pressure trans-ducers; (b) vertical contact pressure distribution for different embedment depths (Ho and Lopes [1969]).

8.4.3. Pressure Transducers

Ho and Lopes (1969) describe the use of commercially available pressure transducers to measure footing normal contact pressures. The transducers of 12.5 mm diameter operate on the deflection of a strain-gauged diaphragm which is flush with the end of the transducer unit. Details of this particular transducer are given by Burn (1963). Eight pressure transducers were located in the 149 mm diameter footing as shown in Figure 245 (a). For a 700 kN/m^2 pressure change the volume change at the transducer diaphragm was 0.0033 mm^3. A force link was connected in the loading shaft. The output signals from the force link and the pressure recorders were monitored simultaneously on an 8-channel recorder. With the instruments and recorder system used, Ho and Lopes could measure static as well as dynamic load. Contact pressure measurements for a range of foundation geometries are shown in Figure 245 (b).

8.4.4. Normal and Shear Stress Measurement

All of the above mentioned earth pressure cells suffer from (i) their inability to measure normal and shear stress values simultaneously at a boundary and (ii) arching effects created in the soil mass by deflection of the pressure transducer unit. As mentioned in Chapter 4, the Cambridge contact stress transducer has overcome these limitations enabling normal and shear stresses and the eccentricity of normal stress to be measured over very small areas. The arrangement of the strain gauges ensures that the relationship between the applied loads and output voltage is linear. Any interaction between the circuits is automatically accounted for during calibration. The standard cell unit has a face area of 33.3 mm by 33.3 mm and is available in the pressure range 0 to 21 kN/m^2 to 0 to 138000 kN/m^2. It is possible to produce cells with a very small face area. Details on the principles of the cell are given by Arthur and Roscoe (1961) and Figure 99 showed a section through a cell. This cell has been used extensively by the Cambridge research group and some examples of the cell use are given by Hambley and Roscoe (1969), James and Bransby (1970, 1971), for example.

Prange (1971) describes the use of telemetry principles for normal and shear stress measurement but the high initial costs of these units will perhaps limit their use to a few laboratories only.

8.4.5. Other

There are many other methods of contact pressure measurement which the ingenious research worker can apply. For example miniature proving rings connected to a machined plate of about 20 to 25 mm diameter can be embedded in a footing and used to measure average normal contact pressures similar to the measurements of Ho and Lopes (1969) who used commercially available diaphragm-type pressure transducers.

Difficulties which arise with the design of all pressure transducers are the flexibility of the measuring system and interaction between different parts of the measuring system. For these reasons all contact pressure measurements are in error to some degree. Use of the principles of measurement developed by Arthur and Roscoe (1961) have minimized these errors to an exceedingly low level.

8.5. Stress Measurement in a Soil Mass

The introduction of any pressure cell into a soil mass causes a change in the stress field in the soil mass. Some of most important and useful work has been carried out at Nottingham University in connection with pressures beneath pavements. A miniature earth pressure cell, which operates on the diaphragm principle, Figure 90, was embedded in the soil beneath foundations and the stresses "at a point" determined. Some details of this work are given by Sparrow and Tory (1966), Brown and Pell (1967) and these workers conclude that their earth pressure cells are satisfactory for both static and dynamic pressure measurement at their relatively large scale of testing.

8.6. Some Examples of Laboratory Instrumentation

To illustrate the power of laboratory scale instrumentation techniques in providing data on behaviour, several examples have been chosen. It will be appreciated that there are many hundreds of examples of instrumentation at the laboratory scale.

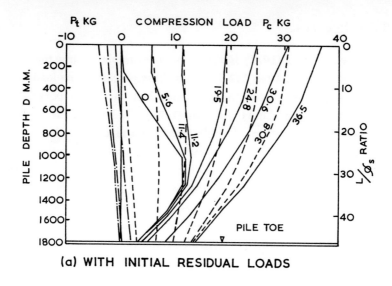

(a) WITH INITIAL RESIDUAL LOADS

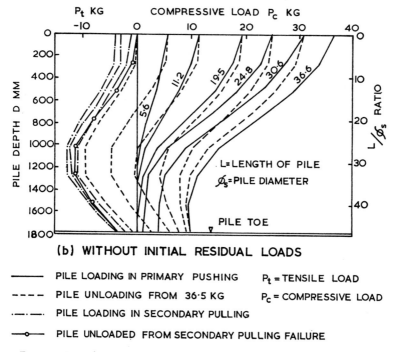

(b) WITHOUT INITIAL RESIDUAL LOADS

———— PILE LOADING IN PRIMARY PUSHING P_t = TENSILE LOAD

- - - - PILE UNLOADING FROM 36·5 KG P_c = COMPRESSIVE LOAD

·—·—· PILE LOADING IN SECONDARY PULLING

—o— PILE UNLOADED FROM SECONDARY PULLING FAILURE

Fig. 246: Distribution of axial load in a 1.78 m long, 25.4 mm diameter pile (a) allowing for initial residual loads, (b) neglecting initial residual loads (Tan [1971]).

8.6.1. Pile Tests

The work of Tan (1971) is taken as an example. Using the load cells shown in Figures 240 to 242 Tan was able to measure the load distribution along the length of the pile and thus check the postulations of Hanna (1968) and Hanna and Tan (1971). He studied the initial stress state along the length of the pile due to the placing of the soil around the pile and how this stress state influenced subsequent loading behaviour of the pile. Load distribution data for a 25.4 mm diameter pile are shown in Figure 246. Part (a) of this figure allows for the initial stress state along the pile while part (b) shows the same data but with the initial stress state neglected, an assumption common to most pile research studies. With this method of instrumentation it was possible to study the load-movement behaviour of elements of the pile subjected to both tensile and compressive loading. Further details of this work will be given by Hanna and Tan (1972).

8.6.2. Footings

By using the lead shot technique in association with X-rays Burland (1969) measured displacements of a large number of points within a clay bed loaded by a surface strip footing under plane strain conditions. Figure 247 (a) gives the measured vertical displacements beneath the edge of the footing for pressure increments of 1, 2 and 3 kN/m². Figure 247 (b) gives the net footing pressure/settlement relationship for this footing. The theoretical predictions, which are based on an elastic finite element analysis, are shown in Figure 247 (a).

In contrast to the very refined and highly accurate displacement measurements of Burland (1969), the much less accurate measurements using embedded instruments such as the coils of Eggestadt (1963) or the movement rods of Carr and Hanna (1971) should be mentioned. Movement data measured in the vicinity of a 0.3 m diameter footing tested on sand using the movement rod technique are shown in Figure 248. Movements for two load increments only are shown.

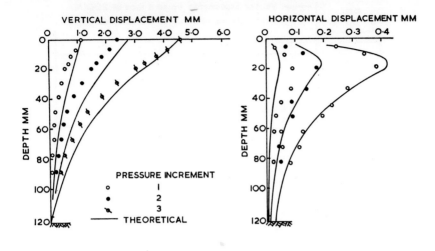

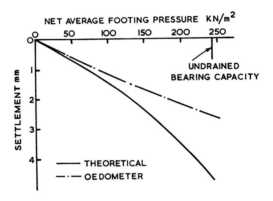

Fig. 247: (a) Comparison of observed and predicted displacements for a model footing test on clay; (b) relationship between average net pressure and consolidation settlement (Burland [1969]).

8.6.3. Retaining Walls

The work of James and Bransby (1970) illustrates the type of data which result from the use of the Arthur and Roscoe (1961) normal and shear earth pressure cell. They tested walls 30.7 mm in height which were caused to rotate about their base and towards the retained sand mass. Figure 249 gives the measured normal and shear stress values as

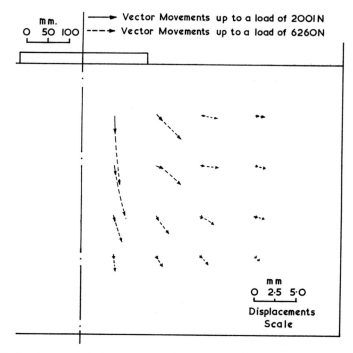

Fig. 248: Sand movements beneath 0.3 m footing in sand measured by the movement rod gauges (Sparks [1972]).

a function of wall rotation for two initial void ratio values, e, of 0.51 and 0.77. The measured angles of wall friction, δ, are also shown in this figure as a function of depth. It will be noted that the stress state along a retaining wall is far from the theoretical assumption of triangular pressure distribution on a frictionless wall which is used in many theories. These authors also used the lead shot technique to provide corresponding patterns of deformation within the soil mass. From a knowledge of the boundary stress state and the displacements within the soil mass the Cambridge research group has been able to apply theory with a fair degree of success. (See Schofield and Wroth [1968] for example).

Unfortunately few laboratories have the luxury of the contact stress cells and the X-ray displacement measuring facility. Despite such shortcomings it is still possible to make a contribution to research on retaining walls at laboratory scale and the studies of Rowe and Peaker (1965), Hanna and Matallana (1970), may be used as examples in support of this statement.

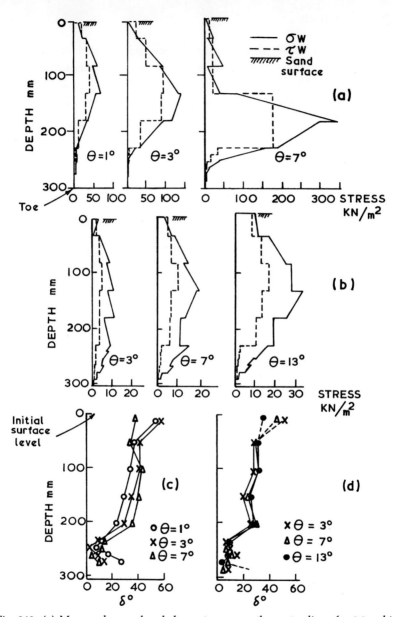

Fig. 249: (a) Measured normal and shear stresses on the centre line of a 0.3 m high wall at three stages of test (e_0 = 0.51); (b) measured normal and shear stresses on the centre line of a wall 0.3 m high at three stages of test (e_0 = 0.77); (c) angle of wall friction measured on each cell at three stages of test (e_0 = 0.51); angle of wall friction measured on each cell at three stages of test (e_0 = 0.77) (James and Bransby [1970]).

8.6.4. Pavements

Brown and Pell (1967) describe the layout and use of instruments for their large scale stress and deformation studies of the dynamic loading of a silty clay. The surface load plate was either 0.15, 0.225 or 0.3 m diameter, the test bed being 2.4 m square by 1.8 m deep. The layout of

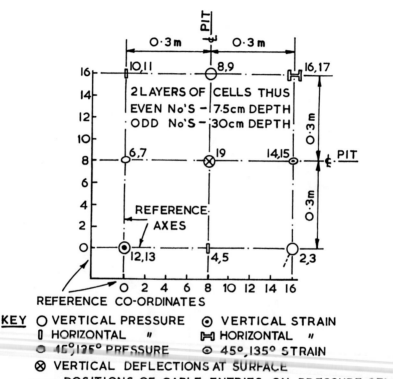

Fig. 250 (a) Layout of instruments in test pit;

the instruments in the test pit is shown in Figure 250 (a) while Figure 250 (b) gives the locations of the various measuring points with respect to the loaded area. It should be pointed out that the distributions of stress, strain and deflection were obtained by superposition because it was appreciated that instruments interfere with the stress and strain distributions even when used singly. To minimize these undesirable errors Brown and Pell placed the cells at 0.3 m horizontal spacing and 0.225 m vertical spacing and the load was moved relative to the instruments. A similar procedure has been used by Sparrow and Tory (1966). Figure 250 (c) gives vertical stress and vertical strain plots as a function of radius for a range of depths, Z/a, a being the radius of the surface loading plate.

Some details of deflection measurement of field scale pavements are given by Finn (1962).

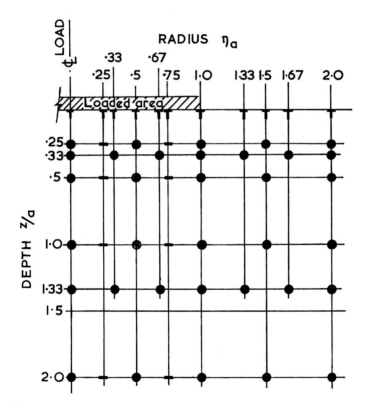

KEY

● FULL SET OF STRESSES AND STRAINS AT POINTS SHOWN THUS, MEASUREMENTS ELSEWHERE ONLY ON PLANES INDICATED

T VERTICAL SURFACE DEFLECTION

Fig. 250 (b): location of measurement points with respect to the footing edge;

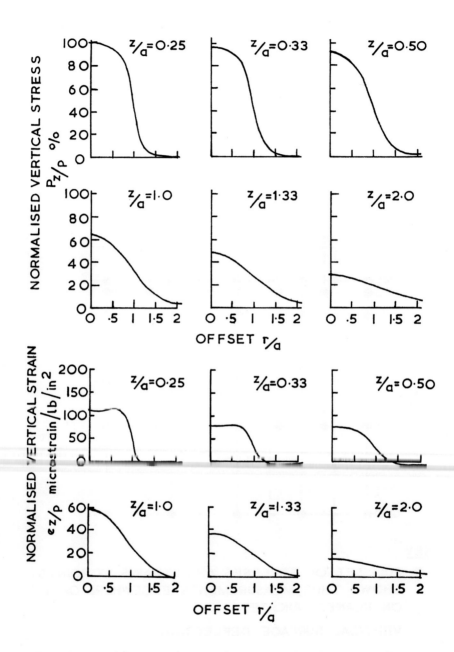

Fig. 250 (c) vertical stress and strain values versus radius (Brown and Pell [1967]).

8.7. The Centrifuge

There are many difficulties and limitations associated with the testing of laboratory scale foundation structures and the extrapolation of such test data to field scale. These include (i) representation of the stress state and its distribution within the soil mass allowing for strata of different relative stiffness, (ii) representation of the foundation (e. g. a retaining wall) to scale. Avgherinos and Schofield (1969) describe the centrifuge test method applied to drawdown failures of slopes. It can be shown that (i) the body forces of corresponding elements in model and prototype should be in the same ratio as their surface areas (N), (ii) the time scale for consolidation effects in model and prototype is given by $t_{model}/t_{prototype} = 1/N^2$. Thus to carry out representative model studies, large models with masses as large as 2000 kg may be required. Centrifugal factors of 100 or greater may be needed. In the pioneering studies of Avgherinos and Schofield (1969) a small centrifuge facility was used and some pertinent features are given in Table 6. In the small scale Cambridge studies displacement fields were recorded by X-ray techniques and pore water pressures were measured at several positions.

Centrifugal Model Test System	Cambridge Mk. 1	Cambridge Mk. 2
Centrifuge location	C.U.E.L. Cambridge	English Electric, Luton
Radius	0.3 m	2.7 m
Model height	2.5 cm	18 cm
Speed Range	400—950 r.p.m.	100—180 r.p.m.
Prototype height range	1.2—1.5 m	5.5—18 m
Soil strength range	3—24 kN/m²	15—58 kN/m²
Test time for 80 % consolidation	35 min	30 hrs
Preliminary consolidation time	27 min	4 hrs
Equivalent prototype time at maximum acceleration	7 years/hour	0.8 years/hour
Date of commission	November 1966	June 1968

Table 6: Centrifuge Data (Avgherinos and Schofield [1969]).

Details of the test specimen preparation and the recording system used are given by Avgherinos and Schofield (1969). Data obtained by them for an embankment 0.18 m high are shown in Figure 251.

Since this early development work much larger centrifuge facilities have been constructed by Schofield (see Lyndon and Schofield [1970] and Rowe [1972]). Work is now in progress on embankment studies, sheet pile walls, excavations and tunnels. Some details are given by Fuglsang (1971).

The application of the centrifuge to test laboratory scale models of foundation structures represents a major advance in research technique.

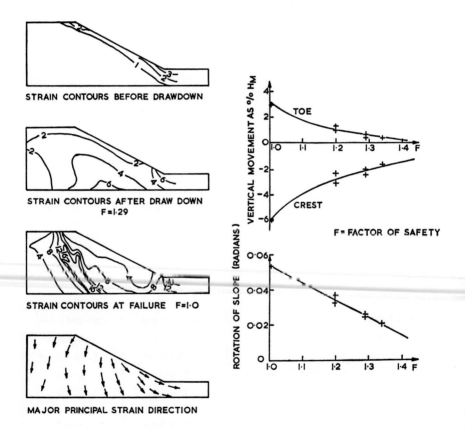

Fig. 251: Strain and deformation data for centrifuge test on a 0.18 m high embankment (Avgherinos and Schofield [1969]).

With these methods of study extensive use is made of small scale instruments to enable performance to be monitored during a test. In such circumstances it is essential to have reliable transducers which can sustain the very large g forces imposed during test. The pick-up and recording devices must have an exceedingly rapid response. At the present time information is not available in the literature on the instrumentation problems associated with the centrifuge testing of soils. However, as very few engineers will ever be called upon to design an instrumentation system for such a facility, but will tend rather to use an already established facility where recording techniques have been developed, this limitation in know-how is not a serious one.

8.8. General

Progress in foundation engineering research has depended on experimental techniques starting with the very early and modest studies of Terzaghi in the 1920's and 1930's and culminating in the relatively sophisticated studies at Cambridge (Roscoe [1970]). During this period techniques of measurement have been modified and improved and new methods have been introduced. In this chapter some of these methods of measurement which are suitable for laboratory use have been mentioned. There are, however, many topics which have not been considered. These include techniques used for the testing of soil specimens, the testing of rock specimens and the modelling of structures in rocks and their subsequent testing. The subject of instrumentation to study laboratory scale foundations under dynamic loadings has not been considered but details will be found in the Proceedings of the Symposium on Soil-Structure Interaction at the University of Arizona (1964) and in the Proceedings of the International Symposium on Wave Propagation and Dynamic Properties of Earth Materials, University of New Mexico (1967).

Some ideas on model testing of foundations are given by Roscoe (1968).

References

ARTHUR, J. R. F., and ROSCOE, K. H., (1961), "An earth pressure cell for the measurement of normal and shear stresses", Civil Engineering and Public Works Review, Vol. 56, No. 659, 765—770.

AVGHERINOS, P. J., and SCHOFIELD, A. N., (1969), "Drawdown failures of centrifuged models", Proceedings, Seventh International Conference on Soil Mechanics and Foundation Engineering, Mexico City, Vol. 2, 497—505.

BROWN, S. F., and PELL, P. S., (1967), "Subgrade stress and deformation under dynamic load", Proceedings, American Society of Civil Engineers, Vol. 93, No. SM 1, 17—46.

BURLAND, J. B., (1971), "A method of estimating the pore pressures and displacements beneath embankments on soft natural clay deposits", Proceedings, Roscoe Memorial Symposium, Cambridge, 505—536.

BURN, K. N., (1963), "A transducer to measure pore water pressure in soil tests", Laboratory Shear Testing of Soils, American Society for Testing and Materials Special Technical Publication No. 361, 390—395.

BUTTERFIELD, R., HARKNESS, R. M., and ANDRAWES, K. Z., (1970), "Stereophotogrammetric method for measuring displacement fields", Geotechnique, Vol. 20, No. 3, 308—314.

BUTTERFIELD, R., and ANDRAWES, K. Z., (1971), "The visualization of planar displacement fields", Proceedings, Roscoe Memorial Symposium, Cambridge, 467—475.

CARR, R. W., and HANNA, T. H., (1971), "Sand movement measurements near anchor plates", Proceedings, American Society of Civil Engineers, Vol. 97, No. SM 5, 833—840.

DAVIS, H. E., and WOODWARD, R. J., (1949), "Some laboratory studies of factors pertaining to the bearing capacity of soils", Proceedings, Highway Research Board, Vol. 29, 467—476.

EGGESTAD, A., (1963), "Deformation measurements below a model footing on the surface of dry sand", Proceedings, European Conference on Soil Mechanics and Foundation Engineering, Wiesbaden, Vol. 1, 233—239.

FINN, F. N., (1962), "Symposium on flexible pavement behaviour as related to deflection. I. Methods of measurement", Proceedings, Technical Session, Association of Asphalt Paving Technology, Vol. 31, 210.

FUGLSAND, L. D., (1971), "Preliminary centrifugal studies of the deformation and failure of uniform earth slopes", M. Sc. Thesis, University of Manchester.

GERBER, E., (1929), "Untersuchungen ueber die Druckverteilung in Oertlich Belastetem Sand", Dissertation, Technische Hochschule, Zürich.

HAMBLEY, E. C., and ROSCOE, H. K., (1969), "Observations and predictions of stresses and strains during plane strain of "wet" clays", Proceedings, Seventh International Conference on Soil Mechanics and Foundation Engineering, Mexico City, Vol. 1, 173—181.

HANNA, T. H., (1968), "The mechanics of load mobilization in friction piles", Journal of Materials, American Society for Testing and Materials, Vol. 4, No. 4, 934—937.

HANNA, T. H., and MATALLANA, G., (1970), "The behaviour of tied-back retaining walls", Canadian Geotechnical Journal, Vol. 7, No. 4, 372—396.

HANNA, T. H., and TAN, R. H. S., (1971), "The load movement behaviour of long piles", Journal of Materials, American Society for Testing and Materials, Vol. 6, No. 3, 532—554.

HANNA, T. H., and TAN, R. H. S., (1972), "The behaviour of long piles under compressive loads in sands", To be published.

HO, M. M. K., and LOPES, R., (1969), "Contact pressure of a rigid circular foundation", Proceedings, American Society of Civil Engineers, Vol. 95, No. SM 3, 791—817.

HOOPER, J. A., (1972), "The theory and design of photoelastic load gauges incorporating glass element transducers", International Journal of Rock Mechanics and Mining Sciences, Vol. 9, No. 3, 363—401.

JAMES, R. G., and BRANSBY, P. L., (1970), "Experimental and theoretical investigations of a passive earth pressre problem", Geotechnique, Vol. 20, No. 1, 17—37.

JAMES, R. G., and BRANSBY, P. L., (1971), "A velocity field for some passive earth pressure problems", Geotechnique, Vol. 21, No. 1, 61—83.

KIRKPATRICK, W. M., and BELSHAW, D. J., (1968), "On the interpretation of the triaxial test", Geotechnique, Vol. 18, No. 3, 336—350.

LYNDON, A., and SCHOFIELD, A. N., (1970), "Centrifugal model test of a short-term failure in London clay", Geotechnique, Vol. 20, No. 4, 440—442.

MORGAN, J. R., and HOLDEN, J. C., (1967), "Deflection prediction in prototype pavements", Proceedings, Second International Conference on Structural Design of Asphalt Pavements, University of Michigan.

MORGAN, J. R., (1971), "Contribution to discussion on Session 4, Proceedings, Roscoe Memorial Symposium, Cambridge, 495, 496.

PEAKER, K., (1964), "Passive earth pressure measurements", Ph. D. Thesis, University of Manchester.

PEAKER, K. R., (1965), "A hydraulic earth pressure cell", Symposium on Instruments and Apparatus for Soil and Rock Mechanics, ASTM, Special Technical Publication No. 392, 75—81.

PLANT, G. W., (1972), "Anchor Inclination: its effect on the performance of a laboratory scale tied-back retaining wall", Proceedings, Institution of Civil Engineers, London, Vol. 53, 257—274.

PRANGE, B., (1971), "The state of telemetry in soil mechanics", Proceedings, Roscoe Memorial Symposium, Cambridge, 476—488.

ROSCOE, K. H., (1968), "Soils and Model Tests", Journal of Strain Analysis, Vol. 3, No. 1, 57—64.

ROSCOE, K. H., (1970), "The influence of strains in soil mechanics", Geotechnique, Vol. 20, No. 2, 129—170.

ROSCOE, K. H., ARTHUR, J. R. F., and JAMES, R. G., (1963), "The determination of strains in soils by an X-ray method", Civil Engineering and Public Works Review, Vol. 58, No. 684, 876, Vol. 58, No. 685, 1009—1012.

ROWE, P. W., and BRIGGS, A., (1961), "Measurements on model strutted sheet pile excavations", Proceedings, Fifth International Conference on Soil Mechanics and Foundation Engineering, Paris, Vol. 2, 473—478.

ROWE, P. W., and PEAKER, K. R., (1965), "Passive earth pressure measurements", Geotechnique, Vol. 15, No. 1, 57—78.

ROWE, P. W., (1972), "The relevance of soil fabric to site investigation practice", Geotechnique. Vol. 22, No. 22, 195—300.

SCHNAEBELI, G., (1957), "Une analogie mécanique pour l'étude de la Stabilité des Ouvrages en Terre à deux dimensions", Proceedings, Fourth International Conference on Soil Mechanics and Foundation Engineering", London, Vol. 2.

SCHOFIELD, A. N., and WROTH, C. P., (1968), Critical State Soil Mechanics", McGraw-Hill, London.

SCOTT, A., (1972), "Strain Gauges", Engineering, London, May, 482—485.

SHENTON, M. J., (1965), "The stresses acting on a driven pile in cohesionless material", Ph. D. Thesis, University of Nottingham, England.

SELIG, E. T., (1964), "A review of stress and strain measurement in soil", Proceedings, Symposium on Soil-structure Interaction, University of Arizona, 172—186.

SPARKS, R., (1972), "An investigation into the behaviour of prestressed plate anchors in sand", M. Eng. Thesis, University of Sheffield, England.

SPARROW, R. W., and TORY, A. C., (1966), "Behaviour of soil mass under dynamic loading", Proceedings, American Society of Civil Engineers, Vol. 92, SM3, 59—86.

TAN, R. H. S., (1971), "Piles in tension and compression", Ph. D. Thesis, University of Sheffield.

TRUESDALE, W. B., and ANDERSON, M. E., (1964), "A new device for soil strain measurement", Proceedings, Symposium on Soil-Structure Interaction, University of Arizona, 129—137.

9 | Appendix

ADDITIONAL REFERENCES

A large number of papers and technical reports are available which deal with foundation instrumentation. The following list includes some of these papers which are not included in the individual chapter reference lists.

BARR, D. J., and SWANSTON, D. N., (1970), "Measurement of creep in a shallow, slide-prone till soil", American Journal of Science, Vol. 269, No. 5, 467—480.

BECKER, P., von, (1970), „Erddruck- und Wandbewegungsmessungen an zwei hohen Flügewänden eines Brückenwiderlagers", Bautechnik Vol. 47, No. 9, 306—313.

BENSON, R. P., CONLON, R. J., MERRITT, A. H., JOLI COEUR, P., and DEERE, D. U., (1971), "Rock Mechanics at Churchill Falls", American Society of Civil Engineers, Special Publication on Underground Rock Chambers (in press).

BJERRUM, L., and ANDERSEN, K. H., (1972), "In-situ measurement of lateral pressures in clay", Proceedings, Fifth European Conference on Soil Mechanics and Foundation Engineering, Madrid, Vol. 1, 11—20.

BOZOZUK, M., (1970), "Field Instrumentation of Soil", Proceedings, Conference on Design and Installation of Pile Foundations and Cellular Structures, Lehigh University, Bethlehem, USA, 145—157.

BOZOZUK, M., (1972), "Downdrag measurements on a 160-ft. floating pipe test pile in marine clay", Canadian Geotechnical Journal, Vol. 9, No. 2, 127—136.

BRETH, H., and WANOSCHEK, H. R., (1972), "The influence of foundation weights upon earth pressure acting on flexible strutted walls", Proceedings, Fifth European Conference on Soil Mechanics and Foundation Engineering, Madrid, Vol. 1, 251—258.

BROMS, B. B., and INGELSON, I., (1972), "Lateral earth pressure on a bridge abutment", Proceedings, Fifth European Conference on Soil Mechanics and Foundation Engineering, Madrid, Vol. 1, 117—123.

BROS, B., (1972), "The influence of model retaining wall displacements on active and passive earth pressures in sand", Proceedings, Fifth European Conference on Soil Mechanics and Foundation Engineering, Madrid, Vol. 1, 241—249.

COLMAN, R. B., and HANCOCK, T. G., (1972), "The behaviour of laterally loaded piles", Proceedings, Fifth European Conference on Soil Mechanics and Foundation Engineering, Madrid, Vol. 1, 339—345.

CRAWFORD, C. B., and SUTHERLAND, J. G., (1971), "The Empress Hotel, Victoria, British Columbia — Sixty five years of foundation settlements", Canadian Geotechnical Journal, Vol. 8, No. 1, 77—93.

D'APPOLONIA, D. J., LAMBE, T. W., and POULOS, H. G., (1971), "Evaluation of pore water pressures beneath an embankment", Proceedings, American Society of Civil Engineers, Vol. 97, No. SM6, 881—898.

DIBIAGIO, E., and ROTI, J. A., (1972), "Earth pressure measurements on a braced slurry trench wall in soft clay", Proceedings, Fifth European Conference on Soil Mechanics and Foundation Engineering, Madrid, Vol. 1, 473—483.

DIBIAGIO, E., and MYRVOLL, F., (1972), "Full scale field tests of a slurry trench excavation in soft clay", Proceedings, Fifth European Conference on Soil Mechanics and Foundation Engineering, Madrid, Vol. 1, 461—471.

EIDE, O., AAS, G., and JOSANG, T., (1972), "Special application of cast-in-place walls for tunnels in soft clay in Oslo", Proceedings, Fifth European Conference on Soil Mechanics and Foundation Engineering, Madrid, Vol. 1, 485—498.

ELIAS, V., and STORCH, H., (1970), "Control and performance during construction of a highway embankment", Highway Research Record No. 323, 60—70.

ESCARIO, V., and SAGASETA, C., (1972), "Empujes lateral en una sección del Metro de Madrid", Proceedings, Fifth European Conference on Soil Mechanics and Foundation Engineering, Madrid, Vol. 1, 499—508.

FAGNOUL, A., BONNECHERE, F., and BOLLE, A., (1972), "Etude sur modèle de l'action des terres sur une paroi rigide, en fonction de son déplacement", Proceedings, Fifth European Conference on Soil Mechanics and Foundation Engineering, Madrid, Vol. 1, 135—142.

FORREST, J. B., and MacFARLANE, I. C., (1969), "Field studies of the response of peat to plate loading", Proceedings, American Society of Civil Engineers, Vol. 95, No. SM4, 949—968.

FOWLER, J., (1970), "Dynamic behaviour of piling during initial test firing on the S-IC and S-II test complexes". Foundation Investigations NASA Mississippi Seat Facility Report 4, Technical Report No. S-69-10 U.S. Army Engineers Waterways Experimental Station, Vicksburg, Mississippi.

FOWLER, J., and STEVENS, J. B., (1970), "Load Transfer by foundations of S-IC and S-II test complexes during construction", Foundation Investigation NASA Mississippi Seat Facility Report 3, Technical Report No. S-69-10 U.S. Army Engineers Waterways Experimental Station, Vicksburg, Mississippi.

FRIMANN CLAUSEN, C. J., and JOHANSEN, S., (1972), "Earth pressure measured against a section of basement wall", Proceedings, Fifth European Conference on Soil Mechanics and Foundation Engineering, Madrid, Vol. 1, 515—516.

GERRARD, C. M., KURZEME, M., ANDREWS, D. C., and TOPP, S., (1971), "Instrumentation of raft foundations in Perth", Proceedings, First Australian-New Zealand Conference on Geomechanics, Melbourne, Vol. 1, 361—368.

Groupe de Travail du Comité National Français (1970), "Quelques dévelopements récents des moyens d'ausculation du massif rocheux", Transactions, Tenth International Congress on Large Dams, Montreal, Vol. 3, 935—960.

HAGERTY, D. J., and PECK, R. B., (1971), "Heave and lateral movements due to pile driving", Proceedings, American Society of Civil Engineers, Vol. 97, No. SM11, 1523—1532.

HALCROW, Sir WILLIAM and Partners (1970), "Instrumentation investigation at Clywedog dam", CIRIA Technical Note 9.

HEDLEY, D. G. F., (1969), "Design criteria for multi-wire borehole extensometer systems", Internal Report MR 69/68 ID, Department of Energy, Mines and Resources, Mines Branch, Mining Research Centre, Ottawa.

HORN, A., (1972), "Resistance and movement of laterally loaded abutments", Proceedings, Fifth European Conference on Soil Mechanics and Foundation Engineering, Madrid, Vol. 1, 143—147.

INGLES, O. G., and NEIL, R. C., (1971), "An infinitely programmable stiff loading frame", Proceedings, First Australian — New Zealand Conference on Geomechanics, Melbourne, Vol. 1, 369—376.

INSLEY, A., (1972), "A deep excavation and a raft foundation in soft clay", Canadian Geotechnical Journal, Vol. 9, No. 3, 237—248.

JAMES, R. G., SMITH, I. A. A., and BRANSBY, P. L., (1972), "The prediction of stresses and deformations in a sand mass adjacent to a retaining wall", Proceedings, Fifth European Conference on Soil Mechanics and Foundation Engineering, Madrid, Vol. 1, 39—46.

JIMINEZ SALAS, J. A., URIEL, S., and SERRANO, A. A., (1972), Comportamiento bajo esfuerzos horizontales de dos pontallas en suelos blandos estratificados", Proceedings, Fifth European Conference on Soil Mechanics and Foundation Engineering, Madrid, Vol. 1, 532—534.

JOSSEAUME, H., (1970), "Facteurs intervenant dans les mesures de pression interstitelle", Bulletin Liason. Laboratoire Rout. Ponts et Chausses, hydraulique des sols, Spec. N. 79—101.

JUSTO, J. L., (1969), "Instrumentation of a new channel in soft clay", Proceedings, Seventh International Conference on Soil Mechanics and Foundation Engineering, Mexico City, Vol. 2, 599—607.

KANY, M., (1972), "Measurements of earth pressure on a cylinder 30 m in diameter (pumped storage plant)", Proceedings, Fifth European Conference on Soil Mechanics and Foundation Engineering, Madrid, Vol. 1, 535—542.

KELLY, W. L., (1969), "Instrumentation methods and results for John Day Dam relocation", Proceedings, Engineering Geology and Soil Engineering Symposium, Boise, Moscow, Idaho, USA, 141—158.

KERISEL, J., FERRAND, J., LARÉAL, P., and CLEMENT, P., (1972), "Measures de poussée et de butée faites avec 42 paires de butons asservis", Proceedings, Fifth European Conference on Soil Mechanics and Foundation Enginering, Madrid, Vol. 1, 265—273.

KJAERNSLI, B., (1970), "An emperical design rule for determining the strut forces in braced excavations in Oslo-clay", Norwegian Geotechnical Instiute, Publication No. 83, Oslo.

LABEQUE, Y., (1972), "Essais de fondations superficielles supportant un effort incliné", Proceedings, Fifth European Conference on Soil Mechanics and Foundation Engineering, Madrid, Vol. 1, 103—171.

LAMBE, T. W., (1972), "The integrated Civil Engineering Project", Proceedings, American Society of Civil Engineers, Vol. 98, No. SM6, 531—556.

LEE, I. K., and HERINGTON, J. R., (1971), "Stresses beneath granular embankments", Proceedings, First Australian — New Zealand Conference on Geomechanics, Melbourne, Vol. 1, 291—297.

MACKEY, R. D., and MASON, P. A., (1972), "Pressure distribution during filling and discharging a silo", Proceedings, Fifth European Conference on Soil Mechanics and Foundation Engineering, Madrid, Vol. 1, 55—62.

MANSUR, C. I., and ALIZADEH, M., (1970), "Tie-backs in clay to support sheeted excavation", Proceedings, American Society of Civil Engineers, Vol. 96, No. SM2, 495—509.

MARCHAL, J., and URSAT, P., (1972), "Experimentation in situ sur paroi moulée ancrée en tete", Proceedings, Fifth European Conference on Soil Mechanics and Foundation Engineering, Madrid, Vol. 1, 275—283.

MEIXNER, H., (1971), Messungen zur Ermittlung von Boden- und Gebirgsbewegungen". Bergbautechnik, Leipzig, Vol. 1, No. 4, 263—266.

MEYERHOF, G. G., and SEBASTYAN, G. Y., (1970), "Settlement studies on an air terminal building and apron, Vancouver International Airport, B. C.", Canadian Geotechnical Journal, Vol. 7, No. 4, 433—456.

MITCHELL, J. K., and GARDNER, W. S., (1971), "Analysis of load-bearing fills over soft subsoils", Proceedings, American Society of Civil Engineers, Vol. 97, No. SM11, 1549—1572.

MORRISON, B., and MENELEY, W. A., (1971), "A bubbler-Manometer water level sensing and recording device", Canadian Geotechnical Journal, Vol. 8, No. 3, 425—433.

NAHRGANG, E., (1972), "Lateral displacements and earth pressures in soft cohesive soils subjected to high surface loads", Proceedings, Fifth European Conference on Soil Mechanics and Foundation Engineering, Madrid, Vol. 1, 181—187.

NARAIN, J., and SINGH, B., (1966), "Design of a differential pore pressure mano-meter and its time lag characteristics", Proceedings, American Society of Civil Engineers, Vol. 92, No. SM5, 93—108.

PANEK, L. A., (1970), "Methods and equipment for measuring subsidence", Third Symposium Salt Cleveland Ohio North, Ohio Geological Society, Vol. 2, 321—338.

REHNMAN, S. E., and BROMS, B. B., (1972), "Lateral pressures on basement wall, results from full scale tests", Proceedings, Fifth European Conference on Soil Mechanics and Foundation Engineering, Madrid, Vol. 1, 189—197.

ROMA, M., OTEO, C. S., and FERNANDEZ-ALLER, A., (1972), "Interpretación de los ensayos de pilotes con esfuerzos laterales en el tercer pantalán petrolero de La Coruña", Proceedings Fifth European Conference on Soil Mechanics and Foundation Engineering, Madrid, Vol. 1, 413—422.

SCHIFFMAN, R. L., WHITMAN, R. V., and JORDAN, J. C., (1970), "Settlement problem oriented computer language", Proceedings, American Society of Civil Engineers, Vol. 96, No. SM2, 649—670.

SCHOLZ, C. H., and FITCH, T. J., (1970), "Strain and creep in central California", Journal of Geophysics Research, Vol. 75, No. 23, 4447—4453.

SHERMAN, W. C., and CLOUGH, G. W., (1968), "Embankment pore pressures during construction", Proceedings, American Society of Civil Engineers, Vol. 94, No. SM2, 527—554.

SIMPSON, B., and WROTH, C. P., (1972), "Finite element computations for a model retaining wall in sand", Proceedings, Fifth European Conference on Soil Mechanics and Foundation Engineering, Madrid, Vol. 1, 85—93.

SINNIGER, R., (1970), "Control measurements on dams, rapid survey methods", Transactions, Tenth International Congress on Large Dams, Montreal, Vol. 3, 7—18.

SLACK, D. C., and WALKER, J. N., (1970), "Deflections of shallow pier foundations", Proceedings, American Society of Civil Engineers, Vol. 96, No. SM4, 1143—1158.

SPRANZA, J. J., and NUR, A. M., (1971), "Seasonal deformation of 2-mile straight line", Proceedings, American Society of Civil Engineers, Vol. 97, No. SM12, 1623—1634.

STEVENS, J. B., FOWLER, J., and GUERNSEY, R. G., (1970), "Static load testing of foundation piles at test stand S-II, A--"; Foundation Investigation NASA Mississippi Test Facility Report 2, Technical Report No. S-69-10 U.S. Army Engineer Waterways Experimental Station, Vicksburg, Mississippi.

SYMONS, I. F., and WILSON, D. S., (1972), „Meaurement of Earth Pressures in pulverised fuel ash behind a rigid retaining wall", Proceedings, Fifth European Conference on Soil Mechanics and Foundation Engineering, Madrid, Vol. 1, 569—575.

TAVENAS, F. A., (1971), "Load test results on friction piles in sand". Canadian Geotechnical Journal, Vol. 8, No. 1, 7—22.

TER-STEPANIAN, G. I., (1972), "Geodetic methods of study of landslide dynamics", (in Russian), Nedra, Moscow, 135 pp.

TROW, W., and BRADSTOCK, J., (1972), "Instrumented foundations for two 43-storey buildings on till, Metropolitan Toronto", Canadian Geotechnical Journal, Vol. 9, No. 3, 290—303.

TURBING, K., (1970), "Ergebnisse langjähriger Messungen und Beobachtungen an einem Erd-Stein-Damm", Wasserwirtschaft, Wassertechnik, Berlin, Vol. 20, No. 3, 99—104.

VALI, V., (1969), "Measuring earth strains by laser", Scientific American, Vol. 221, No. 6, 89—95.

Van WAMBEKE, A., and RENARD, J., (1972), "Determination expérimentale des pressions de terre à l'intérieur d'un massif et contre un mur emboué", Proceedings, Fifth European Conference on Soil Mechanics and Foundation Engineering, Madrid, Vol. 1, 585—595.

VAUGHAN, P. R., and KENNARD, M. F., (1972), "Earth pressures at a junction between an embankment dam and a concrete dam", Proceedings, Fifth European Conference on Soil Mechanics and Foundation Engineering, Madrid, Vol. 1, 215—221.

VIRGOE, R. J., (1972), "Load transducers — design, manufacture and use", Journal of Strain, Vol. 8, No. 2, 68—72.

WALKER, F. C., (1970), "Prevention of cracking in earth dams", Transactions, Tenth International Congress on Large Dams, Montreal, Vol. 1, 361—387.

WANG, M. C., and MITCHELL, J. K., (1971), "New stress and strain gauges for measurements in stabilized soil pavements", Journal of Materials, Vol. 6, No. 4, 774—787.

WEINHOLD, H., (1972), "Analysis of horizontal load tests to clarify the lateral bearing value of large diameter bored piles", Proceedings, Fifth European Conference on Soil Mechanics and Foundation Engineering, Madrid, Vol. 1, 433—441.

WEISSENBACH, A., (1968), „Meßverfahren zur Ermittlung von Größe und Verteilung des Erddruckes auf Bahngrubenwände", Vortrag Baugrundtagung der Deutschen Gesellschaft für Erd- und Grundbau, Essen, 257—287.

WHITMAN, R. V., CASAGRANDE, D. R., KARLSRUD, K., and SIMON, R., (1971), "Performance of foundations for Altari Radar", Proceedings, American Society of Civil Engineers, Vol. 97, No. SM1, 1—18.

WILKES, P. F., (1972), "Kings Lynn Trial Embankment", Journal of the Institution of Highway Engineers, August, 9—16.

WINDISCH, E. J., and YONG, R. N., (1970), "The determination of soil strain rate behaviour beneath a moving wheel", Journal of Terramechanics, Vol. 7, No. 1, 55—67.

WOLFSKILL, L. A., and SOYDEMIR, C., (1971), "Soil instrumentation for the I-95 MIT — MDPW Test Embankment", Journal, Boston Society of Vivil Engineers, Vol. 58, No. 4, 193—229.

ZAVRIEV, G. P., PETROSIAN, G. M., and ZAVARIAN, E. G., (1972), "Pressure of clay on underground structures from data from field studies", Proceedings, Fifth European Conference on Soil Mechanics and Foundation Engineering, Vol. 1, 597—601.

ZOINO, W. S., (1971), "Settlement of Rubbish fill — Yellow Freight System Facility, Boston", Journal, Boston Society of Civil Engineers, Vol. 58, No. 4, 230—242.

TABLE OF CONVERSIONS

A number of unit systems are in use in different countries. In this text an attempt has been made to use the Système International d'Unités (S. I.) which is based on six fundamental metric units. In parts of the text a mixture of units is used and conversion factors are given below.

Quantity	Unit	S. I.
Length	foot	0.3048 m
	inch	25.4 mm
Area	square foot	0.0929 m^2
	square inch	645.2 mm^2
Volume	cubic yard	0.7646 m^3
	cubic foot	0.02832 m^3
	cubic inch	16.39 cm^3
	gallon	4.546 l
Mass	ton	1.016 Mg (1.016 tonne)
	hundredweight	50.80 kg
	pound	0.4536 kg
Density	pound per cubic foot	0.01602 Mg/m^3
	gramme per cubic centimetre	1.0 Mg/m^3 (1 tonne/m^3)
Force	pound force	4.448 N
	ton force	9.964 kN
	kilogramme force	9.807 N
Pressure and stress	pound force per square inch	6.895 kN/m^2
	pound force per square foot	0.04788 kN/m^2
	ton force per square foot	107.3 kN/m^2
	kilogramme force per square centimetre	98.07 kN/m^2
Modulus of Deformation	pound force per square foot	0.04788 kN/m^2
	ton force per square inch	15.44 MN/m^2
Coefficient of Consolidation	square foot per year	0.0929 m^2/year
	square centimetre per second	3154 m^2/year
Coefficient of Permeability	centimetre per second	0.01 m/s
	foot per year	0.3048 m/year (0.9651 x 10^{-8} m/s)
Temperature	degree Fahrenheit (F) degree Centigrade (C)	n $^\circ$F = 0.5556 (n-32) $^\circ$C
Angle	degree	0.01745 rad.

1 ton = 2240 pounds	N = Newton

LIST OF SYMBOLS

Where possible the symbols used by other authors are used and consequently several quantities are denoted by the same symbol. Most of the symbols used are defined below and the numbers after them refer to the section in the book where the full definition may be found.

a	Contact area of soil grains	3.1.
a	Area of grout plug	3.4.3.
a	Loading plate radius	4.5.
a	Distance of X-ray surface from plane of lead shot	Fig. 235
a_1	Area of borehole plug	3.4.3.
A	Area	2.6.
A	Height	
A	$f \cdot k/(a_1 \cdot k_g)$	3.4.3.
b	Distance of plane of lead shot from plane of X-ray film	Fig. 235
B	Pore water pressure coefficient	3.1.
B	Foundation width	Fig. 217
B	Height	
B	$F \cdot k/(a_1 \cdot k_g)$	3.4.3.
c	Earth pressure cell half thickness	4.2.
c', c_d	Cohesion intercepts	Fig. 3
c_u	Undrained shear strength	7.6.
c_v	Coefficient of consolidation	1.3.
C_A	Cell action factor	4.2.
C_c	Compression index	1.3.
d	Cell diameter	4.2.
d	Increment	
D	Plate diameter	7.6.7.
D	Depth to rigid boundary	Fig. 207
D	Cell diameter	4.2.
D	Piezometer diameter	3.2.4.
D	Distance of lens from photograph	Fig. 117
D	Depth	
D_{20}	Ring deflection at 20° C	2.2.
D_t	Ring deflection at t° C	2.2.
e	Eccentricity	4.5.
e	Exponential	3.2.2.

e	Output from load cell	Fig. 29
e	Piezometer reading error	3.4.3.
e_o	Voids ratio	Fig. 249
E	Modulus of Deformation	2.6.
E	Equalization ratio	3.2.2.
E	Supply voltage	Fig. 29
E_s	Modulus of deformation of soil	4.2.
E_c	Modulus of deformation of pressure cell	4.2.
F	Factor of safety	Fig. 251
F	Piezometer shape factor	3.2.2.
F	Force normal to axis of cable	2.7.
f, f_o, f_a, f_b, f_c	Frequency of vibration	2.6.
f	$2T/\log(r_o/r_b)$	3.4.3.
f_d	Skin stress in cell diaphragm	4.2.
g	Gravity constant	2.6.
G	Strain gauge factor	7.2.
G	Gauge pressure	3.3.5.
G	Galvanometer	Fig. 203
h	Depth of soil specimen below ground level	Fig. 1
h	Difference in level	Fig. 128
h_1, h_2, h_3	Successive water levels in standpipe	3.2.2.
h_w	Water head	Fig. 44
H, H_0, H_1, H_2	Head in piezometer standpipe	3.2.2.
H	Length of grouted zone	3.4.3.
H	Pressure head at piezometer inlet	3.3.5.
H	Depth to rough base	Fig. 214
H	Distance of lens from tracing paper	Fig. 117
H	Heave gauge	Fig. 215
H	Excavation depth	Fig. 207
I	Moment of inertia	Table 4
k	Coefficient of permeability	3.2.2.
k_g	Coefficient of permeability of grout	3.4.3.
K	Strain gauge constant	2.6.
K	Constant	
K	Earth pressure coefficient	Fig. 221
K_o	Coefficient of earth pressure at rest	1.3.
{K}	Structure stiffness matrix	7.6.
l	Gauge length	2.6.
l_x, l_y	Spacing of lead shot	8.1.
L	Length of vibrating wire element	2.6.

L	Piezometer length	3.2.4.
L	Lateral deformation gauge	Fig. 217
L	Length of wire or rod	7.2.
L	Length of pile	Fig. 246
m	H/D	Fig. 117
m_v	Coefficient of volume compressibility	1.3.
M	Bending moment	2.7.
M_x, M_y	Bending moment vectors	2.8.
N	Number of nodal points	7.6.
N	Normal force component	Fig. 15
N	Centrifuge scale	8.7.
N	Strain gauge	Fig. 99
N	Soil property constant	4.2.
N	1/(BH + 1)	3.4.3.
N_c	Bearing capacity factor	7.6.
N	Newton	
p	Field stress existing at the plane of the cell in the absence of the cell	4.2.
p	Pressure difference	3.2.2.
p_e	Additional pressure recorded by cell	4.2.
p_{max}	Maximum allowable normal pressure on cell diaphragm	4.2.
P	Strut load	2.6.
P	Tie Rod (Anchor) force	Fig. 12
P	Axial load in cable	2.7.
P_A, P_B, P_C	Load in cell elements	2.8.
p_c	Preconsolidation pressure	Fig. 1
p_0	Overburden pressure	Fig. 1
p_0, p_t	Errors in piezometer reading	3.2.2.
PS	Precision Settlement Gauge	Fig. 215
P_H'	Pore water pressure in impermeable layer	3.4.3.
q	Flow	3.2.2.
q	Foundation pressure	Fig. 7
q_u	Ultimate foundation pressure	Fig. 232
Q	Quantity of flow	3.2.2.
Q, Q_1, Q_2	Shear force	4.5.
r	Radial distance	Fig. 250
r	Piezometer radius	3.2.2.
r_0	Radius of radial flow zone	3.4.3.
$\{r\}$	Nodal point displacement vector	7.6.

R	Electrical resistance	7.2.
R	Temperature coefficient of proving ring	2.2.
R	Radius of pitch circle of load cell elements	2.8.
R_G, R_1 to R_4	Strain gauge resistances	7.2.
{R}	Nodal force vector	7.6.
s	Settlement	Fig. 217
S	Spring pressure	3.3.5.
S	Strain gauge	Fig. 99
S	Surface deformation gauge	Fig. 217
S	Shear strength	Fig. 3
S	Spacing of lenses	Fig. 117
{S}	Transformation matrix	7.6.
t	Cell diaphragm thickness	4.2.
t	Temperature in $^\circ$C	2.2.
t	time	3.2.2.
T	Tangential force component	Fig. 15
T	Basic time lag	3.2.2.
T_V	Time factor	3.2.2.
u	Horizontal displacement	Fig. 209
u, u_w	Pore water pressure	3.1.
u_o	Static pore water pressure in the ground	Fig. 1
u_a	Pore air pressure	3.1.
U_1 to U_4	Displacement components	8.2.4.
v	Vertical displacement	Fig. 209
V	Volume for pressure equalization	3.2.2.
V	Single piezometer	Fig. 215
V	Vertical deformation gauge	Fig. 231
W_1 to W_4	Displacement components	Fig. 237
W	Self weight component	Fig. 15
W	Water pressure	3.3.5.
W	Width	Fig. 207
W	Multiple piezometer	Fig. 215
W	Water level gauge	Fig. 122
y	Height in piezometer standpipe	3.2.2.
z	Depth	Fig. 250
Z	Height of water table above soil specimen	Fig. 1
Z	Depth	
α	Direction	8.2.4.
β	Direction of bending moment axis	2.8.

γ	Saturated bulk density	Fig. 7
γ_w	Density of water	3.1.
δ	Central deflection of cell diaphragm	4.2.
$\varepsilon_x, \varepsilon_y$	Linear strains	8.2.4.
ε_{xy}	Shear strain	8.2.4.
ε	Strain in a tensioned wire	2.6.
ε	Piezometer error	3.4.3.
ε_0	$H/(BH + 1)$	3.4.3.
ε_0	$\text{Tan h}\,(\sqrt{A}.\,H)\,/\,[\sqrt{A} + B\,\text{Tan H}\,(\sqrt{A}.\,H)]$	3.4.3.
Θ	Angle of wall rotation	Fig. 249
μ	Poisson's ratio	4.5.
γ	Poisson's ratio	7.2.
ϱ	Density of wire	2.6.
ϱ	Resistivity of wire	7.2.
σ	Total stress	3.1.
σ'	Effective stress	3.1.
$\sigma_1, \sigma_3, \sigma_v, \sigma_H, \sigma_r, \sigma_a$	Components of stress	1.3.
τ	Shear stress	Fig. 3
Φ_s	Pile diameter	Fig. 246
Φ, Φ', Φ_d	Angles of internal friction	1.3.
χ	Coefficient defining effective stress in a partially saturated soil	3.2.
Δ	Settlement	Fig. 5
Δ	Central deflection	2.4.

Note: dx or δx denotes a small change in the value of the parameter x.

LIST OF ABBREVIATIONS

The following abbreviations have been used:

B A R T	Bay Area Rapid Transport (San Francisco)
B. R. S.	Building Research Station
d. c.	Direct current
F I D A S	Field Instrument Data Acquisition System
i. d.	Internal diameter
I C E S	Integrated Civil Engineering System
I I T R I	Illinois Institute of Technology Research Institute
L N E C	National Laboratory of Civil Engineering (Lisbon)
l. v. d. t.	Linear variable differential transformer
M B T A	Massachusetts Bay Transportation Authority
M. I. T.	Massachusetts Institute of Technology
N. G. I.	Norwegian Geotechnical Institute
N. P. L.	National Physical Laboratory
o. d.	Outside diameter
O. D. N.	Ordnance Datum Newlyn
O R E	Office of Research and Experiments (Utrecht)
p.v.c.	Polyvinylchloride
r. p. m.	Revolutions per minute
S T R U D L	Structural design language
U S B R	United States Bureau of Reclamation
U. K.	United Kingdom
W. E. S.	Waterways Experimental Station

Abbreviations of units.

cm	centimetre
h (hr)	hour
kg	kilogramme
l	litre
m	metre
mm	millimetre
min	minute
N	Newton
s	second
t	tonne

ABOUT THE AUTHOR

T. H. Hanna was born in Northern Ireland on December 29, 1936. In 1957 he received the Degree of Bachelor of Science in Civil Engineering with First Class Honours from The Queens University of Belfast. He received the Degree of Doctor of Philosophy (Ph. D.) from Queens, Belfast, in 1960 with a thesis on the behaviour of pile groups in sand.

Between 1957 and 1961 he held the post of Assistant Lecturer in Civil Engineering at The Queens University of Belfast. He then joined the staff of George Wimpey and Company Ltd., Central Laboratories and was engaged with them for two years, mainly in site investigation and foundation design studies. In 1963 he emigrated to Canada working for nine months with W. A. Trow and Associates, consulting Geotechnical Enginners, followed by over three years as a research engineer with the Structural Research Division of the Hydro Electric Power Commission of Ontario.

In 1967 he returned to England and has been on the staff of the Department of Civil and Structural Engineering, University of Sheffield since that time. He was promoted to a Senior Lectureship in 1969 and appointed to the Chair of Civil and Structural Engineering in 1971. His special interests are in Geotechnical Engineering.

Professor Hanna is a Member of the Institution of Civil Engineers, an Associate Member of the American Society of Civil Engineers and a Member of the International Society of Soil Mechanics and Foundation Engineering.

AUTHOR INDEX

SUBJECT INDEX

LIST OF INSTRUMENT SUPPLIERS
AND THEIR REPRESENTATIVES

In the following list only companies are mentioned which have contributed to this volume. The list, therefore, is not intended to be complete.

Companies in larger print have advertised their products and services in the Advertising Section of this book, where the reader will find additional information on foundation instrumentation.

ABEM Instrument Group, Craelius Svenska Diamant, Fack, S-101 10 Stockholm 1, Sweden

A. M. Erichsen GmbH, P. O. Box 20 15 37, D-5600 Wuppertal 2, Germany

Adlab Ltd., P. O. Box 1, Farnworth, Bolton, BL4 7SM, Lancashire, England

Apparatus Specialties Co., P. O. Box 122, Saddle River, N. J. 07458, USA

Alcock, W. J. & Co. Ltd., P. O. 781, Calcutta, India

Applied Geodata Systems, Inc., 675 Massachusetts Ave., Cambridge, Mass. 02139, USA

Associated Instruments, Manufacturers, Ltd., 468 – 7 Jalan Ipoh, Kuala Lumpur, Malaysia

Atkins Technical, Inc., P. O. Box 14405 University Station, Gainsville, Fla. 32601, USA

Automatic Systems Laboratories Ltd., Construction House, Grovebury Rd., Leighton Buzzard, Bedfordshire, LU 7 8SX, England

Automation Industries (U. K.) Ltd., Albert St., Fleet, Aldershot, Hampshire, England

Axel Johnson Institute for Industrial Research, P. O. Box 13, S-149 01 Nynäshamn, Sweden

BEVAC, Route d'Yverdon 18, CH-1033 Cheseaux-sur-Lausanne, Switzerland

BLH Electronics, Inc., Waltham, Mass. 02154, USA

Bavaria Elektronic GmbH, Lucile Grahnstr. 45, D-8000 München, Germany

Bavaria Elektronik GmbH, Kleiner Glinderberg Str. 28, D-2056 Glinde, Germany

Bison Instruments, Inc. 3401 48th Ave. North, Minneapolis, Minn. 55429, USA

Bleakley Gray Corp. Pty. Ltd., 28 Elizabeth St., Melbourne, Victoria 3000, Australia

Brewer Engineering Labs, Inc., Marion, Mass. 02738, USA

Brewer Engineering Labs, Inc. Marion, Mass. 02738, USA

Clockhouse c/o Testlab Corp., P. O. Box 66310, Chicago, Ill., USA

Constructora NORCO, Apartado Aereo 11–25, Mendellin, Colombia

Corner House Laboratories (1968) (Pty.) Ltd., Private Bag I, Emmarentia, Johannesburg, South Africa

Craelius, Fack, S-101 10 Stockholm I, Sweden

Dartec Ltd., Foster St., Stourbridge, Worcs., England

Deakin Instrumentation Ltd., St. Thomas Rd., Wigston, Leicestershire, LE8 2TA, England

Dillon, W. C. & Co., Inc. P. O. Box 3008, Van Nuys, Calif. 91407, USA

Dwyer Instruments, Inc. P. O. Box 373, Michigan City, Ind. 46360, USA

Earth Sciences Research, Inc., 133 Mt. Auburn St., Cambridge, Mass. 02138, USA
Eastman International Co. GmbH, P. O. Box 1160, D-3005 Hannover-Westerfeld, Germany
Eastronics Ltd., P. O. Box 21029, Tel-Aviv, Israel
Elektronik und Meßtechnik, Postfach A112, CH-8052 Zürich, Switzerland
Endevco, Dynamic Instrument Division, 801 South Arroyo Pkwy., Pasadena, Calif. 91109, USA
Endevco (U. K.) Ltd., Upper King St., Royston, Herts., England
Endevco France S. A., 76 rue des Grand Champs, Paris 20e, France
Engineering Laboratory Equipment Ltd., Durrants Hill Trading Estate, Apsley, Hemel Hempstead, Herts., England
Environmental Equipments Ltd., Eastheath Ave., Wokingham, Berks. RG11 2PP, England
Erichsen, A. M. GmbH, P. O. Box 201537, D-5600 Wuppertal 2, Germany
Erik Ferner AB, P. O. Box 56, Bromma 1, Sweden
Estronic, Klokkerjordet 31, N-1364 Hvalstad, Norway

Farnell Instruments Ltd., Sandbeck Way, Wetherby, Yorkshire, England
Fleming Services, 15 Coppice Ave., Great Shelford, Cambridge, CB2 5AQ, England
Foundation & Soil Ltd., P. O. Box 10107, Tel Aviv, Israel
Franz Glötzl Baumesstechnik, D-7501 Forchheim - Bahnhof, Germany
Fylde Electronic Labs Ltd., Oakham Court, Preston, PR1 3XP, England

Gage Technique Ltd., P. O. Box 30, Trowbridge, Wilts., England
GEC − Elliott Process Instruments Ltd., Century Works, Lewisham, London, SE13 7LN, England
General Scientific & Co., 7 Jalan 222, Petaling Jaya, Malaysia
Geocel Inc., 16027 West 5th St., Golden, Colo. 80401, USA
Geomech Pty. Ltd., 31 Gremore St., Richmond, Victoria 3121, Australia
Geonor, A. S., P. O. Box 99, Oslo 7, Norway
Geoprobe, Division of Warnock-Hersey Ltd., 1438 rue des Gouverneurs, Sinllery, P. Q., Canada
Geoquest Ltd., Buckhill House, Calne, Wiltshire, England
Geosistemas S. A., Aniceto Ortega 1310, Col. del Valle, Mexico 12, D. F. Mexico
Geostrumenti, Via XXV Aprile 10, I-20090 Segrate (Milano), Italy
Geotecna, Via Solari 43/3, I-20144 Milano, Italy
Geotest, P. O. Box 173, Mt. Wawerley, Victoria 3149, Australia
geotechnik Hans Herbert Mennerich, Gabelsberger Str. 5, D-3000 Hannover, Germany
Geo-Testing, Inc., P. O. 4339, San Rafael, Calif. 94903, USA
Gilmore Industries, Inc., 3355 Richmond Rd., Cleveland, Ohio 44122, USA
Glötzl, Franz, Baumesstechnik GmbH, D-7501 Forchheim-Bahnhof, Germany
Göloglu, Sevket, Maliyeciler Koop. Apt., 113/B Kücükesat, Ankara, Turkey
Graham and White Instruments Ltd., 82 London Rd., St. Albans, Herts., England

Hewlett-Packard Inc., P. O. Box 301, Loveland, Colo. 80537, USA
Honeywell Industrial Division, Fort Washington, Pa. 19034, USA
Horstman Ltd., Locksbrook Rd., Bath, England

Hottinger, Baldwin, Messtechnik GmbH, P. O. Box 4151, D-6100 Darmstadt, Germany

Houston Scientific HSI, Inc., 4202 Director's Row, Houston, Tex. 77018, USA

Ilmonen AB, Mikaelsgt. 19, SF-00100 Helsinki 10, Finland

Intercole Systems Ltd., Chandlers Ford Industrial Estate, Eastleigh, Hampshire, SO5 3YU, England

INTERFELS Internationale Versuchsanstalt für Fels GmbH, Schwarzstr. 27, A-5020 Salzburg, Austria

INTERFELS Internationale Versuchsanstalt für Fels GmbH, P. O. Box 75, D-4442 Bentheim, Germany

International Engineering Concessionaires Ltd., Wellington House, Walton-on-Thames, Surrey, England

International Research & Development Co. Ltd., Fossway, Newcastle Upon Tyne, NE6 2YD, England

Intertechnology Ltd., Victor House, Norris Rd., Staines, Middlesex, TW18 4DS, England

Intertechnology Ltd., P. O. Box 219, Don Mills, Ontario, Canada

Irot, S. A. LCDO Poza 69, Bilbao 13, Spain

K. C. Production Sales Ltd., Downhill Rd., Bracknell, Berkshire, England

Keuffel & Esser Co., 20 Whippany Rd., Morristown, N. J. 07960, USA

Koning en Hartman Elektrotechniek, 30 Koperwerf, The Hague 2038, Netherlands

Kyowa Electronic Instrument Co. Ltd., 5-Chofugaoka, 3chome, Chofu-ski, Tokyo 182, Japan

Laser Systems & Electronics, Inc., P. O. Box 858, Tullahoma, Tenn. 37388, USA

Little, Arthur D., Inc., Acron Park, Cambridge, Mass. 02140, USA

Macklow-Smith Ltd., Watchmoor Rd., Off Moorlands Rd., Camberley, Surrey, England

Marubun Corp., Electronics Division II, 1-1, Nihombashi Odemmacho 2-chome, Tokyo 103, Japan

Magnaflux Testing Systems, Inc. 7300 W. Lawrence Ave., Chicago, Ill. 60656, USA

Magnaflux Ltd., 702 Tudor Estate, Abbey Rd., London, N. W. 10, England

Maihak AG, P. O. Box, D-2000 Hamburg 39, Germany

Martin-Decker Co., 1928 S. Grand Ave., Santa Ana, Calif. 92705, USA

Maruto Testing Machine Co., 7,2-chome, Shirakawa-cho, Fukagawa, Koto-ku, Tokyo, Japan

Mayer, Peter, Apartado 1728, Caracas 101, Venezuela

W. H. Mayes & Son Ltd., Vansittart Estate, Arthur Rd., Windsor, Berkshire, England

Measurement Research Ltd., New Row, Norwich End, Whaley Bridge via Stockport, Cheshire, England

Megatronix Ltd., 100 Penn Dr., Unit No. 1, Weston, Ontario, Canada

M. B. Metals Ltd., Portsdale, Sussex, England

Metrosol, Via Almerigo da Schio 8, I-20146 Milano, Italy

Micro-Measurements, A Division of Vishay Intertechnology, Inc., P. O. Box 306, Romulus, Mich. 48174, USA

Morehouse Instrument Co., 1742 Sixth Ave., York, Pa. 17403, USA

Morgal Scientific Co., Jalan 223, Petaling Jaya, Malaysia

Motion Smith & Son Ltd., 88 Jalan Pudu, Kuala Lumpur, Malaysia

Mycalex Instruments Ltd., Charlton Kings Industrial Estate, Cirencester Rd., Cheltenham, GL53 8DZ, England

Nigeria Soil Engineering Co. Ltd., P. O. Box 104, Ikeja, Nigeria

Nold, Walter Co., 24 Birch Rd., Natick, Mass. 01760, USA

Pacific Instrument Co., 1203 Dell Ave., Campbell, Calif. 95008, USA

Panambra Industrial e Tecnica, S. A., Av. Senador Queiros 150, Sao Paulo, Brazil

Peter Smith Instrumentation Ltd., Gosforth Industrial Estate, Newcastle Upon Tyne NE3 1XF, England

Philips' Gloeilampenfabrieken, Eindhoven, Netherlands

Photoelastic, Inc., 67 Lincoln Hwy, Malvern, Pa. 19355, USA

Physik Instrumente Huggenberger AG, Ackersteinstr. 119, CH-80419 Zürich, Switzerland

Prewitt Associates, P. O. Box 365, Lexington, Ky. 40501, USA

Proceq, S. A., P. O. Box 163, CH-8034 Zürich 8, Switzerland

Production Supplies Pty Ltd., 22 Hosker St., Springvale, Victoria 3171, Australia

Pye Unicam Ltd., York St., Cambridge, CB1 2PX, England

Robertson Research Mineral Technology Ltd., "Ty' n-y-Coed", Llanrhos, Llandudno, North Wales, England

RocTest Ltd., 1485 Desaulniers, Longeuil (Montreal), Quebec, Canada

Sangamo Weston Controls Ltd., North Bersted, Bognor Regis, Sussex, England

Scratch Strain Gauge Division, Prewitt Associates, P. O. Box 365, Lexington, Ky. 40501, USA

S. E. I. L., rue du R. P. Christian-Gilbert, 92 Asnieres, Paris, France

SOCOSOR, B. P. 277, F-75827 Paris Cedex 17, France

Sensotec, Inc., 1400 Holly Ave., Columbus, Ohio 43212, USA

Sharples Photomechanics Ltd., Europa Works, Wesley St., Bamber Bridge, Preston, PR5 5PB, England

S. L. Electronics Co., 526 Malvern Rd., Hawksburn, Victoria 3142, Australia

Slope Indicator Co., 3668 Albion Place North, Seattle, Wash. 98103, USA

Smith, Peter, Instrumentation Ltd., Gosforth Industrial Estate, Newcastle Upon Tyne, NE3 1XF, England

Soil & Rock Instrumentation Inc., 377 Elliott St., Newton Upper Falls, Mass. 02164, USA

Soilcrete Australia, 30 Dickson Ave., Atarmon, Sydney, N. S. W. 2064, Australia

Soil Instruments Ltd., Townsend Lane, London, NW9 8TR, England

Soil Mechanics Ltd., Eastern Rd., Bracknell, Berks. RG12 2UP, England

Soil Test International, Inc., 2205 Lee St., Evanston, Ill. 60202, USA

W. F. Sprengnether Instrument Co. Inc., 4567 Swan Ave., St. Louis, Mo. 62110, USA

Standard Controls, Inc., 2401 South Bayview St., Seattle, Wash. 98144, USA

Standard Scientific & Optical Ltd., 26 Jalan 223 Petaling Jaya, Malaysia

Statham Instruments, Inc., 2230 Statham Blvd., Oxnard, Calif. 93030, USA

Stelmo Ltd., Westwell Leacon, Charing, Ashfort, Kent, England
Strainstall Ltd., Harelco House, Denmark Rd., Cowes, Isle of Wight, England
Strainsert, Inc., 24 Summit Grove Ave., Bryn Mawr, Pa. 19010, USA
Stress Engineering Services Ltd., 4 Palmerston Rd., Sheffield S10 2TE, England
Structural Behaviour Engineering Labs, Inc., P. O. Box 9727, Phoenix, Ariz. 85020, USA

Technitron S. R. L., Via Laminia 443-A, I-00196 Rome, Italy
Technitron S. R. 1., Via Dezza 47, I-20141 Milano, Italy
Telemac International, Inc., 5450 Côte des Neiges Room 416, Montreal 249, Quebec, Canada
Telemac S. A., 17, Rue Alfred Roll, Paris 17e, France
Tellurometer (U. K.) Ltd., Oakcroft Rd., Chessington, Surrey KT9 1RQ, England
Telindus N. V., 38 rue Stanley, Brussels 18, Belgium
Terrametrics, Inc. 16027 West 5th Ave., Golden, Colo. 80401, USA
Terrametric (South Africa) Pty. Ltd., 6 Keith Ave., Florida North, Transvaal, South Africa
Terrascience Systems Ltd., P. O. Box 6625, Postal Station G, Vancouver, B. C., Canada
Terrascience Systems Ltd. c/o Intertechnology Ltd., P. O. Box 219, Don Mills, Ontario, Canada
Terra Tec Division Laudes Laboratories, Inc., Overlake Park, Redmond, Wash. 98052, USA
Terratest (Great Britain) Ltd., St. Thomas Rd, Wigston, Leicester LE8 2TA, England
Terratest S. A., BP 2154, CH-1002 Lausanne 2, Switzerland
Terratest, S. à R. L. 3, Villa Dury-Vasellon, 75 Paris XXe, France
Terratest GmbH, Postfach 17, D-6079 Buchschlag, Germany
Texcel Electronics Ltd., 13 Cunningham Hill Rd., St. Albans, Herts., England
The Trow Group, 90 Milvan Dr., Weston 486, Ontario, Canada
Tokyo Sokki Kenkyujo Co. Ltd., 8-ban, 2-go, 6-chome, Minamishi, Singawa-ku, Tokyo, Japan
Tomar Instruments Co. Inc., 7711 N. W. 5th Ave., Vancouver, Wash., USA
Transducers (C. E. L.) Ltd., Trafford Rd., Reading, RG1 8JH, England
Techquipment Ltd., Hooton St., Carlton Rd., Nottingham, NG3 2NJ, England

Vemco Industries, Inc., Pier Seven, The Embarcadero, San Francisco, Calif. 94111, USA
Vergarada, S. A., Guzman el Bueno 121, Parque de las Naciones, Madrid 3, Spain
Vishay Intertechnology, Inc. P. O. Box 306, Romulus, Mich, 48174, USA

Walter Nold Co., 24 Birch Rd., Natick, Mass. 01760, USA
Welwyn Electric Ltd., Strain Measurement & Equipment Div., 70 High St., Teddington, Middlesex, TWI1 8JF, England
Wykeham Farrance Engineering Ltd., Weston Rd., Slough SL1 4HW, England

ADVERTISER'S INDEX

Soil & Rock Instrumentation, Inc., 377 Elliot St., Newton Upper Falls, Mass. 02164, USA

Soil Instruments Ltd., Townsend Lane, London NW9 8TR, England

Soil Mechanics Ltd., Eastern Rd., Bracknell, Berks. RG12 2UP, England (Nicklin Advertising Ltd.)

Strainstall Ltd., Harelco House, Denmark Rd., Cowes, Isle of Wight, England (K. W. Jackson)

Telemac International, Inc., 5450 Cote des Neiges, Room 416, Montreal 249, Quebec, Canada

Terrametrics, Inc., 16027 West 5th Ave., Golden, Colo. 80401, USA

Terrascience Systems Ltd., P. O. Box 6625, Postal Station G, Vancouver, B. C., Canada

Terra Tec Division Lauders Laboratories, Inc., Overlake Park, Redmond, Wash. 98052, USA (Pascoe and Starling)

Terratest S. A., BP 2154, CH-1002 Lausanne 2, Switzerland

Texel Electronics Ltd., 13 Cunningham Hill Rd., St. Albans, Herts., England (Lovell and Rupert Curtis Ltd.)

The Trow Group, 90 Milvan Dr., Weston 486, Ontario, Canada

W. A. Wahler & Associates Inc., P. O. Box 10023, Palo Alto, Calif. 94303, USA

Walter Nold Co., 24 Birch Rd., Natick, Mass. 01760, USA (Publication Services Associates)

Joseph S. Ward Associates, 91 Roseland Ave., Caldwell, N. J. 07006, USA

Wykeham Farrance Engineering Ltd., Weston Rd., Slough SL1 4HW, England

PROFESSIONAL SERVICES

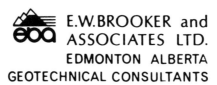

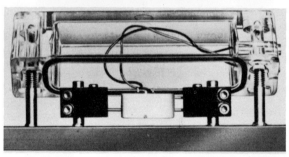

Since Man's First Interest in SOIL...

. . . . life has changed considerably and so has the need for knowledge "in depth". We design and manufacture instrumentation for the in situ measurement and observations of soil behaviour. We also supervise and install equipment and advise on its uses . . . .

. . . . **in any part of the world.**

We manufacture:

Hydraulic piezometers

Pneumatic piezometers

Earth pressure cells

Soil extensometers

Hydraulic settlement gauges

Pneumatic settlement gauges

Electrical settlement gauges

Digital inclinometers

Soil INSTRUMENTS LTD.
TOWNSEND LANE · LONDON NW9 8TR · ENGLAND
Telephone: 01-205 2829

You'll find us the most professional people on Earth.

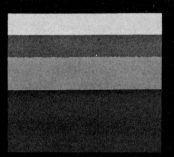

Soil Mechanics Limited, established over 25 years ago, was the first civil engineering company in the United Kingdom to specialise in the solution of geotechnical problems – a science now called – Geotechnology.

From its earliest days the policy of the company has been to offer the widest range of processes in Geotechnology.

In 1967 our **Instrumentation & Field Testing Division** was formed to adopt and pioneer specialised field techniques in soil and rock mechanics. Together with associate company, Rock Mechanics Limited, it now offers a wide range of services which not only complement the conventional site investigation activities of the company internally, but also provide an external service to the engineer, geologist or planner.

A widely experienced staff is available for all field operations whilst overall planning, supervision and interpretation is carried out by engineers, geologists or applied scientists many of whom have post-graduate qualifications in soil and rock mechanics.

Our Instrumentation and Field Testing Division can apply any of the following techniques to your problem . . .

Land Geophysics
☐ Seismic surveys ☐ Resistivity surveys ☐ Gravimetric and magnetic surveys ☐ Downhole and between hole logging

Vibration and Dynamics
☐ Structural dynamics monitoring ☐ Blast monitoring ☐ Traffic vibrations monitoring

Marine Geophysics and Hydrographic Surveys
☐ Continuous sub bottom profiling using sparker, boomer or high resolution boomer ☐ Precision echo sounding ☐ Side scan sonar ☐ Current velocity and direction ☐ Tide and wave studies ☐ Bed sediment sampling

Movement Monitoring
☐ Precise topographical surveys ☐ Surface extenso-meters ☐ Boreholes extenso-meters and inclinometers ☐ Shear detectors ☐ Hydraulic and electromagnetic settlement monitoring

Deformability and Strength Tests
☐ Borehole deformability logging ☐ Dutch deep sounding ☐ Plate bearing tests ☐ In situ shear tests ☐ Portable shear box tests ☐ Anchor and rock bolt tests ☐ Pile tests

Special Sampling
☐ Delft continuous sampling ☐ Piston sampling ☐ Block sampling ☐ Water sampling

Ground Water
☐ Piezometer installation ☐ Field permeability tests ☐ Sand drain trials ☐ Flow and tracer studies

Special Services
☐ Stress measurement ☐ Pressure and load monitoring ☐ Borehole camera studies ☐ Corrosion studies

For further details of the facilities and services available to those professionally involved in Geotechnology, contact Soil Mechanics Limited, Foundation House, Eastern Road, Bracknell, Berkshire RG12 2UP, England. Telephone : Bracknell 24567. Telex : 847253.

ϕ Soil Mechanics: the best on Earth.

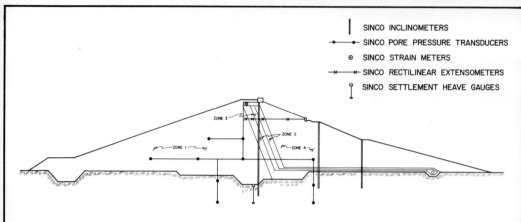

SINCO INCLINOMETERS
SINCO PORE PRESSURE TRANSDUCERS
SINCO STRAIN METERS
SINCO RECTILINEAR EXTENSOMETERS
SINCO SETTLEMENT HEAVE GAUGES

TYPICAL INSTRUMENTED SECTION
OF EARTH OR ROCKFILL DAM

200B - slope indicator........................... **settlement-heave gauges**

digitilt inclinometers........ **goodman jacks for insitu borehole tests**

in-place inclinometers....................... **vibrating-wire strain gauges**

pneumatic pore pressure measuring systems................. **load cells**

strain meters .... **geo-monitors—micro seismic & acoustic**

rectilinear extensometers................ ....**portable vibration monitors**

mechanical extensometers...... **strong motion servo seismographs**

3668 Albion Place North, Seattle, Washington, 98103
(206) 633-3073, cable: SINCO, Seattle
Foundation and Structural Instrumentation

SiNCO
Slope Indicator Company

THE DE AERATOR

. . . . . . at last a portable, compact, simple to use, maintenance free apparatus that permits fast, efficient removal of air from water without the use of heat.

. . . . . . the DeAerator was developed by the **walter nold company** in 1970 during a research program for the geophysical field. The objective of the program was to research, develop, and manufacture equipment that would provide readily obtainable and inexpensive de-aired water.

. . . . . . the **walter nold company** successfully met the challenge and is now offering the results of its research to the technical world. Some areas of expertise where de-aired water would be employed include:

. . . . . . Closed hydraulic piezometer systems
. . . . . . Laboratory permeability testing
. . . . . . Liquid manometer settlement gauges
. . . . . . Specific gravity testing
. . . . . . Laboratory triaxial testing

. . . . . . the **walter nold company** is constantly conducting tests relating to de-aired water and will supply available data upon request. Write or call today for further details.

US Patented
Foreign Patents Pending

24 birch road, natick massachusetts, 01760, u.s.a.   617–653-1635

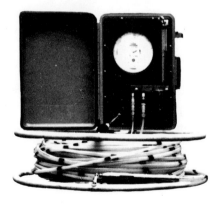

In The Field Hewlett-Packard Can Help You Do But Drive

Now You Can Own A Distance Measuring System For Under $5000.

Join the growing ranks of surveyors who've found how much these measuring systems can increase profits. Over 2,500 HP Distance Meters are already in use in the U.S. and Canada—more than all the competitors put together. You probably know someone who has one. Why not ask him how he likes his HP 3800 System? Fair Warning: He's likely to make you a convert.

Start With The HP Series 3800, The Electronic Distance Meters That Give You The Best Range And Accuracy For The Money.

Get direct readout to 10,000 feet (3800A) or 3,000+ meters (3800B), with repeatable accuracy of 1 part in 100,000 or better—in spite of people, automobiles or branches moving across the line of sight.

Add The Vertical Circle for Convenient Reduction To Horizontal.

It mounts atop your 3800, so you measure vertical angle and slope distance with only one setup. Try it and you'll never go back to separate setups.

Punch Out Your Field Problems On The HP 35 Pocket Calculator.

It gives complete log and trig functions with a single key, and stores constants and intermediate results. Think of it as a speedy 10-digit calculator you can carry into the field.

With HP's Surveying Systems, Your Field Data Can Be In At Four And Your Adjusted Data Out By Five.

Making the field measurements is only half your battle. You still have to process the data—and that takes time. With these systems you can handle the whole day's work of a survey crew in as little as 15 minutes.

Conversational Capability. Just Follow The Printer's Instructions.

Anyone can use the Series 9800 with as little as 15 minutes of training. And you get a fully labled record of your survey data for your client file.

```
PT NO
        1.000
ANG
RGT
DEG/MIN/SEC
        123.000
         22.000
         56.000
DIST
SLOPE
        456.890
ZNTH ANG
DEG/MIN/SEC
         93.000
         32.000
         21.000
HOR.
        456.019
```

Or In Your Office,
Surveying Systems
Most Everything
The Stakes.

(And we'd like to be working on that too.)

Expand Your Data Handling Capacity With Tape Cassettes.

There's nothing quite as comforting as being able to reconstruct a job. Add our cassette peripheral and store all your important data. And don't worry about damaged tape, for its unique precision drive mechanism safeguards your irreplaceable records.

Have Your Forms Prepared Automatically.

Forget the delays in getting results typed. Let the Series 9800 system typewriter automatically prepare your records under calculator control. There's no need for transcribing results from tape printout.

You Have Hewlett-Packard's Experience With Measurement Assuring Your Precision.

Your bread and butter comes from making accurate distance measurements and computations. We understand your problems, for precision measurement is our business. A typical example: An integral part of guidance system for the Apollo program is our Cesium Clock—accurate to 1 second in 30,000 years. If we can help the astronauts come within feet of target at a distance of a quarter million miles, you can be confident of your measurement accuracy and computations with HP surveying systems.

To Solve Surveying Problems, Just Call Your Local HP Office.

There are 57 in the U.S. and Canada to serve you. See them for expert assistance, whether it's help in selecting just the right equipment or suggestions on how to use it best. Hewlett-Packard Civil Engineering Products, P.O. Box 301, Loveland, Colorado 80537

For new standards in Surveying Systems, think Hewlett-Packard.

093/70

HEWLETT **hp** PACKARD

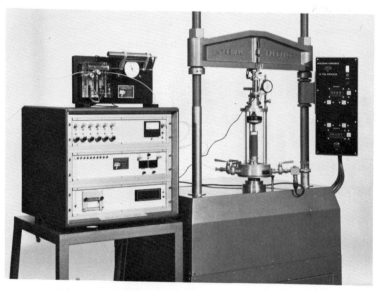

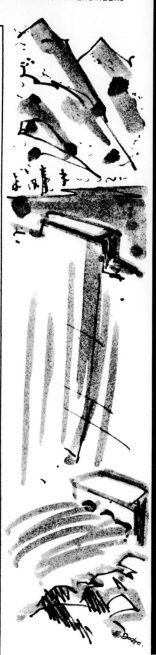

Range choice+Versatility=Strainstall

We have the sum of your strain instrumentation needs.

Here is but a fraction

EMBEDMENT GAUGES

TYPE PC 657NA

Suitable for external hydraulic pressures up to 200 p.s.i.

TYPE RRL/A

Designed especially for strain measurements during concrete curing periods.

SURFACE MOUNTED RECOVERABLE GAUGES

TYPE ST 918

For use in high pressure conditions. On–site tuning capability and mobility without need of re–setting.

TYPE ST1190

An economically priced unit for accurate measurement of surface strains and temperatures.

LOAD CELLS

AN EXAMPLE OF A 35 TON TENSILE LOAD CELL

Compressive vibrating wire units are also manufactured to customer requirements. These incorporate 3 or more elements to counter the effect of non axial loading.

EARTH PRESSURE CELLS

TYPE PC 204

A heavy duty transducer providing stability, high discrimination and measurement accuracy over long periods.

WATER PRESSURE CELLS

TYPE ST 917

For measurement of percolating water pressure variations in foundation soils and bedrocks.

All gauges are individually pressure tested and an inspection certificate is issued with each.

All our instrumentation has full electronic back up of our own manufacture.

strainstall limited

Harelco House, Denmark Road, Cowes, Isle of Wight PO31 7TB
Cowes (STD 098-382) 2219/2360
Telegraphic address 'Strainstall Cowes' Telex 86369.

specialists in stress analysis, strain gauge installation and instrumentation

Remote Measuring Instruments

Load Cells

for abutment pressure
   rock pressure
   rock stress
   tensile and compressive force
   force of anchor

Pore Water Pressure Cells
Bottom Water Pressure Cells

for all kinds of soil
   Special designs for laboratory researches

Earth Pressure Cells

for any kind of measuring problems in soil mechanics.
   Special design for normal– and shear stress
   in boundary zones of structures

Inclinometer

for measuring problems in structural engineering
and soil mechanics
   Stationary– and travelling type

All transmitters operating on the well–proved
Maihak vibrating–wire principle of measurement:

- Measuring error<1%
- Measuring sensitivity 0.2 ....0.03%
- Stability of zero and calibration value for long –term measurements
- Unfalsified remote transmission of measured values
- Measuring results are not affected by variations of electrical quantities
- Simple and robust construction of the instruments
- Temperature –independent, waterproof and rustproof transmitters
- Analog or digital receiving and recording facility
- Measurements static or dynamic
- Universal combination of various measured quantities in one receiving system, for example also strain, temperature, displacement

Measurement of Ground Movements

Vertical settlement– and horizontal displacement
measurements in embankments and in the underground
with radio settlement gauge after Dr. Idel

H. Maihak AG   Hamburg 39
Tel. (0411) 27 10 71   Telex 0211158

GLOETZL PRESSURE CELLS

this is a hydraulic measuring system, which is based upon the compensation method.

— direct measuring: the searched stress is read in kp/cm².
— constant zero value and high accuracy of measurement.
— a robust instrument with a small thickness, qualified for the building site.
— a simple and quick installation.

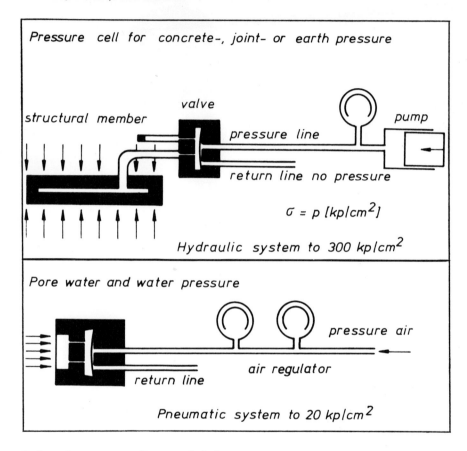

Pressure cell for concrete-, joint- or earth pressure

structural member   valve   pressure line   pump

return line no pressure

$$\sigma = p \ [kp/cm^2]$$

Hydraulic system to 300 kp/cm²

Pore water and water pressure

pressure air

air regulator

return line

Pneumatic system to 20 kp/cm²

Delivery Programme — Pressure Cells for:

— concrete stress	load limits 0—50, 200, 300 kp/cm²
— joint pressure	load limit 0—50 kp/cm²
— earth pressure	load limit 0—50 and 200 kp/cm²
— shuttering girder pressure	load limit 0—50 kp/cm²
— pore water and water pressure	load limit 0—10 and 20 kp/cm²
— power cells, various dimensions	

The measurement can be operated with
— hand- or motor pump.
— automatic measuring equipment.

Franz Glötzl, Baumesstechnik — West Germany

D-7501 Forchheim/Bhf., Tel.: Karlsruhe 07 21 / 55 58 20
Telegrammadresse: Baumessglötzl Karlsruhe.

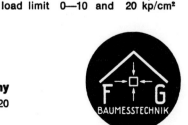

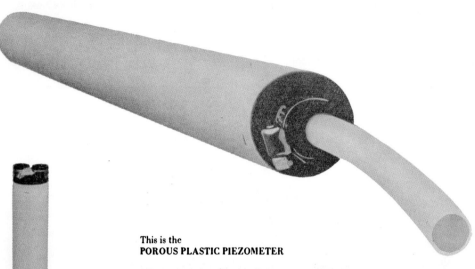

This is the
POROUS PLASTIC PIEZOMETER

It is a new product developed to overcome the
deficiencies of its predecessors.

Answering previous field assembly problems,
the pre-assembled porous plastic unit only
requires attaching to the lead-in tubing. The
unit is robust and relatively immune to rough
field handling.

The porous plastic has an average pore size of
50 microns. This small pore size enables the
material to be used in direct contact with silt or
clay with no worries about clogging. The great
profusion of pores results in high permeability.
Stability of the plastic is ensured within the
temperature range normally encountered. As
constructed the plummet has a negative
buoyancy for ease of installation.

Model PFF is available for circulating de-airing
water through the unit.

Same day air express shipment
from our factory.

TERRATEST PIEZOMETERS
90 Milvan Drive
Weston (Toronto) Ontario
Canada
1-416-749-1294

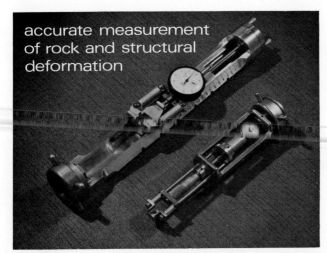

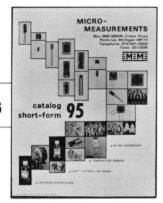

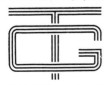

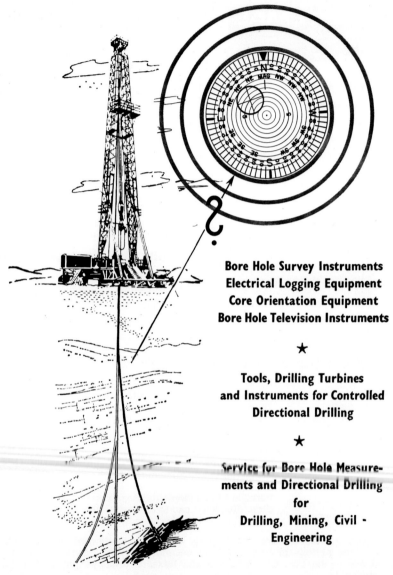

Announcement of the forthcoming book

No. 5 of Vol. 1 (1971/73)

Series on Rock and Soil Mechanics

THE TENSILE STRENGTH OF ROCK

by

Dr. John A. Hudson

Transport and Road Research Laboratory, Crowthorne, England

Table of Contents

If you are interested in this book, please give us your name and address, so that we may send you a detailed brochure on this volume.

Tentative Publication Date: Fall 1973

Bins and Bunkers for Handling Bulk Materials

— Practical Design and Techniques —

By **W. Reisner, M. v. Eisenhart Rothe** and **H. Colijn**

1971, 280 pages, 333 references, 15 tables, 178 illustrations
Second Printing November 1972, Price: US $ 20.00 paperback
Vol. 1 (1971/73) No. 1, Series on Rock and Soil Mechanics

International Standard Book No: 0-87849-001-9
Library of Congress Catalog Card No: 74-149275

Handling and storing of bulk materials has become increasingly important in recent years to the mining, mineral processing, chemical, railroading, shipping and farming industries. This is primarily due to the ever increasing capacities of individual plants and installations.

This book is the first attempt to gather the widely scattered literature on the subject of bins and bunkers and gives a survey of the state of the art. The text treats the theoretical considerations of bulk solids in bins, bunkers and silos, but concentrates on the practical aspects.

Contents:

1. **Flow Behavior of Bulk Solids**

2. **Design Based on Flow Properties of Bulk Solids**

3. **Loads of Bins and Bunkers**

4. **Shapes of Bins and Bunkers**

5. **Activation of Bins and Bunkers**

6. **Feeding and Recovery**

7. **Functions of Bins and Bunkers**

8. **Treatment of Bulk Solids**

9. **Control and Automatic Equipment**

This book found such great interest worldwide, that it had to be reprinted 18 months after its first publication in 1971 and was also translated into German language.

Typical Book Reviews
Bins and Bunkers for Handling Bulk Materials

"It is, in effect, a design handbook incorporating a large number of figures and diagrams illustrating designs and listing 61 equipment manufacturers engaged in the production of bins, bunkers and ancilliary equipment. As such, the book should prove a useful tool for engineers in industry who are concerned with bulk materials handling."
Solid Liquid Flow Abstracts, July 1971

"The planning and design engineer will appreciate this survey, and also the possibility of being able to quickly locate publications which deal with his special problems in more detail."
The Australian Concrete Journal, November 1971

"From the few criticisms that can be made about this publication, it is obviously the most comprehensive guide to the design of storage hoppers printed to date and as such must be considered as a reference book for the shelves of all designers of bulk storage equipment."
The Mining Engineer, March 1972

"All important publications in the major world languages have been evaluated and listed with full bibliographic details, each title being translated into English."
Journal of the Institution of Engineers, Australia, 1971

"This is a good introduction to hopper theory with detailed description of the apparatus available to the foundry industry and can be recommended as a useful reference work."
BCIRA Journal, September 1971

"Here is a book of reference which will be invaluable to the structural engineers and designers, and as such, it should find a prominent place on their bookshelves and in all technical or engineering libraries."
Indian Concrete Journal, September 1971

"This book could be useful for design and production engineers and for students."
The Australasian Institute of Mining & Met., September 1971

"The authors' 280-page review of modern developments makes full use of available information and they are not averse to bringing in fairly involved calculus to define the theory of bulk flow behaviour, as one would expect in an up-to-date treatise on the subject."
Steel Times, August 1971

"With many bulk carriers becoming the self-discharging type and reclamation of minerals from the seabed requiring the use of hoppers onboard recovery vessels the information contained in this publication should prove most useful."
Marine Engineers Review, October 1971

The Science of Rock Mechanics

PART 1
STRENGTH PROPERTIES
OF ROCKS

By Prof. Dr. **W. Dreyer,** Technical University Clausthal, Germany

1972, 500 pages, 200 references, 86 tables, 137 figures, price: US $ 25.00

Vol. I (1971/73) No. 2, Series on Rock and Soil Mechanics.

Library of Congress Catalog Card Number: 78-149276.
International Standard Book Number: 0-87849-002-7.

The present volume is the first — in itself complete — part of the monography "The Science of Rock Mechanics". It comprises primarily the relationship between state of stress, strength of rocks and their determining textural data. As the description of the mechanical behavior of rocks under compressive load is extremely incomplete without adequate consideration of the petrographic parameters such as mineral composition, mineral interlocking, granulation, grain density and porosity, the author has treated the mineral content of all investigated rock samples quantitatively and formulated them mathematically.

The operation of caverns in salt deposits for the purpose of storage requires intimate knowledge of stability and convergence behavior of an underground system. The solution to this highly complex rock mechanics problem is discussed in a special chapter.

Several series of biaxial and triaxial deformation tests and model studies have the objective to solve stress conditions existing in room and pillar systems. Of special interest to the engineer will be a few newly developed methods for measuring absolute rock pressure at specific points in a mine.

It is hoped that this volume will lead to a deeper understanding of the mechanical and tectonic behavior of all kinds of rocks. The book should not only be of value to the mineralogist, geologist and petrographer but also to the civil, geological and especially the mining engineer.

Typical Book Reviews:

The Science of Rock Mechanics

"Originality in its true and good sense of the word is the great advantage of this book. Here, a professor has not written a seventh book out of six others, but a researcher has presented his field of interest and especially the results of his own studies, extending over almost two decades, among them many to be published for the first time.

G. B. Fettweis, ERZMETALL, November 1972

"Une part importante de l'ouvrage est réservée aux methodes des mesure et aux essais sur la portance des roches soumises a des charges homogènes et hétérogènes, aux études de convergence des excavations minières, et aux conditions de stabilité des réservoirs souterrains. Cet ouvrage constitue en fait une excellente introduction aux problèmes de la mécanique des roches, et pour le praticien, une source de renseignements précieux."

Industrie Minérale, May 1972

„Es ist zu erwarten, daß das vorliegende Buch bei Gebirgsmechanikern international große Beachtung finden wird."

Kali und Steinsalz, Februar 1972

"I am certain that this text will become a standard reference throughout the world for practitioners in evaporite geotechnology."

D. R. Richner, Chairman, Terraneers, Ltd., January 1973

„Das Buch ist nicht nur für die Ingenieurgeologie von Interesse, sondern kann jedem Bau- und Bergingenieur, der sich im Rahmen von Felsbauarbeiten mit den Festigkeitseigenschaften von Gestein und Gebirge befassen muß, empfohlen werden."

Geologische Mitteilung, Juli 1972

"Because of its nature, the book will be mostly useful to those who are directly concerned with the design of mine openings and storage cavities in halite rocks, but some of the reported results are also of interest in general rock mechanics. The book is well and clearly presented and the English translation is very good."

Institution of Mining & Metallurgy, London, July 1972

E X P L O S I V E S

for

North American Engineers

by

Cedric E. Gregory
Professor of Mining Engineering
The University of Idaho

1973, 300 pages, 80 figures, 15 tables, 130 references,
price: US Dollar 20.00, hard cover.

Vol. 1 (1971/73) No. 4 Series on Rock and Soil Mechanics
International Standard Book Number: ISBN 0-87849-007-8
Library of Congress Catalog Card Number: LCCC 72-96512

"North American Engineers at graduation have had little opportunity to embrace much of the rudimentary lore and practice of explosives. Many of them gain little more knowledge throughout their professional careers. Yet, to my mind, the intelligent use of explosives represents an important tool in many fields of engineering endeavor.

Although a sound knowledge of explosives principles is basic to the mining engineer, and very important to the civil engineer, I found, as a University teacher at three American universities, that the competition for lecture hours in our already congested curricula precludes the opportunity to cover the ground, even superficially, in formal lectures.

But it would be significantly easier if there were available some publication dealing with the elementary principles and practices of those particular explosives marketed in North America and used under American and Canadian conditions.

Hence, I have been inspired to write this "primer" or elementary monograph on the basic principles, types available, and methods applicable to the North American scene."

Dr. C. E. Gregory

Contents